Framework 9

MATHS S

David Capewell   Formerly Westfield School, Sheffield

Marguerite Comyns   Queen Mary's High School, Walsall

Gillian Flinton   All Saints Catholic High School, Sheffield

Paul Flinton   Chaucer School, Sheffield

Geoff Fowler   Maths Strategy Manager, Birmingham

Derek Huby   Mathematics Consultant

Peter Johnson   Waitakere College, Auckland, N.Z.

Jayne Kranat   Langley Park School for Girls, Bromley

Ian Molyneux   St. Bedes RC High School, Ormskirk

Peter Mullarkey   Netherhall School, Maryport, Cumbria

Nina Patel   Ifield Community College, West Sussex

Claire Turpin   Sidney Stringer Community Technology College,
                            Coventry

OXFORD

UNIVERSITY PRESS

OXFORD
UNIVERSITY PRESS

Great Clarendon Street, Oxford OX2 6DP

Oxford University Press is a department of the University of Oxford.
It furthers the University's objective of excellence in research,
scholarship, and education by publishing worldwide in

Oxford New York

Auckland Bangkok Buenos Aires Cape Town Chennai
Dar es Salaam Delhi Hong Kong Istanbul Karachi Kolkata
Kuala Lumpur Madrid Melbourne Mexico City Mumbai Nairobi
São Paulo Shanghai Taipei Tokyo Toronto

Oxford is a registered trade mark of Oxford University Press
in the UK and in certain other countries

British Library Cataloguing in Publication Data

Data available

ISBN 019 914 859 7

10 9 8 7 6 5 4 3 2

Typeset by Mathematical Composition Setters Ltd.

Printed in Italy by Rotolito Lombarda

Acknowledgements

The photograph on the cover is reproduced courtesy of Pictor.

The Publisher would like to thank the following for permission to reproduce
photographs:
Dave Capewell: pp 148, 152, 154, 158, (both); Corbis/Tibor Bognar: p 147
right; Corel Professional Photos: p 66 top right; Empics: p 66 top left; Oxford
University Press: pp 212, 214; Photodisc: pp 51, 147 (left), 156, 200;

Figurative artwork is by Paul Daviz

Pie charts on p 80 from www.statistics.gov.uk.

About this book

This book has been written for students who are working below but towards the objectives in Year 9 of the Framework for Teaching Mathematics. The content of the book is based on the Year 8 teaching programme from the Framework and leads to the 4–6 tier of entry in the NC tests.

The authors are experienced teachers and maths consultants who have been incorporating the Framework approaches into their teaching for many years and so are well qualified to help you successfully meet the Framework objectives.

The book is made up of units based on the sample medium term plans which complement the Framework document, thus maintaining the required pitch, pace and progression.

The units are:

The last four units in this book are designed to consolidate KS3 work and bridge to KS4 work.

Each unit comprises double page spreads that should take a lesson to teach. These are shown on the full contents list.

Problem solving is integrated throughout the material as suggested in the Framework.

How to use this book

This book is made up of units of work that are colour coded into: Algebra (Blue), Data (Pink), Number (Orange), Shape, space and measures (Green), Problem solving (Light Green) and a Bridging unit (Red).

Each unit of work starts with an overview of the content of the unit, as specified in the Framework document, so that you know exactly what you are expected to learn.

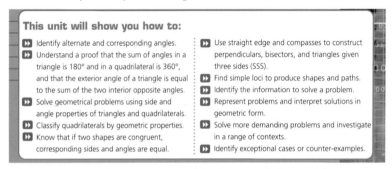

This unit will show you how to:

▶▶ Identify alternate and corresponding angles.
▶▶ Understand a proof that the sum of angles in a triangle is 180° and in a quadrilateral is 360°, and that the exterior angle of a triangle is equal to the sum of the two interior opposite angles.
▶▶ Solve geometrical problems using side and angle properties of triangles and quadrilaterals.
▶▶ Classify quadrilaterals by geometric properties.
▶▶ Know that if two shapes are congruent, corresponding sides and angles are equal.

▶▶ Use straight edge and compasses to construct perpendiculars, bisectors, and triangles given three sides (SSS).
▶▶ Find simple loci to produce shapes and paths.
▶▶ Identify the information to solve a problem.
▶▶ Represent problems and interpret solutions in geometric form.
▶▶ Solve more demanding problems and investigate in a range of contexts.
▶▶ Identify exceptional cases or counter-examples.

The first page of a unit also highlights the skills and facts you should already know and provides Check in questions to help you revise before you start so that you are ready to apply the knowledge later in the unit:

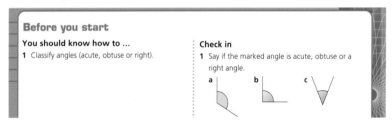

Before you start

You should know how to ...
1 Classify angles (acute, obtuse or right).

Check in
1 Say if the marked angle is acute, obtuse or a right angle.

a   b   c

Inside each unit, the content develops in double page spreads which all follow the same structure.

The spreads start with a list of the learning outcomes and a summary of the keywords:

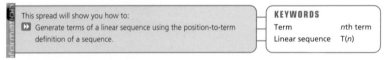

This spread will show you how to:
▶▶ Generate terms of a linear sequence using the position-to-term definition of a sequence.

KEYWORDS
Term nth term
Linear sequence $T(n)$

The keywords are summarised and defined in a Glossary at the end of the book so you can always check what they mean.

Key information is highlighted in the text so you can see the facts you need to learn.

▶ A term-to-term rule links a term with the next term.
▶ A position-to-term rule links a term to its position in the sequence.

Examples showing the key skills and techniques you need to develop are shown in boxes. Also hint boxes show tips and reminders you may find useful:

The nth term of a sequence is $T(n) = 2n + 1$.
Write the first five terms, then describe the sequence.

$T(1) = 2 \times \mathbf{1} + 1 = 3$
$T(2) = 2 \times \mathbf{2} + 1 = 5$
$T(3) = 2 \times \mathbf{3} + 1 = 7$
$T(4) = 2 \times \mathbf{4} + 1 = 9$
$T(5) = 2 \times \mathbf{5} + 1 = 11$ The first five terms are 3, 5, 7, 9, 11.

The sequence is the odd numbers starting at 3.

The **term-to-term** rule is add 2.

The **position-to-term** rule is: multiply the position by 2 then add 1, or $2n + 1$.

Each exercise is carefully graded, set at three levels of difficulty:

» The first few questions provide lead-in questions, revising previous learning.
» The questions in the middle of the exercise provide the main focus of the material.
» The last few questions are challenging questions that provide a link to the Year 9 learning objectives.

At the end of each unit is a summary page so that you can revise the learning of the unit before moving on.

Check out questions are provided to help you check your understanding of the key concepts covered and your ability to apply the key techniques. They are all based on actual Key Stage 3 past paper questions so they give you practice at the standard required in your examination.

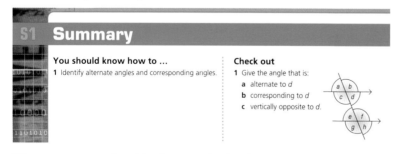

S1   Summary

You should know how to ...
1 Identify alternate angles and corresponding angles.

Check out
1 Give the angle that is:
  a alternate to d
  b corresponding to d
  c vertically opposite to d.

The answers to the Check in and Check out questions are produced at the end of the book so that you can check your own progress and identify any areas that need work.

Contents

1 Sequences

This unit will show you how to:

- Use formulae from mathematics and other subjects.
- Derive simple formulae.
- Generate and describe integer sequences.
- Generate terms of a linear sequence using term-to-term and position-to-term definitions.
- Begin to use expressions to describe the *n*th term of an arithmetic sequence.
- Express simple functions in symbols.
- Solve more demanding questions and investigate in a range of contexts.
- Suggest extensions to problems, conjecture and generalise.

The notes on a piano describe a sequence.

Before you start

You should know how to ...

1 Count on or back in steps, including counting back past zero.

2 Use the correct order of operations.

3 Substitute numbers into simple expressions.

Check in

1 Continue these sequences:

   a 5, 8, 11, __, __   **b** 12, 8, 4, __, __

2 Work out:

   a $2 \times 5 - 1$ **b** $3 - 12 \div 6$

   c $2 - 3 - 5 \times 2$ **d** $2(6 \times 4) - 2$

3 Work out the value of these expressions when $x = 4$ and $y = {}^{-}1$.

   a $x + 2y$ **b** $3y - x$

   c $\dfrac{4y}{x}$ **d** $\dfrac{4x}{y}$

Revising sequences

This spread will show you how to:
▶▶ Generate and describe integer sequences.
▶▶ Generate terms of a linear sequence using the term-to-term definition of a sequence.
▶▶ Express simple functions in symbols.

KEYWORDS
Generate
Term
Linear sequence
Flow chart

Nadia delivers leaflets for one week.
She decides which payment scheme is better:

Scheme 1: £2 the first day then double the amount the next day.

Scheme 2: £10 the first day and an extra £2 each day.

She works out the total for each scheme:
She chooses Scheme 2 – it pays £8 more.

Each scheme generates a sequence of numbers:
Scheme 1: The first term is £2 and the rule is ×2
Scheme 2: The first term is £10 and the rule is +£2.

	Mon	Tue	Wed	Thurs	Fri	**Total**
Scheme 1	£2	£4	£8	£16	£32	**£62**
Scheme 2	£10	£12	£14	£16	£18	**£70**

▶ **To describe a sequence you need a start number and a rule.**

You can use the rule of a sequence to find more terms.

example

Find the first five terms of these sequences:
a 1st term 12   rule: add 4
b 1st terms 2, 4, ...   rule: add the two previous terms

a 12, 16, 20, 24, 28, ...
b 2, 4, 6, 10, 16, ...

▶ **You can use a flow chart to generate a sequence.**

example

Find the first five terms of the sequence generated by this flow chart.

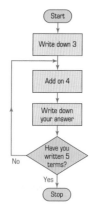

Start
Write down 3
Add on 4
Write down your answer
Have you written 5 terms?
No
Yes
Stop

The first term is 3: T(1) = 3

The term-to-term rule is 'add 4'

So T(2) = 3 + **4** = 7
T(3) = 7 + **4** = 11
T(4) = 11 + **4** = 15
T(5) = 15 + **4** = 19

You have written the first five terms, so stop.

The sequence is: 3, 7, 11, 15, 19, ...

Exercise A1.1

1 Copy and complete these sequences by filling in the missing numbers.
Explain each rule in writing.

a 15, ☐, 35, 45, ☐, ...   **b** 5, 3, ☐, ¯1, ☐, ☐, ...   **c** 5, ☐, 20, 40, ☐, 160, ☐, ...

2 Describe these sequences in words, giving the first term and the rule.
Use your rule to find the next two terms.

a 12, 16, 20, 24, ...   **b** 6, 12, 24, 48, ...   **c** 243, 81, 27, 9, ...

3 These cards are all jumbled up. Match each sequence to its correct name.

4 Here are four flow charts. Follow the instructions to generate a
sequence from each flow chart.

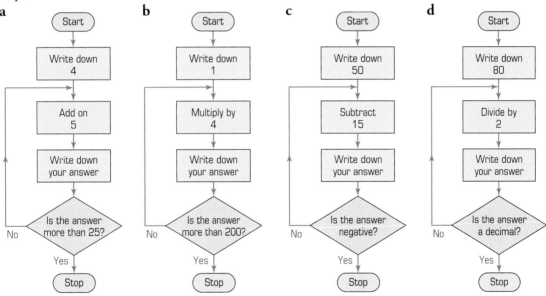

5 Here is a rule for a sequence:
  ▶ To find the next term of the sequence add ☐.
Choose a first number for the sequence and a number to add,
so that all the terms in the sequence are:

a even numbers   **b** odd numbers
c numbers ending in a 5   **d** every other number is a whole number.

This spread will show you how to:

▶▶ Generate terms of a linear sequence using the position-to-term definition of a sequence.

KEYWORDS

Term nth term
Linear sequence $T(n)$

▶ Each number in a sequence is called a **term**.
▶ A term is described by its **position** in the sequence.

You can write a term in shorthand using $T(n)$:

$T(1)$ = 1st term
$T(2)$ = 2nd term
$T(3)$ = 3rd term
$T(4)$ = 4th term
...
$T(10)$ = 10th term
...
$T(n)$ = nth term

The numbers 3, 7, 11, 15, 19, 23, ... form a sequence as they follow a rule:

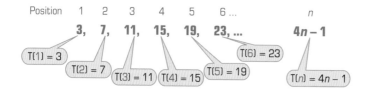

The **term-to-term** rule is: add 4.

The **position-to-term** rule is: multiply the position by 4 then subtract 1, or $4n - 1$.

▶ A **term-to-term** rule links a term with the next term.
▶ A **position-to-term** rule links a term to its position in the sequence.

The position-to-term rule is often called the nth term, or the general term.

The nth term of a sequence is $T(n) = 2n + 1$.
Write the first five terms, then describe the sequence.

$T(\mathbf{1}) = 2 \times \mathbf{1} + 1 = 3$
$T(\mathbf{2}) = 2 \times \mathbf{2} + 1 = 5$
$T(\mathbf{3}) = 2 \times \mathbf{3} + 1 = 7$
$T(\mathbf{4}) = 2 \times \mathbf{4} + 1 = 9$
$T(\mathbf{5}) = 2 \times \mathbf{5} + 1 = 11$ The first five terms are 3, 5, 7, 9, 11.

The sequence is the odd numbers starting at 3.

Exercise A1.2

1 The nth term of a sequence is $n + 3$.
Write down the first five terms of the sequence.

2 The nth term of a sequence is:
   a $n - 1$
   b $3n$
   c $10n - 1$
   d $2n - 1$
   e $4n + 4$
Write down the first five terms of each sequence.
Describe each sequence in words or using a term-to-term rule.

3 Here are 16 cards all jumbled up.
   ▶ Match three cards together so that each sequence has a
      term-to-term rule and a position-to-term rule.
   ▶ For the remaining card, write the sequence and the term-to-term rule.

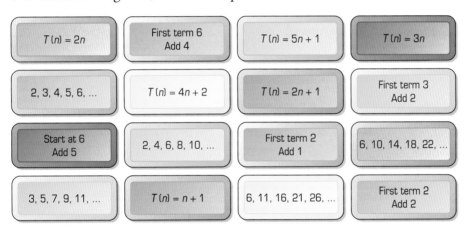

4 Write the first five terms of a sequence whose nth term or $T(n)$ is:
   a $4n + 2$
   b $5n - 8$
   c $50 - 2n$
   d $n + 0.6$
   e $10 - 0.5n$

5 Here is a sequence:

   5, 12, 19, 26, 33, 40, ...

   a Write the next three terms in the sequence.
   b Explain the rule for finding the next term.
   c What is the 30th term?
   d What is the nth term?

5

Describing sequences

This spread will show you how to:

▶▶ Use expressions to describe the *n*th term of an arithmetic sequence.

▶▶ Derive simple formulae.

▶▶ Use formulae from mathematics and other subjects.

KEYWORDS

Formula   *n*th term

Term

Arithmetic sequence

Charlotte and Steve are building a fence.
They have pieces of wood all 1 metre long.

They start with one
vertical post:

Then add two horizontal
pieces and one vertical post:

They add three more
pieces of wood each time:

1

1 + 3

1 + 3 × 2

Their garden is 10 metres long.
They work out how many pieces of wood they need.

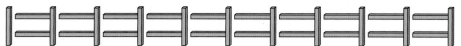

Number of pieces of wood = 1 + 3 × 10 = 31 pieces

They want another fence that will be 22 metres long.
This is too long to draw so they need to use a rule.

Number of pieces of wood = 1 + 3 × 22 = 67 pieces

> 3 pieces of wood are added 22 times.

> This is the first vertical post.

You can work out the number of pieces of wood for any length using this formula:

Number of pieces of wood = 1 + 3 × *n* = 1 + 3*n*

> This is the first vertical post.

> 3 pieces of wood are added *n* times (*n* is the length of the fence).

▶ You can describe a pattern using a rule or formula (the *n*th term).

example

Use the formula to find the number of pieces of wood for a fence that is 50 metres long.

....

Number of pieces of wood = 1 + 3 × 50 = 1 + 150 = 151 pieces

Exercise A1.3

1 A line of counters is set out in a pattern: 4 white, 3 blue, 4 white, 3 blue, ...

What colour is the 50th counter?
What position in the line is the 22nd blue counter?

2 Draw the next two patterns in these sequences.

a

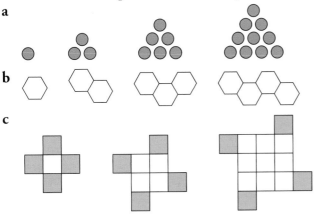

b

c

3 Here is a sequence of grey and white tiles:

cross 1   cross 2   cross 3

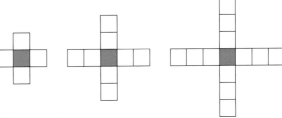

  a Draw a picture of cross 4.
  b How many grey tiles will there be
    in cross 10?
  c How many white tiles will there be
    in cross 10?
  d Which of the two rules gives you
    the total number of tiles:
    Number of tiles = $1 + 4c$ or Number of tiles = $c + 4$
    (where c is the cross number)?
    Explain why this rule works.

> **Hint:** Look at how many are on each arm, and how many arms there are.

  e How many tiles will be needed to make cross 100?

4 Justin wants to make a fence to go around his garden.
It must have 4 horizontal pieces of wood and all of the
pieces of wood are 1 metre long.

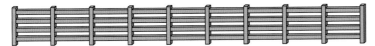

  a How many pieces of wood are needed for a fence 10 metres long?
  b How many pieces of wood are needed for a fence 30 metres long?
  c Copy and complete the formula:
    Number of pieces of wood = ____ + ____ × n (where n is the fence length)
  d If there were 501 pieces of wood, how long would the fence be?

You should know how to ...

1   Generate terms of a linear sequence using term-to-term and position-to-term definitions of the sequence.

2   Begin to use linear expressions to describe the nth term of an arithmetic sequence.

Check out

1   Write the first five terms in these sequences.

   a   Start at 3. Add 4 each time.

   b   Start at 1. Multiply by 3. Subtract 1.

   c   First term 5. Add 3. Multiply by 2.

   d $3n + 2$

   e $6n - 5$

   f $3 - 2n$

2   Here is a pattern of squares:

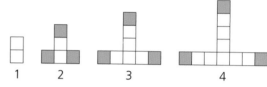

1   2   3   4

   a   Write down the number of squares in each pattern.

   b   Describe in words how the pattern grows.

   c   Predict the number of squares in the 5th, 7th and 10th patterns.
       Explain how you worked out your answer.

   d   Write an expression for the nth term of the pattern.

This unit will show you how to:

▶▶ Express simple functions in symbols.

▶▶ Represent mappings expressed algebraically.

▶▶ Generate points in all four quadrants and plot the graphs of linear functions, where *y* is given explicitly in terms of *x*.

▶▶ Recognise that equations of the form $y = mx + c$ correspond to straight-line graphs.

▶▶ Construct linear functions arising from real-life problems and plot their corresponding graphs.

▶▶ Discuss and interpret graphs arising from real situations.

▶▶ Solve more demanding problems and investigate in a range of contexts.

▶▶ Represent problems and interpret solutions in algebraic or graphical form.

You can program a washing machine to carry out a function. The results may be surprising.

Before you start

You should know how to ...

1 Use letter symbols.

2 Add, subtract and multiply with negative numbers.

3 Plot points in all four quadrants.

Check in

1 Write expressions for each of the following statements. Use *n* for the unknown number.

  a A number multiplied by 3

  b Add 10 to a number

  c 6 minus a number

  d A number divided by 3

  e A number multiplied by 3 then 4 added

2 Work out:

  a ⁻3 + ⁻4   b 5 − 7

  c ⁻2 + 4   d 2 × ⁻2

  e ⁻4 × 3   f ⁻2 + 2

3 Draw a grid from ⁻5 to 5 in both directions. Plot the points (4, 1) (⁻1, 4) (⁻5, 1) (⁻4, ⁻4) (2, ⁻5) (4, 1) on the grid and join them up. Name the shape you have made.

Revising functions

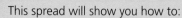

This spread will show you how to:
▶▶ Express simple functions in symbols.
▶▶ Represent mappings expressed algebraically.

KEYWORDS
Function machine
Function   Input
Mapping   Output

To continue this pattern, add four extra tiles each time.

pattern 1
5 tiles

pattern 2
9 tiles

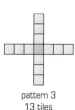

pattern 3
13 tiles

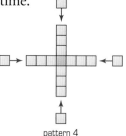

pattern 4
17 tiles

You can write: Total number of tiles = 4 × pattern number + 1
$$T = 4n \qquad\qquad + 1$$

T = Number of tiles
n = pattern number

You can write this in a function machine:

This is the number of yellow tiles.
4 arms with n tiles on each arm.

This is the one pink tile in the middle
of each pattern.

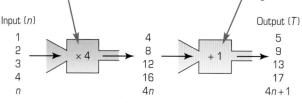

The function machine is: $n \longrightarrow 4n + 1$ — The *input* **turns into** $4n + 1$
The rule for the sequence is: $T(n) = 4n + 1$ — The *output* **equals** $4n + 1$

You can write a function using a mapping arrow or as an equation using an equals sign.

example

Complete this function machine.
Write the function as a mapping
and as an algebraic equation.

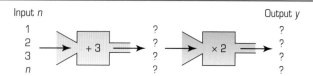

The function machine is:

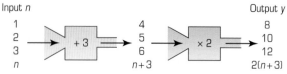

Function is $n \longrightarrow 2(n + 3)$
Equation is $y = 2(n + 3)$

You can show the pairs on a mapping
diagram:

Exercise A2.1

1 Find the missing outputs for each function machine.

a

Input		Output
4		?
6	-8	?
10		?
n		?

b

Input		Output
1		?
0.5	$+0.5$	?
4.5		?
n		?

2 Copy and complete these function machines and match each one with one of the functions in the box (there are two spare!)

$y = 3x + 3$	$y = 3x + 9$	$y = 3(x + 3)$	$y = \frac{x}{2} - 3$
$y = 3(x + 1)$	$y = 3x + 1$	$y = \frac{x-6}{2}$	$y = \frac{x}{2} - 6$

a

Input x			Output y
1			?
2	$\times 3$	$+ 9$	?
3			?

b

Input x			Output y
1			?
2	$\times 3$	$+ 3$	?
3			?

c

Input x			Output y
1			?
2	$\div 2$	$- 3$	?
3			?

d

Input x			Output y
1			?
2	$- 6$	$\div 2$	?
3			?

e

Input x			Output y
1			?
2	$+ 3$	$\times 3$	?
3			?

f

Input x			Output y
1			?
2	$+ 1$	$\times 3$	?
3			?

3 In question 2, function machines **b** and **f** are equivalent.
The same inputs produce the same outputs.
List the other pairs of equivalent functions in question 2. Explain your reasons.

4 Draw a function machine for each of these functions.
   a $y = 2x - 1$ **b** $y = \frac{x}{3} + 2$ **c** $y = 3(x + 1)$ **d** $y = \frac{x-4}{2}$

5 Challenge
For each of these function machines, find the missing inputs.

a

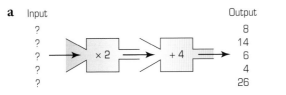

Input			Output
?			8
?			14
?	$\times 2$	$+ 4$	6
?			4
?			26

b

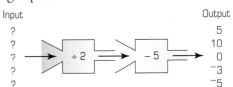

Input			Output
?			5
?			10
?	$\div 2$	$- 5$	0
?			$^-3$
?			$^-5$

For each function machine, write the function and the inverse function,
using a mapping arrow ($\rightarrow$).

This spread will show you how to:
▶▶ Generate points in all four quadrants and plot the graphs of linear functions, where y is given explicitly in terms of x.
▶▶ Recognise that equations of the form $y = mx + c$ correspond to straight-line graphs.

KEYWORDS

Coordinate pair	Intercept
Function machine	Input
Linear function	Output
Straight-line graph	

This function 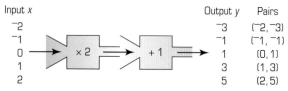 $y = 2x + 1$ is written as an algebraic equation.

y is the output x is the input

The function machine for $y = 2x + 1$ forms pairs of values. You can plot these values on a coordinate grid.

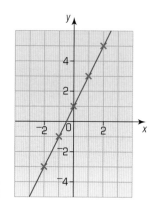

Input x		Output y	Pairs
⁻2		⁻3	(⁻2, ⁻3)
⁻1		⁻1	(⁻1, ⁻1)
0	→ ×2 ⟹ +1 ⟹	1	(0, 1)
1		3	(1, 3)
2		5	(2, 5)

The coordinate pairs lie on a straight-line graph.

▶ **You can use a straight-line graph to work out unknown values.**

Plot the graph $y = 3x - 1$.
Use your graph to find:
a the value of y when $x = 1.5$ **b** the value of x when $y = {}^-5.5$

....

A table of values helps keep track of the pairs.
$y = 3x - 1$ for x-values from ⁻2 to 2.

These are the coordinate pairs to plot.

Join the points together to form a straight-line graph.
Label the line $y = 3x - 1$

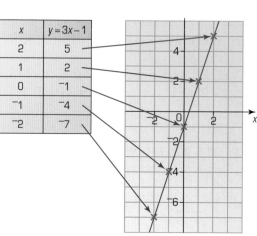

x	$y = 3x - 1$
2	5
1	2
0	⁻1
⁻1	⁻4
⁻2	⁻7

a Start from $x = 1.5$
The y-coordinate of the point on the line when $x = 1.5$ is $y = 3.5$
b Start from $y = {}^-5.5$
The x-coordinate of the point on the line when $y = {}^-5.5$ is $x = {}^-1.5$

▶ **A function of the form $y = mx + c$ will produce a straight-line graph.**

Exercise A2.2

1 Copy the grid onto squared paper.

   a Plot these coordinate pairs.
Join each point to the next point with a straight line.

     (1, 4) (3, 2) (3, 0) (1, ⁻2) (⁻1, ⁻2)
     (⁻3, 0) (⁻3, 2) (⁻1, 4) (1, 4)

   b What shape have you drawn?

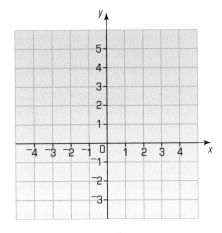

2 For each of these functions:

   ▶ copy and complete the table of values
   ▶ copy the grid, plot the coordinate pairs on the same grid,
     and join up with a straight line
   ▶ label each line.

   a $y = 3x + 1$

x	⁻2	⁻1	0	1	2
y					

   b $y = 3x + 4$

x	⁻2	⁻1	0	1	2
y					

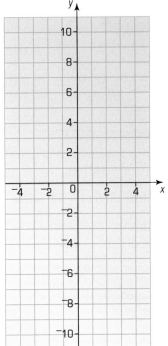

   c $y = 3x - 2$

x	⁻2	⁻1	0	1	2
y					

   d Look at all three straight-line graphs.
What is similar about the lines?
Look at the equations. What is similar about the equations?

   e Look at where each line crosses the y-axis (called the
intercept). Look at each equation.
Compare these and comment on your findings.

3 Challenge
These equations belong to two families.

   ▶ Family A: the straight-line graphs are all parallel.
   ▶ Family B: the straight-line graphs all intercept the
     y-axis at 3.

Can you sort the equations into their two families,
without drawing them?

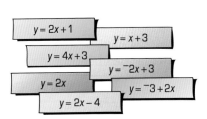

13

This spread will show you how to:
▶▶ Construct linear functions arising from real-life problems and plot their corresponding graphs.
▶▶ Discuss and interpret graphs arising from real situations.

KEYWORDS
Convert
Conversion graph
Distance–time graph

Dominique is on holiday in Cyprus.
The distance from the airport to her hotel in Limassol is 50 kilometres.

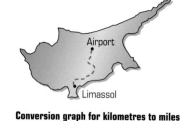

Dominique wants to convert 50 kilometres to miles.
She decides to draw a conversion graph.

I know:
| 8 kilometres | = | 5 miles |
So:
| 80 kilometres | = | 50 miles |
| 160 kilometres | = | 100 miles |
and
| 0 kilometres | = | 0 miles |

She draws lines on her conversion graph to convert 50 kilometres to miles.

50 kilometres = 31 miles

Dominique goes on a coach trip.
The distance–time graph illustrates her journey.

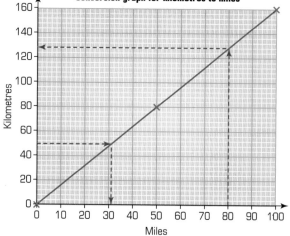

The coach travels 40 miles to their destination and 40 miles back to the resort, a total of 80 miles.
Dominique uses her conversion graph to convert 80 miles into kilometres.

80 miles = 128 kilometres

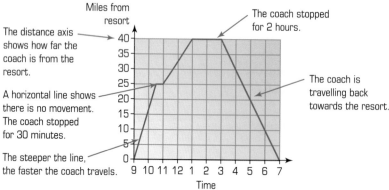

The distance axis shows how far the coach is from the resort.

A horizontal line shows there is no movement. The coach stopped for 30 minutes.

The steeper the line, the faster the coach travels.

The coach stopped for 2 hours.

The coach is travelling back towards the resort.

▶ A distance–time graph illustrates a journey by showing how far you have travelled during a period of time.

The mathematical term for how far something has moved is displacement.

Exercise A2.3

1 Use the conversion graph for miles to kilometres on page 14 to change this road sign into kilometres.

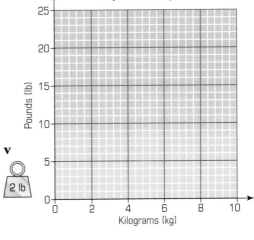

Birmingham 100 miles ___ km
Coventry 75 miles ___ km
Rugby 60 miles ___ km

2 **a** Copy the axes for the conversion graph for pounds, lb, to kilograms, kg.

b Plot the conversion graph, using these three conversions:

0 kg = 0 lb
5 kg = 11 lb
10 kg = 22 lb

c Use the conversion graph to convert these weights into kilograms.

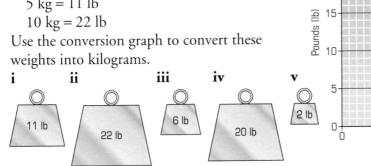

i 11 lb ii 22 lb iii 6 lb iv 20 lb v 2 lb

Conversion graph for pounds to kilograms

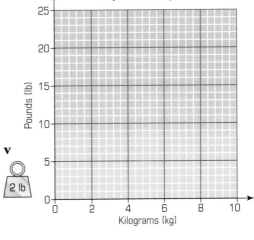

3 Sonia takes her dog to the park for a walk. This is her distance–time graph.

a What happens when Sonia is 800 metres from home?

b How long does it take her to reach the park?

c How long does she stay at the park?

d How far does she walk in total?

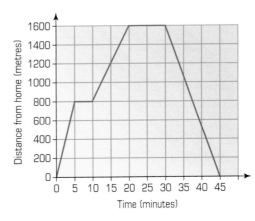

4 Here are two containers. Water is poured into the containers at a steady rate. The graphs show depth of water against time.

A

B

a Match the correct container to its graph.

i

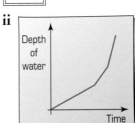

ii

b Sketch a graph to show depth of water against time when this container is filled.

15

You should know how to ...

1 Plot the graphs of linear functions, where y is given explicitly in terms of x.

Check out

1 a Copy and complete the table of values for the function $y = 2x - 1$.

x	⁻3	⁻2	⁻1	0	1	2	3
y		⁻5					5

b Copy the grid and plot the graph of $y = 2x - 1$. Join the points to make a straight line.

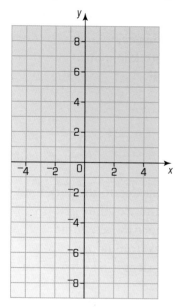

2 Recognise that equations of the form $y = mx + c$ correspond to straight-line graphs.

2 On the same grid as question 1, plot the graph of $y = 2x + 1$.
Describe how the two graphs are the same.
Which of the following graphs will have the same feature as the two you have drawn?
A $y = 3x + 2$
B $y = 2x - 5$
C $y = 4x - 2$
D $y = 3 + 2x$

3 Represent problems in algebraic and graphical form, using correct notation and appropriate diagrams.

3 Draw a sketch graph to show the depth of water against time when this container is filled.

1 Proportional reasoning

This unit will show you how to:

- Know that a recurring decimal is a fraction.
- Use division to convert a fraction to a decimal.
- Order fractions.
- Add and subtract fractions.
- Calculate fractions of quantities.
- Multiply and divide an integer by a fraction.
- Interpret % as an operator and express one number as a percentage of another.
- Use the equivalence of fractions, decimals and percentages to compare proportions.
- Calculate percentages and find the outcome of a given percentage increase or decrease.
- Consolidate understanding of the relationship between ratio and proportion.
- Reduce a ratio to its simplest form.
- Divide a quantity into two or more parts in a given ratio.
- Use the unitary method to solve problems involving ratio and direct proportion.
- Use inverse operations.
- Use the order of operations, including brackets.
- Recall known facts, including fraction to decimal conversions.
- Consolidate and extend mental methods.
- Use a calculator efficiently and effectively.
- Compare and evaluate solutions.
- Use logical argument to establish the truth of a statement.

You can use percentages to solve problems.

Before you start

You should know how to ...

1 Multiply two numbers up to 10 × 10 and the related division facts.

2 Write numbers as fractions and write one number as a fraction of another.

3 Find equivalent fractions and write fractions in their simplest form.

4 Calculate 10% of an amount.

Check in

1 Work out: **a** 7 × 5   **b** 36 ÷ 6   **c** 45 ÷ 9

2 **a** What fraction of 7 is 5?
   b What fraction of 12 is 7?
   c What fraction of 10 is 9?

3 Simplify each of these fractions to their simplest form.
   a $\frac{8}{10}$ **b** $\frac{12}{15}$ **c** $\frac{21}{24}$ **d** $\frac{35}{55}$

4 Calculate 10% of: **a** 50p   **b** £120   **c** 65 m

Adding and subtracting fractions

This spread will show you how to:

▶▶ Add and subtract fractions by writing them with a common denominator.

▶▶ Order fractions.

KEYWORDS

Order	Add
Compare	Subtract
Fraction	Equivalent
Ascending	
Common denominator	

The diagrams show different fractions of a whole:

$\frac{1}{2}$ is shaded $\frac{1}{4}$ is shaded $\frac{1}{3}$ is shaded

You can write the fractions in size order.

$\frac{1}{4}$ is the smallest, then $\frac{1}{3}$, then $\frac{1}{2}$.

It is harder to order these fractions:

$$\frac{7}{12} \qquad \frac{5}{6} \qquad \frac{2}{3}$$

The denominators are 12, 6 and 3.

To compare the fractions, you need a common denominator:

3, 6 and 12 are all factors of 12:

> You could use a suitable diagram to compare them.

$$\frac{2}{3} \xrightarrow{\times 4} = \frac{8}{12} \qquad \frac{5}{6} \xrightarrow{\times 2} = \frac{10}{12}$$

> You say,
> '$\frac{2}{3}$ is equivalent to $\frac{8}{12}$.'

You can see that $\frac{7}{12}$ is the smallest, then $\frac{2}{3}$, then $\frac{5}{6}$.

▶ **You can compare fractions when they have the same denominator.**

You can add and subtract fractions with the same denominator.

example

Work out:

a $\frac{1}{8} + \frac{1}{8} + \frac{1}{8}$ **b** $\frac{1}{2} - \frac{1}{3}$

a The denominators are all eighths, so you can add:

$\frac{1}{8} + \frac{1}{8} + \frac{1}{8} = \frac{3}{8}$

b You need a common denominator.

2 and 3 are factors of 6 (= 2 × 3)

$$\frac{1}{2} \xrightarrow{\times 3} = \frac{3}{6} \qquad \frac{1}{3} \xrightarrow{\times 2} = \frac{2}{6}$$

$\frac{1}{2} - \frac{1}{3} = \frac{3}{6} - \frac{2}{6} = \frac{1}{6}$

Exercise N1.1

1 Put these fractions in ascending order.

   a $\frac{3}{8}, \frac{6}{8}, \frac{1}{8}, \frac{4}{8}$ **b** $\frac{6}{7}, \frac{3}{7}, \frac{2}{7}, \frac{4}{7}$

   c $\frac{4}{9}, \frac{3}{9}, \frac{7}{9}, \frac{8}{9}, \frac{5}{9}$ **d** $\frac{3}{10}, \frac{1}{10}, \frac{4}{10}, \frac{8}{10}, \frac{5}{10}$

2 Work out the answers to these fraction problems.

   a $\frac{1}{6} + \frac{1}{6} + \frac{1}{6} + \frac{2}{6}$ **b** $\frac{3}{9} + \frac{2}{9} + \frac{2}{9}$ **c** $\frac{3}{12} + \frac{5}{12} + \frac{3}{12}$

   d $\frac{7}{8} - \frac{4}{8}$ **e** $\frac{7}{9} - \frac{5}{9} - \frac{1}{9}$ **f** $\frac{2}{11} + \frac{7}{11} - \frac{3}{11} - \frac{1}{11}$

3 Work out the answers to these fraction problems.

   a $\frac{1}{3} + \frac{1}{4}$ **b** $\frac{1}{3} - \frac{1}{6}$ **c** $\frac{3}{5} + \frac{1}{4}$

   d $\frac{1}{2} + \frac{1}{5} + \frac{1}{4}$ **e** $\frac{2}{5} - \frac{1}{6}$ **f** $\frac{9}{10} - \frac{2}{5} + \frac{1}{6}$

4 Copy and complete these magic squares.
  The rows, columns and diagonals all add up to the same amount.

a

$\frac{8}{20}$		
	$\frac{5}{20}$	
	$\frac{9}{20}$	$\frac{2}{20}$

   Use these fractions: $\frac{1}{20}, \frac{3}{20}, \frac{4}{20}, \frac{6}{20}, \frac{7}{20}$.

b

		$\frac{3}{5}$
$\frac{3}{10}$		$\frac{7}{10}$
		$\frac{1}{5}$

   Use these fractions: $\frac{1}{10}, \frac{2}{5}, \frac{1}{2}, \frac{4}{5}, \frac{9}{10}$.

5 Copy and complete these puzzles. You must only use the numbers
  given for each question.

   a $\frac{\square}{\square} + \frac{\square}{\square} = \frac{3}{4}$ $\boxed{1}$ $\boxed{1}$ $\boxed{4}$ $\boxed{2}$ **b** $\frac{\square}{\square} + \frac{\square}{\square} = \frac{11}{12}$ $\boxed{2}$ $\boxed{4}$ $\boxed{3}$ $\boxed{1}$

   c $\frac{\square}{\square} + \frac{\square}{\square} = \frac{5}{12}$ $\boxed{1}$ $\boxed{3}$ $\boxed{3}$ $\boxed{4}$ **d** $\frac{\square}{\square} + \frac{\square}{\square} = \frac{39}{40}$ $\boxed{3}$ $\boxed{3}$ $\boxed{5}$ $\boxed{8}$

6 A fraction from Box A added to a fraction from Box B makes a
  fraction in Box C. Find the four fraction additions.

Box A

$\frac{7}{18}$	$\frac{1}{10}$
$\frac{3}{9}$	$\frac{1}{4}$

+

Box B

$\frac{1}{3}$	$\frac{2}{5}$
$\frac{5}{12}$	$\frac{4}{9}$

=

Box C

$\frac{2}{3}$	$\frac{5}{6}$
$\frac{1}{2}$	$\frac{12}{18}$

Hint: Not all the fractions
are in simplest form.

This spread will show you how to:

▸▸ Calculate fractions of quantities.

▸▸ Multiply an integer by a fraction.

To find a half of something, you divide it into 2.

$\frac{1}{2}$ of £20 = £20 ÷ 2 = £10

$\frac{1}{2}$ is a unit fraction because the numerator is 1.

To find other unit fractions of amounts, you divide by the denominator:

$\frac{1}{5}$ of 30 kg = 30 kg ÷ 5 = 6 kg

6 kg	6 kg	6 kg	6 kg	6 kg

You can use this information to find $\frac{3}{5}$ of 30 kg.

3 lots of $\frac{1}{5}$ is $3 \times \frac{1}{5} = \frac{3}{5}$

| $\frac{1}{5}$ | $\frac{1}{5}$ | $\frac{1}{5}$ |

So $\frac{3}{5}$ of 30 kg = $3 \times \frac{1}{5}$ of 30 kg = 3 × 6 kg = 18 kg

| 6 kg | 6 kg | 6 kg |

▸ In maths, the word 'of' or 'lots of' means you multiply.

Find:

a $\frac{2}{3}$ of £45

b $\frac{3}{20}$ of 1 kg.

....

a $\frac{1}{3}$ of £45 = £45 ÷ 3

= £15

$\frac{2}{3}$ of £45 = $2 \times \frac{1}{3}$ of £45

= 2 × £15

= £30

b 1 kg = 1000 g

$\frac{1}{20}$ of 1000 g = 1000 g ÷ 20

= 50 g

$\frac{3}{20}$ of 1000 g = $3 \times \frac{1}{20}$ of 1000 g

= 3 × 50 g

= 150 g

Exercise N1.2

1 **a** How many minutes are there in an hour?
   b Work out how many minutes there are in:
   i $\frac{1}{2}$ an hour   **ii** $\frac{1}{4}$ of an hour   **iii** $\frac{1}{3}$ of an hour   **iv** $\frac{1}{6}$ of an hour?

2 **a** How many degrees are there in a right angle?
   b Work out how many degrees there are in:
   i $\frac{1}{2}$ a right angle   **ii** $\frac{1}{3}$ of a right angle   **iii** $\frac{1}{9}$ of a right angle.

3 Work out:
   a $\frac{1}{2}$ of £32   **b** $\frac{1}{3}$ of £18   **c** $\frac{1}{5}$ of 30 cm
   d $\frac{1}{7}$ of 35p   **e** $\frac{2}{3}$ of 30 kg   **f** $\frac{3}{5}$ of 20 litres
   g $\frac{5}{7}$ of 35p   **h** $\frac{7}{10}$ of 50 cm

4 Here are five time statements.

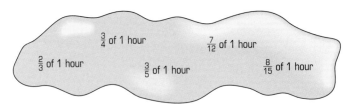

$\frac{3}{4}$ of 1 hour $\frac{7}{12}$ of 1 hour $\frac{2}{3}$ of 1 hour $\frac{3}{5}$ of 1 hour $\frac{8}{15}$ of 1 hour

   Work out the time in minutes for each statement.
   Then put the statements in order, starting with the shortest.

5 Each number in Box A goes with numbers in
   Box B and Box C to make four 'fraction of'
   statements.
   Find and write down these four statements.

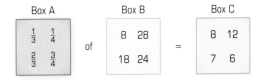

6 Tim is offered three choices for his pocket money.
   Which choice should he take to get the most
   pocket money?
   Explain your answer with calculations.

Choice 1 $\frac{2}{5}$ of £4.50

Choice 2 $\frac{4}{7}$ of £3.50

Choice 3 $\frac{5}{12}$ of £3.60

7 Use the multiplication fact that $2 \times 3 = 3 \times 2$ to help you do these.
   a $3 \times \frac{1}{4}$ **b** $\frac{1}{7} \times 5$ **c** $\frac{1}{56} \times 4$
   d $\frac{2}{11} \times 4$ **e** $3 \times \frac{2}{12}$ **f** $4 \times \frac{3}{15}$
   g $\frac{3}{20} \times 9$ **h** $11 \times \frac{3}{30}$

8 Work out each of these.
   Give your answers as a simplest form fraction or as a mixed number.
   a $5 \times \frac{2}{9}$ **b** $\frac{3}{7} \times 5$ **c** $\frac{5}{6} \times 3$
   d $3 \times \frac{3}{4}$ **e** $10 \times \frac{5}{7}$ **f** $\frac{3}{8} \times 9$
   g $\frac{4}{5} \times 8$ **h** $\frac{5}{12} \times 7$

This spread will show you how to:
▶▶ Divide an integer by a fraction.
▶▶ Use inverse operations.

KEYWORDS
Divide   Inverse
Multiplication Fraction

These 6 counters divide into 3 lots of 2 counters:

The division $6 \div 2$ means 'how many 2s are there in 6?'

$6 \div 2 = 3$

These 6 counters divide into 12 lots of $\frac{1}{2}$ counters:

The division $6 \div \frac{1}{2}$ means 'how many $\frac{1}{2}$s are there in 6?'

$6 \div \frac{1}{2} = 12$

▶ Division and multiplication are inverse operations
  – one undoes the other: $12 \div 3 = 4$ so $4 \times 3 = 12$.

When you multiply an amount by $\frac{1}{2}$, you divide by 2:
$$\frac{1}{2} \times 20 = 20 \div 2 = 10$$

When you divide an amount by $\frac{1}{2}$, you do the opposite so you multiply by 2:
$$20 \div \frac{1}{2} = 20 \times 2 = 40$$

example

Find $6 \times \frac{2}{3}$ and use it to find $6 \div \frac{2}{3}$.

$6 \times \frac{2}{3} = 6 \times \frac{1}{3} \times 2$
$\qquad = 6 \div 3 \times 2 \qquad$ divide by 3 then multiply by 2
$\qquad = 2 \times 2$
$\qquad = 4$

To find $6 \div \frac{2}{3}$ you must do the opposite:
$6 \div \frac{2}{3} = 6 \times 3 \div 2 \qquad$ multiply by 3 then divide by 2
$\qquad = 18 \div 2$
$\qquad = 9$

▶ When you divide an amount by a fraction less than 1, the result will be larger.

Exercise N1.3

1 Look at these circles.
  a How many halves are there in:
    i 1   **ii** 2   **iii** 3?
  b How many quarters are there in:
    i 1   **ii** 2   **iii** 3?

2 Look at these circles.
  a How many $\frac{1}{3}$s are there in:
    i 1   **ii** 2   **iii** 3?
  b How many $\frac{1}{6}$s are there in:
    i 1   **ii** 2   **iii** 3?

3 Imagine four circles.
  a How many $\frac{1}{4}$s are in the four circles?
  b How many $\frac{1}{5}$s are in the four circles?
  c How many $\frac{1}{10}$s are in the four circles?
  d How many $\frac{1}{15}$s are in the four circles?

4 Work out each of these. The first one is done for you.

> Division is the inverse of multiplication.

  a **i** $6 \times \frac{1}{2}$ **ii** $6 \div \frac{1}{2}$
  i $6 \times \frac{1}{2} = 6 \div 2 = 3$ **ii** so $6 \div \frac{1}{2} = 6 \times 2 = 12$
  b **i** $9 \times \frac{1}{3}$ **ii** $9 \div \frac{1}{3}$ **c** **i** $8 \times \frac{1}{4}$ **ii** $8 \div \frac{1}{4}$
  d **i** $6 \times \frac{1}{6}$ **ii** $6 \div \frac{1}{6}$ **e** **i** $10 \times \frac{1}{5}$ **ii** $10 \div \frac{1}{5}$

5 Work out:
  a $12 \div \frac{1}{2}$ **b** $5 \div \frac{1}{2}$ **c** $7 \div \frac{1}{3}$ **d** $2 \div \frac{1}{8}$ **e** $3 \div \frac{3}{4}$ **f** $8 \div \frac{2}{3}$
  g $10 \div \frac{4}{8}$ **h** $6 \div \frac{3}{5}$ **i** $9 \div \frac{2}{3}$ **j** $7 \div \frac{2}{8}$ **k** $6 \div \frac{3}{4}$ **l** $11 \div \frac{2}{3}$

6 Copy and complete this magic square using the calculations in the cloud. Each row, column and diagonal should add up to the same amount.

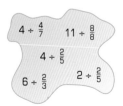

	$1 \div \frac{1}{4}$	
$2 \div \frac{1}{3}$	$6 \div \frac{3}{4}$	
	$6 \div \frac{1}{2}$	

$4 \div \frac{4}{7}$ $11 \div \frac{8}{8}$
$4 \div \frac{2}{5}$
$6 \div \frac{2}{3}$ $2 \div \frac{2}{5}$

7 Copy and complete this spider diagram.

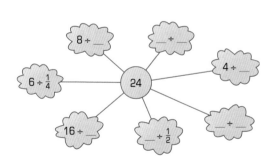

This spread will show you how to:

▶▶ Use division to convert a fraction to a decimal.

▶▶ Interpret percentage as an operator.

▶▶ Calculate percentages.

▶▶ Consolidate and extend mental methods.

KEYWORDS

Per cent	Fraction
Percentage	Decimal
Divide	Justify
Profit	

Per cent means 'per 100'. You use the symbol %.

37% means 37 for every 100.
You can write it
as a fraction: $\frac{37}{100}$ and as a decimal: $37 \div 100 = 0.37$

Many everyday percentages are easy to work out in your head.

▶ **25% is the same as $\frac{1}{4}$ – you divide by 4.**

▶ **10% is the same as $\frac{1}{10}$ – you divide by 10.**

You can use these facts to work out other percentages.

---

example

Find:

a 20% of 60 m

b 15% of 60 m.

. . . .

a 10% of 60 m = 60 m ÷ 10
              = 6 m
   20% of 60 m = 2 × 10% of 60 m
               = 2 × 6 m
               = 12 m

b 10% of 60 m = 6 m
   5% of 60 m = $\frac{1}{2}$ × 10% of 60 m
              = $\frac{1}{2}$ × 6 m
              = 3 m
   15% of 60 m = 10% of 60 m + 5% of 60 m
                    = 6 m + 3 m
                    = 9 m

You can use a calculator to find other percentages of amounts.

example

Calculate:

a 12% of 64 cm

b 127% of 63 kg.

. . . .

a 12% means $\frac{12}{100}$ = 12 ÷ 100
               = 0.12
   You can input 0.12 × 64 = 7.68
   Or press [1] [2] [%] [×] [6] [4] [=]
   The answer is 7.68 cm

b 127% means $\frac{127}{100}$ = 127 ÷ 100
               = 1.27
   You can input 1.27 × 63 = 80.01
   Or press [1] [2] [7] [%] [×] [6] [3] [=]
   The answer is 80.01 kg

The sequence of keys depends on the calculator you use.
Check yours using the example.

Exercise N1.4

1 Change each of these percentages into decimals by dividing by 100.
  a 40% **b** 22% **c** 83% **d** 6%
  e 125% **f** 105% **g** 228% **h** 3.5%

2 Work out 10% of each of these amounts by dividing by 10.
  a 40p **b** 60 cm **c** 120 km **d** 6000 mm
  e 83 cm **f** 12 seconds **g** 108 m **h** 5 mm

3 Work out the answers to these by finding what 10% is first.
  a 20% of 60 **b** 5% of 40 **c** 30% of 20
  d 15% of 120 **e** 95% of 200 **f** $2\frac{1}{2}$% of 40

4 There are three good ways for working out percentages.
  A Find 10% first, then use this to find the percentage.
  B Change the percentage into a decimal, then use a calculator.
  C Change the percentage into a fraction and work out the fraction of the amount.

  State which method you would use to work out each of these questions
  and then work out the answers. Remember to show your working.
  a 25% of 50 cm **b** 13% of 83 mm **c** 30% of 70p
  d 35% of 150 m **e** 55% of 60 mm **f** 11% of 80
  g 37% of 65 **h** 75% of 124 **i** 85% of 230

5 Copy and complete this spider diagram.

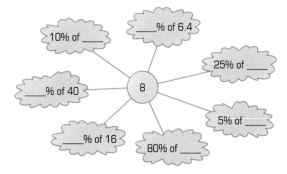

6 Which of these statements is true? Use calculations to justify your answer.
  a 75% of £6 > 60% of £7.50
  b 25% of 72 > 35% of 60
  c 35% of 60 > 65% of 30

7 A TV hire firm paid £900 to advertise in a local paper.
  That month its profits rose from £7200 by 15%.
  Do you think the firm should advertise again? Use calculations to justify your answer.

Fractions, decimals and percentages

This spread will show you how to:

▶▶ Use division to convert a fraction to a decimal.

▶▶ Express one number as a percentage of another.

▶▶ Use the equivalence of fractions, decimals and percentages to compare proportions.

KEYWORDS

Fraction   Compare

Decimal   Proportion

Percentage

Recurring decimal

You can use a fraction, a decimal and a percentage to express the same amount:

$\frac{1}{2}$, 50% and 0.5 are equivalent.
They all show the same proportion.

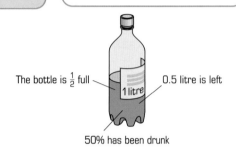

The bottle is $\frac{1}{2}$ full   0.5 litre is left

50% has been drunk

You should know these equivalent forms:

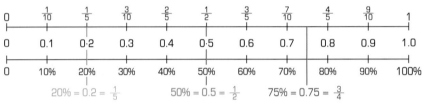

$20\% = 0.2 = \frac{1}{5}$ $50\% = 0.5 = \frac{1}{2}$ $75\% = 0.75 = \frac{3}{4}$

You can convert between the different forms.

Fraction ⟶ Decimal

$\frac{9}{40} = 9 \div 40 = 0.225$

Decimal ⟶ Fraction

$$0.44 = \frac{44}{100} \overset{\div 4}{\underset{\div 4}{=}} \frac{11}{25}$$

Fraction ⟶ Percentage

$\frac{5}{12} = \frac{5}{12} \times 100\% = 5 \times 100 \div 12\%$
$\quad = 41.7\%$ (1 dp)

Percentage ⟶ Fraction

$$28\% = \frac{28}{100} \overset{\div 4}{\underset{\div 4}{=}} \frac{7}{11}$$

Percentage ⟶ Decimal

$23\% = 23 \div 100 = 0.23$

Decimal ⟶ Percentage

$0.31 = 0.31 \times 100\% = 31\%$

Notice that $\frac{5}{12}$ gives a recurring decimal: $\frac{5}{12} = 0.41666666\ldots$

Decimals that stop are called terminating decimals:
$\frac{9}{40} = 0.225$

You can compare proportions if they are in the same form.

example

Three friends share a pizza. Bob eats 35%, Jim eats $\frac{2}{5}$ and Tom eats 0.25.
Who eats the most pizza?

$35\% = 35 \div 100 = 0.35 \qquad \frac{2}{5} = 2 \div 5 = 0.4$
$0.4 > 0.35 > 0.25$ so Jim eats the most.

Exercise N1.5

1 A pair of 'cotton rich' socks is 62% cotton. What percentage is not cotton?

2 **a** Change these percentages into decimals.
    i 40%   **ii** 32%   **iii** 7%   **iv** 135%
  b Change these decimals into percentages.
    i 0.71   **ii** 0.8   **iii** 0.03   **iv** 1.72
  c Change these fractions into decimals.
    i $\frac{3}{4}$ **ii** $\frac{2}{5}$ **iii** $\frac{1}{8}$ **iv** $\frac{3}{8}$
  d Change these decimals into fractions.
    i 0.7   **ii** 0.05   **iii** 0.39   **iv** 0.25
  e Change these percentages into simplest form fractions.
    i 30%   **ii** 80%   **iii** 15%   **iv** 24%
  f Change these fractions into percentages.
    i $\frac{2}{5}$ **ii** $\frac{5}{8}$ **iii** $\frac{7}{50}$ **iv** $\frac{3}{20}$

3 This pie chart shows the lessons a teacher takes.
Copy and complete the table, estimating the fraction, decimal and percentage of time spent teaching each subject.

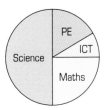

	Fraction	Decimal	%
Maths			
Science			
PE			
ICT			

4 A pair of trousers is made from three materials. $\frac{3}{5}$ is polyester, 25% is Lycra. The rest is cotton.
  a What percentage is cotton?
  b What fraction is cotton?

5 This pie chart shows the income from books sold by a market stallholder.
The stallholder got £160 from selling science fiction books. Estimate how much he got from:
  a other fiction   **b** crime   **c** romance.

6 Each year group in Stanway School has equal numbers of boys and girls.
The pie charts show the proportions of students in each year. There are 135 boys in Year 7.

Copy and complete this table.
From your table, how many students are in each year?

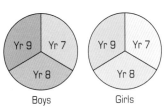

	Yr 7	Yr 8	Yr 9	Total
Boys	135			
Girls				

 **Percentage change**

This spread will show you how to:

▶ Calculate percentages and find the outcome of a given percentage increase or decrease.

▶ Round decimals to the nearest whole number.

KEYWORDS

Percentage	Increase
Decrease	Change
Subtract	Interest

Percentages are often used to describe changes:

increases   or   decreases

You can find a percentage increase in two steps:

Calculate the amount of change

Add it on to the original amount

Increase £35 by 5%

5% of £35 $= \frac{1}{2} \times 10\% \times £35$
$\qquad = \frac{1}{2} \times £3.50$
$\qquad = £1.75$

£35 + £1.75 = £36.75

You can find a percentage decrease in two steps:

Calculate the amount of change

Subtract it from the original amount

Decrease £16 by 25%

25% of £16 $= \frac{1}{4} \times £16$
$\qquad = £16 \div 4$
$\qquad = £4$

£16 − £4 = £12

Not all calculations give whole-number answers.

example

A loaf of bread cost 40p in 1990. The price has increased by 37%.
What is the current price?

....

Find the amount of change: 37% of 40p $= 37 \div 100 \times 40p$
$\qquad\qquad\qquad\qquad\qquad = 14.8p$
$\qquad\qquad\qquad\qquad\qquad = 15p$ to the nearest penny

The current price is 40p + 15p = 55p.

You can change an amount by more than 100%.

A 100% increase doubles the amount – you add the amount on to itself.
A 100% decrease leaves zero – you take the whole lot away!
A 200% increase trebles the amount.
A 200% decrease leaves a negative amount.

Exercise N1.6

1　**a**　Calculate these percentages by finding 10% first.
　　　i 20% of 30　　**ii** 5% of 60　　**iii** 95% of 60
　　b　Change each of these percentages to fractions, then find the fraction of the amount.
　　　i 25% of 84　　**ii** 40% of 42　　**iii** 60% of 20

2　**a**　Increase these amounts by the percentage shown.
　　　i £40 by 10%　　**ii** £60 by 5%　　**iii** 88 cm by 15%
　　b　Decrease these amounts by the percentage shown.
　　　i £120 by 5%　　**ii** 300 cm by 60%　　**iii** 73p by 100%

3　A shop is having a sale.
　　Find the sale price of each of these items.

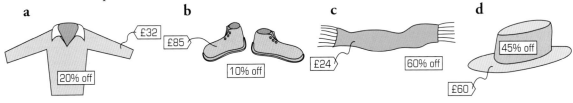

a £32　20% off　　**b** £85　10% off　　**c** £24　60% off　　**d** 45% off　£60

4　Joanne puts £100 in a bank account with an interest rate of
　　5% per year.
　　She neither puts any more money in nor takes any out.
　　Find out, to the nearest penny, what she has in her account after:
　　a 1 year　　　**b** 2 years　　　**c** 3 years

> An interest rate of 5% means that the bank adds 5% to the balance in the account each year.

5　Henry bought his house in 1998 for £80 000.
　　Since then it has increased in value by 150%.
　　Find the present value of Henry's house.

6　Samantha invested £2000 in shares on the stock market in 2002.
　　Her shares have since decreased in value by 23%.
　　Find out what her shares are worth at present, to the nearest penny.

7　Tony says 'If you increase an amount by 10% then decrease the
　　new amount by 10%, you get back to the original amount.'
　　Is Tony correct? Use calculations to back up your answer.

8　Chloe says 'To increase £40 by 15%, you just multiply it by 1.15.'
　　Try her calculation and the normal two-step method to see whether she is correct.

9　Four numbers are increased by the
　　percentages shown to make four new
　　numbers. Copy and complete the table
　　using the numbers in the cloud.

Original number	% increase	Increased number
	20%	48
	150%	60
	25%	45
	75%	56

24　32　36　40

This spread will show you how to:
▶▶ Consolidate understanding of the relationship between ratio and proportion.
▶▶ Reduce a ratio to its simplest form.
▶▶ Divide a quantity in a given ratio.

KEYWORDS

Fraction	Proportion
Ratio	
Simplest form	

▶ A proportion compares a part with the whole.

▶ A ratio compares a part with another part.

You can use a fraction, decimal or percentage to show a proportion.

$\frac{1}{4}$ of this circle is blue.

The proportion shaded blue is $\frac{1}{4}$ or 25%.
The ratio of blue : yellow is 1 : 3.

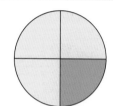

▶ You can simplify a ratio by dividing both parts by the same number.

$\frac{4}{8}$ of this circle is blue.

The proportion shaded blue is $\frac{4}{8}$ or 50%.

In its simplest form, $\frac{4}{8} = \frac{1}{2}$ (÷4)

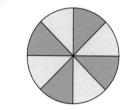

The ratio of blue : yellow is 4 : 4

In its simplest form the ratio is ÷4 (4:4 → 1:1) ÷4

You can compare parts in a ratio when they both use the same units.

example

Simplify the ratio 30 minutes : 3 hours.

3 hours = 3 × 60 minutes = 180 minutes

The ratio is ÷30 (30:180 → 1:6) ÷30

You can use fractions to divide a quantity in a given ratio.

example

Share £20 in the ratio 3 : 2.

The total number of parts is 3 + 2 = 5.
You can write the ratio using proportions $\frac{3}{5} : \frac{2}{5}$
$\frac{1}{5}$ of £20 = £20 ÷ 5 = £4
so $\frac{2}{5}$ of £20 = 2 × £4 = £8 and $\frac{3}{5}$ of £20 = 3 × £4 = £12

£12 = $\frac{3}{5}$ of £20
£8 = $\frac{2}{5}$ of £20

You share £20 in the ratio £12 : £8.

Exercise N1.7

1 Here is a shaded stick.
  a Write the shaded proportion as:
    i a fraction   **ii** a percentage.
  b What is the ratio of shaded to unshaded parts?

2 27 boys and 23 girls are going on a school trip.
  a What fraction of the pupils going are boys?
  b Write this as a percentage.
  c What is the ratio of girls to boys?

3 Which two of these ratios are equivalent to $6:8$?
  a $3:4$ **b** $8:6$ **c** $18:24$ **d** $18:12$ **e** $4:4$

4 Reduce these mixed-unit ratios to their simplest form.
  a $20\,\text{cm}:1\,\text{m}$ **b** $£2:25\text{p}$ **c** $2\,\text{hours}:15\,\text{minutes}$ **d** $3\,\text{cm}:6\,\text{mm}$
  e $15\text{p}:£1.80$ **f** $24\,\text{minutes}:2\,\text{hours}$ **g** $400\,\text{m}:5\,\text{km}$ **h** $125\,\text{g}:2\,\text{kg}$

5 In a test, Jim scored 8, Ewan scored 4 and Becky scored 6.
  a Write their scores in the ratio Jim : Ewan : Becky.
  b Reduce this ratio to its simplest form.
  c What proportion of their total score did Ewan score?
  d What proportion of Jim's score did Ewan get?
  e What proportion of Becky's score did Ewan get?

6 Alex and Morag share a paper round that pays £16. Alex does 2 mornings, Morag does 3.
  a In the ratio Alex : Morag, write down the ratio in which they should share the money.
  b Work out how much one day of the round is worth.
  c Work out how much they each get.

7 Fran and Anna share a lottery win in the ratio $3:4$.
If Anna gets £60, how much does Fran get?

8 A map has a scale of $1:2500$.
  a What distance does 4 cm on the map represent in real life
    i in cm   **ii** in m?
  b What distance on the map would represent these real-life distances?
    i 50 m   **ii** 125 m

9 A concrete mix is made of 7 parts of sand, 5 parts of cement and 3 parts of stones.
  a Express this as a ratio of sand : cement : stones.
  b Work out how much of each goes to make 150 kg of concrete.
  c If 63 kg of sand is used, work out how much of the other materials needs to
    be used in the mix.

This spread will show you how to:
▸▸ Understand the relationship between ratio and proportion.
▸▸ Use the unitary method to solve problems involving ratio and direct proportion.

KEYWORDS

Ratio   Constant
Proportion   Strategy
Unitary method
Direct proportion

One muffin costs 30p

2 muffins cost $2 \times 30p = 60p$

3 muffins cost $3 \times 30p = 90p$

4 muffins cost $4 \times 30p = 120p$ (£1.20)

The cost of muffins is proportional to the number you buy.

The ratio number of muffins : cost is always the same.

1 : 30p
↓
1 : 30p

$\div 2 \left(\begin{array}{c} 2:60p \\ 1:30p \end{array} \right) \div 2$

$\div 3 \left(\begin{array}{c} 3:90p \\ 1:30p \end{array} \right) \div 3$

$\div 4 \left(\begin{array}{c} 4:120p \\ 1:30p \end{array} \right) \div 4$

The ratio between the two amounts is constant, so the amounts are in direct proportion.

You can use proportionality to help solve problems.
A good strategy is the unitary method: you find what one item is worth.

example

Three bars of chocolate cost 78p.
How much do seven identical bars cost?

....

Find out what one bar costs: $78p \div 3 = 26p$
One bar costs 26p so 7 bars cost $7 \times 26p = 182p$
Seven bars cost £1.82.

example

Joe travels 20 km. How many miles is this?
5 miles = 8 km

....

You want to know how many miles in 1 km:

$8\text{ km} = 5\text{ miles}$

so $1\text{ km} = \frac{5}{8}\text{ miles}$

$20\text{ km} = 20 \times \frac{5}{8}\text{ miles}$
$= 12.5\text{ miles}$

20 km is 12.5 miles.

Exercise N1.8

1 Copy and complete these direct proportion tables.

  a Loose apples

Weight	1 kg	2 kg	3 kg	4 kg	5 kg
Cost	35p				

  b Bars of chocolate

Number of bars	1	2	3	4
Cost	45p			

  c Loose potatoes

Weight	1 kg	2 kg	3 kg	4 kg	5 kg
Cost		36p			

  d Fruit pastilles

Number of packs	1	2	3	4
Cost			96p	

2 8 packets of pork pies cost £18.
  Work out the cost of:
  a 1 packet   **b** 3 packets   **c** 7 packets

3 A tree grown from seed increases in height by the same amount each year.
  After 8 years it is 168 cm high.
  Work out its height after:
  a 1 year   **b** 5 years   **c** 20 years

4 Another tree grown from seed also increases in height by the same amount each year.
  After 5 years its height is 85 cm.
  Work out how old it was when it reached these heights.
  a 51 cm   **b** 204 cm   **c** 2.89 m

5 A 250 g tin of tuna costs 75p.
  How much per 100 g of tuna is this?

6 A 350 g jar of honey costs £1.47.
  A 500 g jar of the same honey costs £1.95.
  a Work out the cost of 100 g of honey for:
     i the 350 g jar   **ii** the 500 g jar
  b Which jar represents the best value?
  Explain your answer using your calculations for part **a**.

7 A box is filled with identical packets of biscuits.
  The contents of the box weigh 3.6 kg.
  Five of the packets are eaten.
  The contents now weigh 2.475 kg.
  How many packets of biscuits were in the box to start with?

8 £1 is worth 2.8 New Zealand dollars (NZ$).
  Edmund changed £750 into NZ dollars, went to Auckland and spent NZ$1764.
  At the end of the holiday, he changed the NZ$s back into £s.
  How much did he get?

This spread will show you how to:

▶▶ Use the order of operations, including brackets.

▶▶ Use a calculator efficiently and effectively.

Ms Take has set the class this calculation to do:

$(7 - 3) \times 3^2 + 15$

The class have different answers:

	$(7 - 3) \times 3^2 + 15$
Brackets	
Indices	$4 \times 3^2 + 15$
Division	$4 \times 9 + 15$
or	
Multiplication	$36 + 15$
Addition	51
or	
Subtraction	Peter was correct.

On a scientific calculator, you input the calculation in order.

$$(\quad 7 \quad - \quad 3 \quad) \quad \times \quad 3 \quad x^2 \quad + \quad 1 \quad 5 \quad =$$

The key sequence depends on your calculator.

Check that you know how yours works.

To find the correct answer you must follow the order of operations:

▶ The correct order of operations is **BIDMAS**.

Some calculations have hidden brackets.

---

example

Work out: $\dfrac{8 + 4}{13 + 2}$

··

The fraction means you divide the numerator by the denominator.

You need brackets to show this:

$\dfrac{(8 + 4)}{(13 + 2)} = \dfrac{12}{15} = \dfrac{4}{5} = 0.8$

On a calculator you press:

This calculation also has hidden brackets: $\sqrt{20^2 - 12^2}$

You work out $20^2 - 12^2 = 400 - 144 = 256$

$\sqrt{256} = 16$ so $\sqrt{20^2 - 12^2} = 16$

On some calculators you input the √ first, on others you input it last.

Exercise N1.9

1 Work out the answer to each of these.
   a $18 + 14 - 19$ **b** $4 + 6 \times 2$ **c** $24 \div 4 + 7$
   d $15 + 20 \div 5$ **e** $4 \times 2 + 3 \times 2$ **f** $4 \times 2^2 - 5$

2 Work out each of these bracket questions.
   a $2 \times (3 + 5)$ **b** $(2 + 4) \times (7 - 5)$ **c** $(13 + 12) \div 5$
   d $6 \times (10 - 7) + 12$ **e** $(80 \div 10) \div 2$ **f** $40 - (10 \div 2) \times 6$

3 Copy these questions.
   Put a pair of brackets into each of the calculations to get
   the correct answer.
   a $7 - 3 \times 2 = 8$ **b** $8 + 5 - 3 \times 5 = 50$ **c** $2 \times 3 \times 4 + 5 = 54$

4 Hannah says that these three calculations will all have the
   same answer
   a $40 \div 10 \div 2$ **b** $(40 \div 10) \div 2$ **c** $40 \div (10 \div 2)$
   Hannah is wrong. Work out which one is different.
   Explain why it gives a different answer.

5 Solve each of these calculations. You will need to decide
   whether to use a mental, written or calculator method.

   a $\dfrac{80}{5+3}$ **b** $12 \times 8 + 6 \times 4$ **c** $\dfrac{7 \times 8}{13 - 5}$ **d** $3 \times 8^2 - 100 \div 4$

6 Copy and complete this operation puzzle.
   You must place an operator in each blank box to make
   each calculation correct.

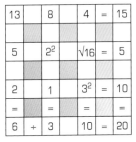

7 Work out as many whole-number answers as you can by
   putting brackets into this calculation.
   $4 \times 5 + 4 - 2 \times 6 + 1$

8 Jo and Will are discussing a problem.
   Jo says 'Adding two numbers and then squaring that number
   is the same as squaring each number then adding the two square numbers.'
   Will says 'These two methods will never give the same answer.'
   Who do you think is correct?
   Explain your answer using calculations.

9 You are told that $(13 - 5 \times 2)(8 \div 4 + 3) = 15$
   What does this tell you that two brackets next to each other means?

10 Work out:
   a $(3 \times 5)(8 - 6)$ **b** $\sqrt{(26^2 - 24^2)}$ **c** $(2^2 + 3^2)(8 \div (4 \div 2))$

You should know how to ...

1 Use the equivalence of fractions, decimals and percentages to compare proportions.

Check out

1 This pie chart shows how Jim's typical 24-hour weekday is split up.

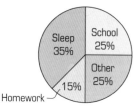

Copy and complete this table for the proportion of the day he spends on each activity.

	Fraction	Decimal	%
School			
Sleep			
Homework			
Other			

2 Calculate percentages and find the outcome of a given percentage increase or decrease.

2 Work out:

  a 50% of 60p   **b** 25% of 24p
  c 10% of 64 cm   **d** 5% of 40 mm
  e 15% of £1.20   **f** 30% of 60 cm
  g 35% of £2.60   **h** 85% of 60 mm
  i Increase:
      i 8 by 10%   **ii** 24 by 15%
  j Decrease:
      i 32 by 10%   **ii** 50 by 85%

3 Divide a quantity into two or more parts in a given ratio.

3 Share £60 in these ratios.

  a 2 : 1   **b** 1 : 5
  c 5 : 1   **d** 5 : 7
  e 1 : 2 : 3   **f** 2 : 5 : 3

4 Use the unitary method to solve problems involving ratio and direct proportion.

4 a 3 singly-packed Scotch eggs cost £1.26. Find the cost of:
      i 1 egg   **ii** 5 eggs
  b 25 g of herbs cost 40p. Find the cost of:
      i 10 g   **ii** 40 g   **iii** 75 g

5 Use logical argument to establish the truth of a statement.

5 Jim says: 'If I decrease 80 by 10% then I can get back to 80 simply by increasing my new number by 10%.'
Use calculations to explain whether Jim is correct or not.

3 Solving equations

This unit will show you how to:

▶▶ Begin to distinguish the different roles played by letter symbols.

▶▶ Know the meaning of *formula* and *function*.

▶▶ Use index notation for small positive integers.

▶▶ Simplify or transform linear expressions by collecting like terms.

▶▶ Know that algebraic operations follow the same conventions and order as arithmetic operations.

▶▶ Construct and solve linear equations with integer coefficients.

▶▶ Substitute integers into simple formulae.

▶▶ Begin to use graphs and set up equations to solve problems involving direct proportion.

▶▶ Substitute positive integers into expressions involving small powers.

▶▶ Solve more demanding problems and investigate in a range of contexts.

▶▶ Represent problems and interpret solutions in algebraic or graphical form.

▶▶ Solve more complex problems by breaking them down into smaller steps, choosing and using efficient techniques.

In algebra, you need to balance both sides.

Before you start

You should know how to ...

1 Simplify expressions by collecting like terms. For example:

▶ $a + a + a = 3a$

▶ $a \times a = a^2$

2 Add and subtract using negative numbers.

3 Substitute numbers into simple expressions.

4 Use direct proportion in simple contexts.

Check in

1 Simplify these expressions:

   a $n + n + n + n + n$ **b** $2n + 2n$

   c $3 \times n$ **d** $n \times n$

   e $n + p + n + p$ **f** $2n + 3p + n + p$

2 Work out:

   a $^-3 + ^-4$ **b** $4 - 6$

   c $^-2 - ^-3$ **d** $^-3 + 3$

3 Substitute $x = 4$ into each expression.

   a $2x$ **b** $2x + 3$

   c $x - 5$ **d** $\frac{20}{x}$

4 Three pencils cost 90p. How much will:

   a six cost?   **b** twelve cost?   **c** ten cost?

Using letter symbols

This spread will show you how to:
- ▶▶ Distinguish the different roles played by letter symbols.
- ▶▶ Know the meaning of the words *expression, equation, formula* and *function.*

You can use letter symbols in different ways.

Naomi and Sîan are sorting these algebra cards into equations, formulae and functions.

$y = 2x + 4$	$a + 9 = 12$	$y = 10 - x$	$C = kd$	$\dfrac{x}{2} = 10$	$A = \frac{1}{2} bh$

Sîan says:

In the **equation** $2x + 4 = 14$ the letter x has an **unknown value,** which you can work out.

In the **formula** $V = IR$ the letters V, I, R are **variables,** they can take any value.
You use two of them to work out the third.

In the **function** $y = x + 3$ the y-value can be worked out for any value of x.

$$2x + 4 = 14$$
$$2x = 10$$
$$x = 5$$

If $I = 5$ and $R = 10$ find the value of V.
$$V = IR$$
$$V = 5 \times 10 = 50$$

If $y = x + 3$
when $\quad x = 2 \quad y = 5$
$\quad\quad\quad x = 6 \quad y = 9$

Naomi sorts the algebra cards into three piles:

Equations	Formulae	Functions
$a + 9 = 12$	$C = kd$	$y = 10 - x$
$\dfrac{x}{2} = 10$	$A = \frac{1}{2} bh$	$y = 2x + 4$

- ▶ Letters represent numbers.
- ▶ An expression is a collection of letter and number terms.

example

Match equivalent expressions. Write an equivalent expression for each of the two left over.

$n \times 2$	$2n$	$n + 2$	n^2	$n + n + 2$
$n \div 2$	$2 + n$	$\frac{n}{2}$	$n \times n$	$n + n + n$

Multiplication and addition are associative:
$$(n \times 2) \times 3 = n \times (2 \times 3)$$
$$(n + n) + 2 = n + (n + 2)$$

| $n \times 2 = 2n$ | ↔ | $2n$ | $2 + n$ | ↔ | $n + 2$ | $n \div 2 = \frac{n}{2}$ | ↔ | $\frac{n}{2}$ | $n \times n$ | ↔ | n^2 |

Simplify each of the expressions by collecting like terms.
$$n + n + 2 = 2n + 2 \quad n + n + n = 3n$$

Exercise A3.1

1 Simplify these expressions by collecting like terms.

  a $3 \times a$ **b** $a + a + a$ **c** $d + d + d - d - d$

  d $b + b + b + a + a$ **e** $b \times 5$ **f** $10d \div 2$

> **Hint:** 'Like terms' contain exactly the same letter.

2 Sort these algebra cards into three piles: equations, formulae and functions.

$A = B \times H$ $y = 4x - 8$ $5x = 10$ $y = 3 + x$ $A = \frac{1}{2}(a + b)h$ $\frac{x}{8} = 10$

3 The number in each brick is the result of adding the numbers in the two bricks beneath it.
Copy the walls and write expressions for the numbers in each brick.
Write each expression as simply as possible.

a   **b**   **c**

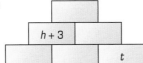
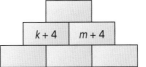

4 Here are some algebra cards.

  a Which card will always give the same answer as $3 \times n$?

  b Which cards added together will give $6n + 6$?

  c Which cards will always give the same answer as $3n - 6m$?

  d Which card simplifies to $\frac{n}{3}$?

  e Write a new card that will always give the same answer as $n + n$.

$2n - 7m + n + m$ $\frac{n}{3}$ $3n - 6m$ $3 \times n$

$3m$ $\frac{2n}{6}$ $3n$ $n + n$

$3n + 6$ $^-4m + n - 2m + 2n$

5 Simplify these expressions.

  a $2p + 3p$ **b** $5m - 6 + 2m - 3$ **c** $4a + 3b + 3a - 2b$

  d $3s + 2p - 3s - p$ **e** $5x + 8 + 2x - 5 - x$ **f** $9w - 4x + w - 3$

  g $3n + 4 - 5m + n + 1$ **h** $2a - 2b - 2a + 2b + 1$ **i** $^-y + 4x - 2y + x$

6 **a** Write an expression for the perimeter of each of these shapes.

  i   **ii**   **iii**

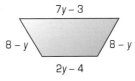

Regular hexagon

  b If every shape in part **a** has a perimeter of 30 cm, find the unknown value in each.

Arithmetic in algebra

This spread will show you how to:

▶▶ Know that algebraic operations follow the same conventions and order as arithmetic operations.

▶▶ Substitute integers into simple expressions.

Algebraic operations follow the same order of operations as arithmetic:

Order of operations

Brackets ————————————————————

Indices or Powers

Division and Multiplication ————————

Addition and Subtraction ——————————

Work out:

$9 - 4(3 - 1)$

$= 9 - 4 \times 2$

$= 9 - 8$

$= 1$

Use the word **BIDMAS** to help you remember the order.

Remember this special rule for algebra:

▶ You do not use multiplication or division signs.
  ▶ $5 \times a = 5a$
  ▶ $2b \div 3 = \frac{2b}{3}$

You use a fraction instead of the division sign.

Brackets often contain a hidden multiplication.

▶ When you multiply by a bracket, you do not use the multiplication sign.
  $2 \times (5 + 2) = 2(5 + 2)$
  $3 \times (b + 4) = 3(b + 4)$

You can use these rules to help substitute values into algebraic expressions.

example

Find the value of these algebraic expressions when $q = 2$, $r = 4$ and $s = 6$.

a $5q + 4$ 　　　 b rs 　　　 c $10 - qrs$ 　　　 d $3(2s - 5)$ 　　　 e $q(r - s)$

....

a $5q + 4$
　$= 5 \times 2 + 4$
　$= 10 + 4$
　$= 14$

b rs
　$= 4 \times 6$
　$= 24$

c $10 - qrs$
　$= 10 - 2 \times 4 \times 6$
　$= 10 - 48$
　$= {}^-38$

d $3(2s - 5)$
　$= 3 \times (2 \times 6 - 5)$
　$= 3 \times (12 - 5)$
　$= 3 \times 7$
　$= 21$

e $q(r - s)$
　$= 2 \times (4 - 6)$
　$= 2 \times {}^-2$
　$= {}^-4$

Exercise A3.2

1 This is a game for two players.
- ▶ Player 1 picks a question from the table and its answer from the second table.
- ▶ Player 2 uses a calculator to check the answer.
- ▶ If the answer is correct Player 1 claims the question square, if incorrect Player 2 claims the square.
- ▶ Players take turns to choose questions and answers.
- ▶ The winner is the first player to get 4 in a row.

$4 + 2 \times 3$	$3(4 + 2)$	$10 - 2 \times 4$	$44 \div 4 + 30 \div 2$
$6(4 + 2)$	$22 - 10 \div 2$	$10 + 3(2 + 6)$	$16 - 2 \times 4$
$100 \times 5 + 40$	$2 \times 10 + 4$	$5 \times 4 + 20$	$6 \times 12 - 2 \times 9$
$40 \div 2 + 12$	$2 \times 3 + 4 \times 4$	$2(10 - 2)$	$25 \times 4 + 4$

2	8	10	16
17	18	22	24
26	32	34	36
40	54	104	540

2 Find the value of each expression when $x = 8$.
- **a** i $2x$ ii $2x - 4$ iii $3(2x - 4)$
- **b** i $x + 1$ ii $5(x + 1)$ iii $2(x + 1)$
- **c** i $5x$ ii $5x - 10$ iii $\frac{5x}{2}$
- **d** i $x - 2$ ii $3(x - 2)$ iii $\frac{3(x - 2)}{2}$
- **e** i $\frac{1}{2}x$ ii $\frac{1}{2}x + 5$ iii $\frac{1}{2}x - 5$
- **f** i x^2 ii $x^2 - 3$ iii $2(x^2 - 3)$

3 Work out the expressions in question 2 when $x = 1$.

4 Find the value on each algebra card when $a = 4$, $b = 3$ and $c = 6$.
Sort them into order of size, starting with the smallest.

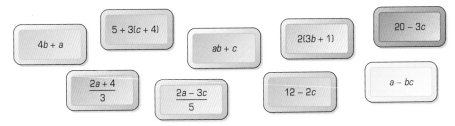

$4b + a$ $5 + 3(c + 4)$ $ab + c$ $2(3b + 1)$ $20 - 3c$
$\frac{2a + 4}{3}$ $\frac{2a - 3c}{5}$ $12 - 2c$ $a - bc$

5 Challenge
- **a** Find the value of each expression when $p = 2$, $q = {}^{-}3$ and $r = {}^{-}4$.
  - i $3r + p$ ii pqr iii $p^2 + r$ iv $\frac{3r}{p}$ v r^2 vi $\frac{p + q}{r + 3}$
- **b** Using p, q and r, make up five expressions of your own with a value of $^{-}24$.
  (You can use all or some of the letters.)

This spread will show you how to:
- ▶▶ Construct and solve linear equations with integer coefficients.
- ▶▶ Simplify or transform linear expressions by collecting like terms.
- ▶▶ Represent problems in algebraic form.

There are different ways of solving the equation $5p + 6 = 21$.

Stephen uses inverse function machines.

Paul uses inverse operations.

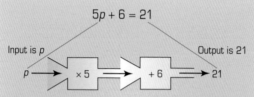

To work out the input you go backwards using the inverse function machine.

The input was 3.

Both methods give the same answer.

The equation is
$$5p + 6 = 21$$
Subtraction is the inverse of addition:
$$5p = 21 - 6$$
$$5p = 15$$
Division is the inverse of multiplication:
$$p = 15 \div 5$$
$$p = 3$$

example

In an arithmagon, the numbers in a square are the sum of the numbers in the two circles either side of it.

What are the numbers A, B and C in this arithmagon?

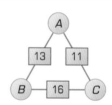

Let A stand for the number in the top circle.
Form expressions for the numbers in the other circles.

$A + B = 13$ ⠀⠀⠀ $A + C = 11$ ⠀⠀⠀ $B + C = 16$
⠀⠀ $B = 13 - A$ ⠀⠀⠀ $C = 11 - A$

Then form an equation and solve it.

$(13 - A) + (11 - A) = 16$
$24 - 2A = 16$
$2A = 8$
$A = 4$

Think⠀ $24 - ? = 16$
⠀⠀⠀$24 - 8 = 16$

so $A = 4$, $B = 9$, $C = 7$

Check: ⠀ $A + B = 13$ ⠀⠀⠀ $A + C = 11$ ⠀⠀⠀ $B + C = 16$
⠀⠀⠀⠀ $4 + 9 = 13$ ✓ ⠀⠀ $4 + 7 = 11$ ✓ ⠀⠀ $9 + 7 = 16$ ✓

Exercise A3.3

1 Copy and complete these spider diagrams using related equations in the boxes (some have been filled in).

a

3 + 2 = 5

2 + 3 = 5

b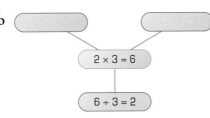

2 × 3 = 6

6 ÷ 3 = 2

c

24 − b = a

a + b = 24

d

b × a = 24

a × b = 24

2 Use inverse function machines to solve these equations.

a $2a + 4 = 18$

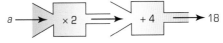
$a \rightarrow$ ×2 $\rightarrow$ +4 $\rightarrow$ 18

b $4n - 5 = 7$

$n \rightarrow$ ×4 $\rightarrow$ −5 $\rightarrow$ 7

c $\frac{x}{2} + 3 = 12$

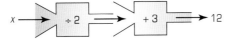
$x \rightarrow$ ÷2 $\rightarrow$ +3 $\rightarrow$ 12

3 The number in each brick is the result of adding the numbers in the two bricks beneath it.
By writing equations, find the unknown letter in each wall.

a

17	
4 + n	n + 3
4	n	3

b

25	
15	6 + p
9	6	p

c

24	
?	?
q	5	8

4 Solve these equations.
a $4a + 5 = 21$ **b** $\frac{e}{3} + 4 = 9$ **c** $4(x - 3) = 20$ **d** $\frac{r + 4}{5} = 2$

5 In an arithmagon, the number in a square is the sum of the numbers in the two circles on either side of it.
Find the numbers in the circles in these arithmagons.

a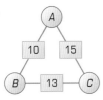

b

c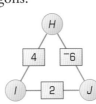

This spread will show you how to:

▶▶ Construct and solve linear equations with integer coefficient unknowns on both sides, using appropriate methods.

KEYWORDS

Equation Substitute

Solve

You can solve equations by using the balancing method.

You must do the same thing to both sides of the equation.

Solve this equation: $\qquad$ $6a + 45 = 9a + 15$

You can take $6a$ off both sides: Take off **6a** $\quad$ a a a $\qquad$ a a a $\quad$ Take off **6a**

a a a $\qquad$ a a a

a a a + 45 $\qquad$ a a a + 15

You can take 15 off both sides: Take off **15** $\quad$ 45 $\qquad$ a a a + 15 $\quad$ Take off **15**

30 $\qquad$ a a a

Each a must be equal to 10. $\qquad$ $3a = 30$

$a = 10$

Check the solution by substituting $a = 10$:

Left-hand side	Right-hand side
$6a + 45$	$9a + 15$
$6 \times 10 + 45$	$9 \times 10 + 15$
$60 + 45$	$90 + 15$
$\boxed{105}$	$\boxed{105}$

The left-hand side and right-hand side are equal so the solution is correct.

example

Work out the value of y in this rectangle.

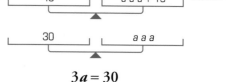

4y + 3

21 − 2y

You know that the opposite sides of a rectangle are equal.

So $\qquad$ $4y + 3 = 21 - 2y$

Take off 3 from both sides: $\quad$ $- 3 \quad - 3$

$4y = 18 - 2y$

Add $2y$ to both sides: $\quad$ $+ 2y \qquad + 2y$

$6y = 18$

Divide both sides by 6: $\quad$ $\div 6 \quad \div 6$

$y = 3$

Check: Left-hand side $= 4y + 3 = 4 \times 3 + 3 = 12 + 3 = 15$

Right-hand side $= 21 - 2y = 21 - 2 \times 3 = 21 - 6 = 15$ $\quad$ So the solution is correct.

Exercise A3.4

1 Find the value of in each question.

a

b

c

2 Solve each of these equations.

a $3b + 14 = 2b + 16$ b $5c + 4 = 3c + 22$ c $2d + 3 = d + 7$

d $5e - 5 = 2e + 16$ e $3f + 11 = 5f + 3$ f $5g - 1 = 2g + 14$

g $9h + 4 = 5h + 20$ h $5i - 10 = i + 2$ i $2j + 11 = j + 20$

> Transform the equations by doing the same to both sides.

3 Work out the value of x in each of these shapes.

a

2x + 10

3x + 5

b

x + 12   4x + 3

4 David and Teresa each have the same number of sweets.
David has 4 full bags of sweets and 3 loose sweets.
Teresa has 3 full bags of sweets and 15 loose sweets.

    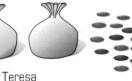

David   Teresa

a Form an equation from the above information.

b Solve the equation to find out how many sweets there are in one bag.

5 The number in each cell is the result of adding the numbers in the two cells beneath it.
By writing equations, find the unknown letter in each wall.

a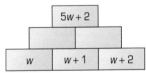

b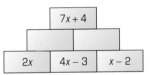

c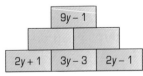

6 Sonia plays a number game. She says: 'Multiplying my number by 4 then subtracting 3 gives the same answer as multiplying my number by 3 then adding 2.'
Work out the value of Sonia's number.

7 Which equation has a different solution to the other two?

| $4x + 3 = 5x - 4$ | $4x + 1 = 6x - 9$ | $3x - 4 = 2x + 3$ |

Write three equations that all have the same solution as the odd one out.

This spread will show you how to:
▶▶ Begin to use graphs and set up equations to solve simple problems involving direct proportion.

Rhiannon takes her holiday photos to be developed.

She can have them developed into different sizes.
All the photos are in the same proportion.

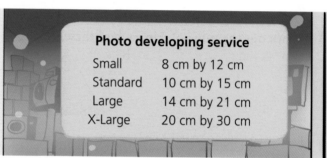

Photo developing service

Small	8 cm by 12 cm
Standard	10 cm by 15 cm
Large	14 cm by 21 cm
X-Large	20 cm by 30 cm

Rhiannon decides to choose her own size. She wants the length to be 45 cm.
She plots a graph and extends the line to work out the width of the photo.

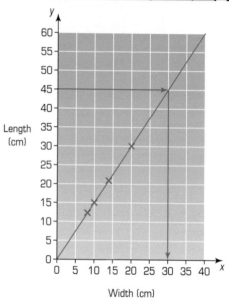

▶ When two quantities are in direct proportion, the coordinate pairs will lie on a straight line which will go through the origin.

A photo of length 45 cm, in the same proportion, will have a width of 30 cm.
The relationship between the length and the width can be written as a formula:

$$\text{length} = 1.5 \times \text{width}$$
$$y = 1.5x$$

Remember:
$1.5 \times x$ is written $1.5x$

If the width is 40 cm you can work out the length using the formula:

$$y = 1.5 \times 40 = 60 \text{ cm}$$

Exercise A3.5

1 James mixes 1 litre of red paint with 2 litres of white paint to make 3 litres of pink paint.
James wants 9 litres of pink paint.
How many litres of red paint will he need?

2 You make 5 litres of purple paint by mixing 1 litre of red paint with 4 litres of blue paint.

a Copy and complete:
To make 10 litres of purple paint, mix __ litres of red paint with __ litres of blue paint.
To make 15 litres of purple paint, mix __ litres of red paint with __ litres of blue paint.
To make 25 litres of purple paint, mix __ litres of red paint with __ litres of blue paint.

b Draw a graph to show how purple paint can be mixed. You can copy these axes.

c Use the graph to work out:
  i How many litres of blue paint you would mix with 8 litres of red paint.
  ii How many litres of red paint you would mix with 14 litres of blue paint.

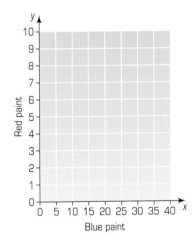

3 Which of these pictures is not in proportion to the others?

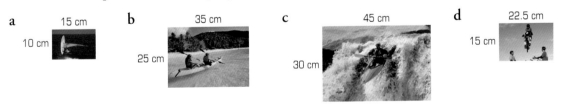

Hint: Plot a graph to help.

4 Draw four rectangles, with their dimensions labelled, that are all in proportion to each other.

A3.6 Substitution

This spread will show you how to:

▶▶ Use index notation for small positive integers.

▶▶ Substitute positive integers into expressions involving small powers (e.g. $3x^2 + 4$ or $2x^3$).

KEYWORDS

Index	Substitute
Algebra	Indices
To the power of n	

When you add repeatedly, you can write the expression using a multiplication:

$$4 + 4 + 4 + 4 + 4 = 5 \times 4$$

When you multiply repeatedly, you can write the expression using an index:

$$4 \times 4 \times 4 \times 4 \times 4 = 4^5$$

This is called the **index** or the **power**.

This is the same in algebra: $\quad p \times p \times p \times p \times p \times p \times p \times p = p^8$

▶ $5 \times 5 = 5^2$ you say 'five squared'.

▶ $6 \times 6 \times 6 = 6^3$ you say 'six cubed'.

▶ $4 \times 4 \times 4 \times 4 \times 4 = 4^5$ you say '4 to the power of 5'.

You can simplify expressions with numbers and different letters combined:

$$3 \times p \times p = 3p^2 \qquad 4 \times p \times p \times r \times r \times r = 4p^2 r^3$$

You can substitute values to find the value of an expression.

example

Find the value of each expression when $p = 2$ and $q = 4$.

a q^2 b pq^2 c $q(p^2 + 4)$

....

a $\quad q^2 = 4 \times 4 = 16$

b $\quad pq^2 = 2 \times 4 \times 4 = 32$

c $\quad q(p^2 + 4) = 4 \times (2 \times 2 + 4) = 4 \times (4 + 4) = 4 \times 8 = 32$

Remember the order of operations:

Brackets
Indices
Division
Multiplication
Addition
Subtraction

You can solve some harder equations by estimating the value and substituting.

example

Winston substitutes a number into the expression on this card. The value he gets is 85. What was the number?

$4x^2 - 3x$

....

You need to substitute different values into the expression until you find the correct number.

First guess $x = 8$	$4 \times 8^2 - 3 \times 8 = 256 - 24 = 232$	Too big – try a smaller value
Second guess $x = 4$	$4 \times 4^2 - 3 \times 4 = 64 - 12 = 52$	Too small – try a bigger value
Third guess $x = 5$	$4 \times 5^2 - 3 \times 5 = 100 - 15 = 85$	Correct value!

Winston must have substituted $x = 5$ into the expression.

Exercise A3.6

1 Copy these repeated multiplications and match them to their index form.
The first one has been done for you.

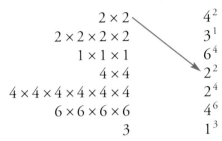

2×2 4^2
$2 \times 2 \times 2 \times 2$ 3^1
$1 \times 1 \times 1$ 6^4
4×4 2^2
$4 \times 4 \times 4 \times 4 \times 4 \times 4$ 2^4
$6 \times 6 \times 6 \times 6$ 4^6
3 1^3

2 Write down these expressions in their simplified form.
   a $p \times p$ **b** $r \times r \times r$ **c** $p \times p \times p \times p$ **d** $3 \times p \times p$
   e $r^2 \times r^3$ **f** $2p^3 \times p^2 \times p$ **g** $2 \times p \times p \times r \times r \times r$ **h** $r \times r \times r + p \times p$

3 Match five pairs of expressions that have the same meaning.
For the remaining expressions, write a simplified expression which is equivalent.

$y \times y \times y$	$2y$	$y^3 \times y^4$	$3y$	$y^2 + y^2$	$y \times y$
y^3	y^2	$y + y + y$	$2y \times 2y$	$2y^2$	$y + y$

4 Find the value of each expression when $a = 3$, $b = 2$ and $c = \frac{1}{2}$.
   i a^2 **ii** $10 - 3a$ **iii** $b^2 + a^2$ **iv** $2c + ab$ **v** $(b+1)^2 + 2a$
   vi $b^3 + 7$ **vii** cb^3 **viii** $(b-1)^2$ **ix** $a^3 - b^3 + 1$ **x** $b^4 + a$
   xi $a(3b + 2c)$ **xii** $(a-b)^5 + 2c$ **xiii** $2b^3 + a$ **xiv** $5b^2$ **xv** $\frac{a^3}{3}$
   xvi $2a^2 + b$ **xvii** $a^2b + a$ **xviii** $b^4 + b^2$ **xix** $ac(b^2 + 2)$ **xx** $cb^5 - 1$
   xxi $c(1 + a^3)$

Use this code to change your answers to letters.

A	B	C	D	E	F	G	H	I	J	K	L	M	N	O	P	Q	R	S	T	U	V	W	X	Y	Z
1	2	3	4	5	6	7	8	9	10	11	12	13	14	15	16	17	18	19	20	21	22	23	24	25	26

Read your letters as words – what does it say?

5 Catherine substitutes a number into the expression on this card:

$2x^2 + 3x$

The value she gets for the expression is 44.
Work out what number she substituted into the expression.

6 Find the exact value of x for each of the following.
   a $3x^2 + 12 = 120$ **b** $5x^2 - 10x = 75$ **Hint:** x is a decimal.
   c $10x - x^2 = 21$ **d** $4x^2 + 3x = 32.5$

You should know how to ...

1 Simplify or transform linear expressions by collecting like terms.

Check out

1 Write an expression for the perimeter of each shape.

a

$3x + 2$
$2x$

b

$x - 2$

2 Construct and solve linear equations with integer coefficients.

2 a The perimeter of each shape in question 1 is 24 cm. Construct an equation and solve it to find the value of x in both shapes.

b Solve these equations:

   i $3x + 6 = 12$

   ii $4x - 10 = 2$

   iii $\frac{x}{2} + 3 = 9$

   iv $2(x - 1) = 18$

   v $\frac{x+3}{3} = 21$

   vi $3x + 4 = 5x - 2$

   vii $x + 6 = 3x + 8$

3 Substitute integers into simple formulae.

3 Find the value of each expression when $a = 2$ and $b = \frac{1}{2}$.

  a a^2 **b** b^2

  c $a + 2b$ **d** $a - b$

  e a^3 **f** $2(a + b)$

  g $a^2 b$ **h** $\frac{2b + a}{2}$

4 Represent problems in algebraic, geometric or graphical form, using correct notation and appropriate diagrams.

4 Use algebra to write this statement correctly: 'Jez thinks of a number, adds 3, then multiplies by 2. The answer is 14.'
Now solve the equation to find the number Jez thought of.

This unit will show you how to:

▶▶ Identify alternate and corresponding angles.

▶▶ Understand a proof that the sum of angles in a triangle is 180° and in a quadrilateral is 360°, and that the exterior angle of a triangle is equal to the sum of the two interior opposite angles.

▶▶ Solve geometrical problems using side and angle properties of triangles and quadrilaterals.

▶▶ Classify quadrilaterals by geometric properties.

▶▶ Know that if two shapes are congruent, corresponding sides and angles are equal.

▶▶ Use straight edge and compasses to construct perpendiculars, bisectors, and triangles given three sides (SSS).

▶▶ Find simple loci to produce shapes and paths.

▶▶ Identify the information to solve a problem.

▶▶ Represent problems and interpret solutions in geometric form.

▶▶ Solve more demanding problems and investigate in a range of contexts.

▶▶ Identify exceptional cases or counter-examples.

You can find geometric shapes in many games.

Before you start

You should know how to ...

1 Classify angles (acute, obtuse or right).

2 Solve simple equations.
For example:

$$a + 35 = 180$$
so $\quad a \quad = 180 - 35$
$\quad\quad a \quad = 145$

Check in

1 Say if the marked angle is acute, obtuse or a right angle.

   a   **b**   **c**

2 Solve these equations:

   a $a + 105 = 180$

   b $2b = 90$

S1.1 Geometrical language

This spread will show you how to:

▶▶ Correctly use vocabulary, notation and labelling conventions.
▶▶ Identify parallel and perpendicular lines.
▶▶ Recognise vertically opposite angles.
▶▶ Know that if two 2-D shapes are congruent, corresponding sides and angles are equal.

KEYWORDS

Parallel   Right angle
Perpendicular   Congruent
Intersect

Lines, angles and shapes are all around.

Parallel lines are always the same distance apart.	Perpendicular lines meet or intersect at right angles or 90°.	All other lines intersect at an angle other than 90°.
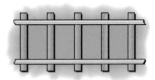	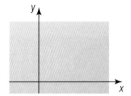	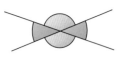
Train tracks are parallel.	Coordinate axes are perpendicular.	The vertically opposite angles are equal.

You need to know these properties of shapes.

▶ Regular shapes have equal sides and equal angles.

A square is a regular quadrilateral.

▶ Congruent shapes are exactly the same shape and size.

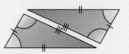

The shapes fit exactly on top of each other. Corresponding sides are the same length.

You can describe a shape using its geometric properties.

example

Describe the geometrical properties of these two shapes.

a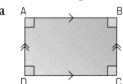

b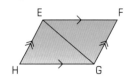

....

a AB is parallel to DC.
AB is perpendicular to BC.
AB is perpendicular to AD.
AB = DC and AD = BC
Angle DAB = 90°, angle ADC = 90°
The rectangle is not regular.

b EF is parallel to HG.
EH is parallel to FG.
EF = HG and EH = FG
∠H = ∠F and ∠E = ∠G
Triangles EHG and GFE are congruent.
The parallelogram is not regular.

Exercise S1.1

1 Write down the letters of the shapes that are congruent.

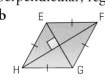

2 Describe some geometrical properties of these shapes by using the words parallel, perpendicular, regular and congruent.

a **b** 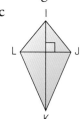 **c** 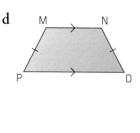 **d**

3 Look up the meaning of these mathematical words.
Write down the meaning and draw a diagram to help explain each word.
  a equidistant
  b parallel
  c perpendicular
  d regular
  e polygon
  f congruent
  g quadrilateral

4 Draw each of these shapes.
Draw in one of the diagonals.
Describe the two resulting congruent triangles for each diagram.
  a parallelogram
  b square
  c rhombus
  d rectangle
  e kite (choose the diagonal that gives two congruent triangles).

5 Divide a 3 by 3 pinboard into two congruent halves, in as many different ways as possible. For example,

6 Divide a 4 by 4 pinboard into two congruent halves in as many different ways as possible.

Properties of triangles

This spread will show you how to:
- ▶▶ Solve geometrical problems using side and angle properties of triangles.
- ▶▶ Understand a proof that the exterior angle of a triangle is equal to the sum of the two interior opposite angles.

KEYWORDS
Interior angle   Triangle
Exterior angle   Equal
Angles on a straight line
Right angle
Angles at a point

You should know these angle properties:

There are 360° in a full turn at a point.

There are 180° on a straight line.

The angles in a triangle add to 180°.

$\angle A + \angle B + \angle C = 180°$

The angles inside a shape are called interior angles.

interior angles

Any interior angle has an associated exterior angle.

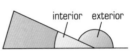

interior   exterior

You should know the properties of these special triangles:

Right-angled	Equilateral	Isosceles	Scalene

One 90° angle, marked	3 equal angles 3 equal sides	2 equal angles 2 equal sides	No equal angles No equal sides

You can use these properties to solve triangle problems.

example

Find the unknown angles in these triangles.

a
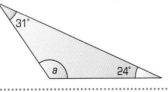

b
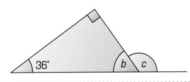

a $a + 31° + 24° = 180°$
    $a + 55° = 180°$
    $a = 125°$

b $b + 36° + 90° = 180°$
    $b + 126° = 180°$
    $b = 54°$
    $b + c = 180°$
    $54° + c = 180°$
    $c = 126°$

Notice that the exterior angle, c is equal to the sum of the two interior opposite angles.

Exercise S1.2

1 List all the different types of triangle you can find in these diagrams.

a
b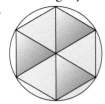
c
d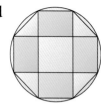

2 Find the unknown angles in each diagram.

a
b
c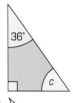
d

e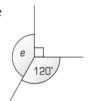
f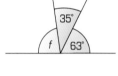
g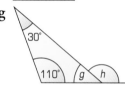
h

i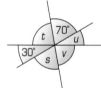
j
k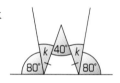

3 Copy and complete this table, putting three types of triangle, equilateral, isosceles and scalene, in the correct spaces.
Explain why some of the spaces in the table can never be filled.

	Some equal angles	No equal angles
Some equal sides		
No equal sides		

4 **a** Copy this diagram, and find *a*.
b Write down the value of *a* + *b* + *c*.
c Show that *b* + *c* = 125°.

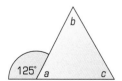

5 Use this diagram to show that *x* = *m* + *n*.
Copy and complete this sentence:
'The exterior angle of a triangle is equal to the sum of the _____ _____ _____.'

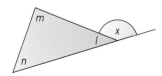

Lines and angles

This spread will show you how to:
- ▶▶ Identify alternate angles and corresponding angles.
- ▶▶ Understand a proof that the sum of the angles in a triangle is 180°.
- ▶▶ Understand a proof that the exterior angle of a triangle is equal to the sum of the two interior opposite angles.

KEYWORDS
Parallel
Acute
Obtuse
Corresponding angles
Angles on a straight line
Alternate
Tessellation
Proof

When a line crosses parallel lines, eight angles are formed:

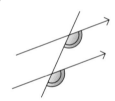

There are four acute angles and four obtuse angles.

The acute angles are the same size.
The obtuse angles are the same size.

Acute + obtuse = 180°.
They lie on a straight line.

Alternate angles are equal.

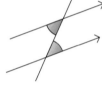

Corresponding angles are equal.

You can see the properties in these tessellations:

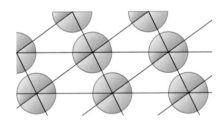

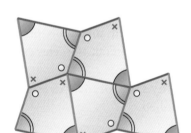

You can use these facts to solve problems.

example

Find the unknown angles in these diagrams. Give reasons for your answers.

a

b

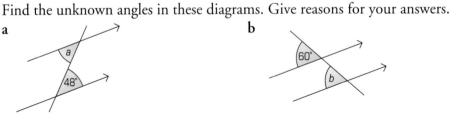
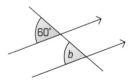

....

a $a = 48°$ (alternate angles)   b $b = 60°$ (corresponding angles)

Exercise S1.3

1 Copy these diagrams and colour in the alternate angles to those shown.

a    **b**    **c**

2 Copy these diagrams and colour in the corresponding angles to those shown.

a    **b**    **c**

3 Calculate the lettered angles. Give a reason in each case.

a 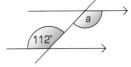   **b** 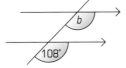   **c**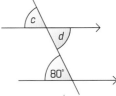

d 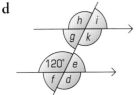   **e** 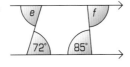   **f**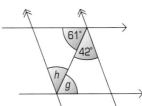

Now add g and h.
What does this show?

4 Copy and complete this proof. It proves that the sum of the angles in a triangle is 180°.

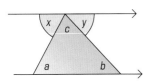

$x = a$ (alternate angles)
$y = b$ (alternate angles)
$x + c + y = 180°$ (angles on a straight line)
$\_\_ + c + \_\_ = 180°$

The sum of the angles in a triangle is _____.

5 Copy and complete this proof. It proves that the exterior angle of a triangle is equal to the sum of the two interior opposite angles.

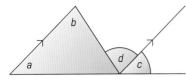

$a = c$ (corresponding angles)
$b = d$ (alternate angles)
So $a + b = \_\_ + \_\_$

The exterior angle of the triangle is equal to _____.

Classifying quadrilaterals

This spread will show you how to:

▶▶ Classify quadrilaterals by their geometric properties.

KEYWORDS
Triangle   Diagonal
Quadrilateral   Parallel

A quadrilateral has four straight sides and four angles.

You can split it into two triangles by drawing in a diagonal.

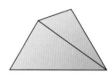

You should know these special quadrilaterals and their properties:

Square	Rhombus	Parallelogram	Rectangle
4 equal angles 4 equal sides 2 sets parallel sides	2 pairs equal angles 4 equal sides 2 sets parallel sides	2 pairs equal angles 2 sets equal sides 2 sets parallel sides	4 equal angles 2 sets equal sides 2 sets parallel sides

Trapezium	Isosceles trapezium	Kite	Arrowhead (Delta)

Usually: No equal angles No equal sides Always: 1 set parallel sides	2 sets equal angles 1 set equal sides 1 set parallel sides	1 pair equal angles 2 sets equal sides No parallel sides	1 pair equal angles 2 sets equal sides No parallel sides

example

a Describe the geometric properties of this shape.
b Name the shape.
c Describe its sides.

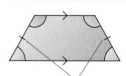

....

a It has 2 equal sides, 2 pairs of equal angles and 1 set of parallel sides.
b It is an isosceles trapezium.
c Two sides are parallel.
  The two sides that are not parallel are equal in length.

The marks show equal sides.

Exercise S1.4

1 List all the different types of quadrilateral you can find in each of these diagrams.

a  b  c d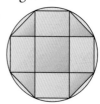

2 Use isometric paper to draw these quadrilaterals.
 a parallelogram
 b rhombus
 c isosceles trapezium
 On each diagram, mark the equal angles, the equal sides, the
 parallel sides and the perpendicular lines (⌐).

3 Draw and cut out two copies of each of the eight special quadrilaterals on page 58.
 Two squares can be put together to form a rectangle.

Shape	Possible new shapes
square	rectangle

 Copy and complete this table for all eight quadrilaterals.

4 a Draw a quadrilateral and join up the midpoints of each side.

 b Name the new quadrilateral.
 c Repeat this process for each of the eight special quadrilaterals on page 58.

5 Copy and complete this table, putting the eight different special
 quadrilaterals on page 58 in the correct place.

	Diagonals are perpendicular	Diagonals are not perpendicular
2 sets of parallel sides		
1 set or no sets of parallel sides		

Properties of quadrilaterals

This spread will show you how to:

▶▶ Solve geometric problems using side and angle properties of special quadrilaterals.

▶▶ Understand a proof that the sum of angles in a quadrilateral is 360°.

KEYWORDS

Triangle   Prove
Diagonal
Alternate angles
Corresponding angles
Angles on a straight line
Complementary angles
Supplementary angles

You know that the sum of the angles in a triangle is 180°.

You can use this to work out the sum of the angles in a quadrilateral:

Draw in a diagonal ...   to make two triangles: $2 \times 180° = 360°$.

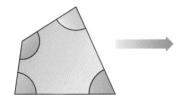 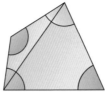 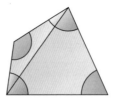

▶ The sum of angles in a quadrilateral is 360°.

You can prove this result for any quadrilateral using algebra:

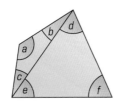

$a + b + c = 180°$ (angles in a triangle)
$d + e + f = 180°$ (angles in a triangle)

So $a + b + c + d + e + f = 360°$
You can use this fact to help solve angle problems.

example

Find the unknown angles.

a

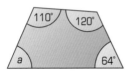

b

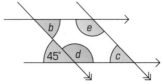

....

a $a + 110° + 120° + 64° = 360°$
$a + 294° = 360°$
$a = 66°$

b $b = 45°$ (alternate angles)
$c = 45°$ (corresponding angles)
$d = 135°$ (angles on a straight line)
$e = 135°$ (angles in a quadrilateral)

Exercise S1.5

1 Write down the meaning of:
  a complementary angles
  b supplementary angles.

Use this diagram to help explain your answer.

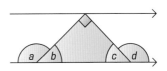

2 Find the unknown angles in these shapes.

a
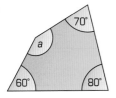

b
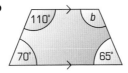

c
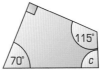

d

e

f
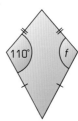

g
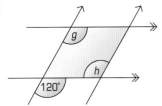

This shows the opposite angles of a parallelogram are equal.

h
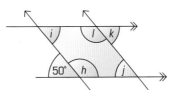

Now add $h + i + j + l$.
What does this show?

3 The angle shown on the isometric grid is 60°.

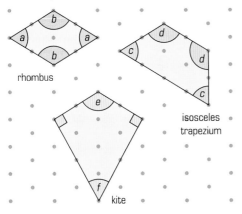

rhombus

isosceles
trapezium

kite

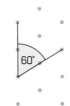

a Find the values of the unknown angles for each shape.
b What is the sum of the four angles in each quadrilateral?

Constructing perpendiculars

This spread will show you how to:
▶▶ Use a straight edge and compasses to construct:
  ▶ the perpendicular from a point to a line
  ▶ the perpendicular from a point on the line.

KEYWORDS
Perpendicular bisector
Perpendicular
Arc
Construction lines
Equidistant
Compasses

The shortest distance from a point to a line is the perpendicular distance:

You construct a perpendicular from a point P to a line like this:

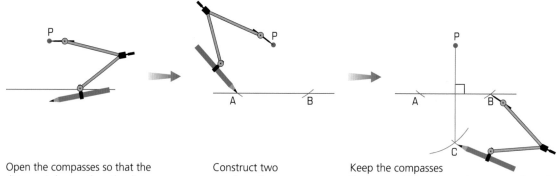

Open the compasses so that the distance is longer than the distance from the point to the line.

Construct two arcs from the point to the line.

Keep the compasses the same width and construct an arc from A and from B to meet at C. Join C to point P.

You construct the perpendicular from a point P on the line like this:

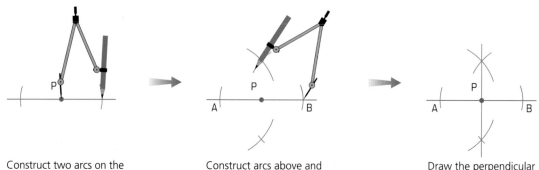

Construct two arcs on the line equidistant from P.

Construct arcs above and below the line from point A and similarly from point B.

Draw the perpendicular bisector of AB.

▶ **A perpendicular bisector divides a straight line into two equal parts at right angles.**

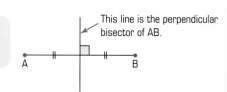

This line is the perpendicular bisector of AB.

Exercise S1.6

1 Copy this diagram of a road. You are standing at A.
Draw your path so that you cross the road in the shortest possible distance.

2 Copy this diagram. Construct a vertical wall at the dot using compasses.

Hint: Always show your construction lines.

3 Draw a line AB so that AB = 10 cm.

| 4 cm | 6 cm |
| A | P | B |

Mark a point P so that AP = 4 cm.
Draw the perpendicular from the point P.

4 **a** Accurately construct this triangle.
b Measure the angle C.
c Copy and complete this sentence: 'The line
_____ is perpendicular to the line _____.'

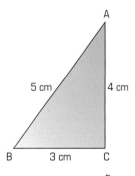

5 **a** Construct this triangle using compasses.
b Measure the length AB.
c Copy and complete this sentence:
'The line _____ is perpendicular to the line _____.'

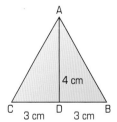

6 **a** Construct this kite using compasses.
b Calculate the area of the kite.

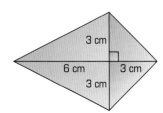

Constructing triangles

This spread will show you how to:
▶▶ Construct a triangle given three sides (SSS).

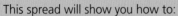

KEYWORDS
Compasses   Arc
Construct   Straight edge
Construction lines

You can construct a triangle accurately when you know:

| Two sides and the included angle (SAS) | or | Two angles and the included side (ASA) | or | Three sides (SSS) |

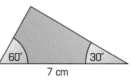

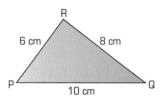

You will need a ruler and a protractor for SAS and ASA.

You will need a ruler and compasses for SSS.

The example shows you how to construct an SSS triangle.

example

Construct the triangle PQR with lengths PR = 6 cm, QR = 8 cm and PQ = 10 cm.

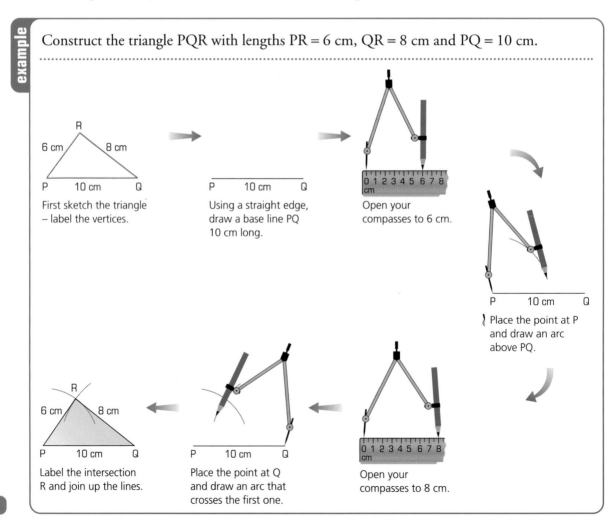

First sketch the triangle – label the vertices.

Using a straight edge, draw a base line PQ 10 cm long.

Open your compasses to 6 cm.

Place the point at P and draw an arc above PQ.

Open your compasses to 8 cm.

Place the point at Q and draw an arc that crosses the first one.

Label the intersection R and join up the lines.

Exercise S1.7

1 Accurately construct these triangles. Show your construction lines.
State the type of triangle for each one.

a
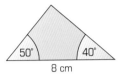

b

c
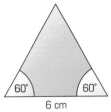

d
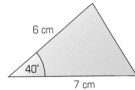

e
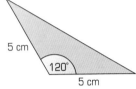

f
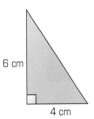

2 Accurately construct these triangles.

a
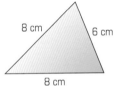

b
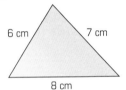

c
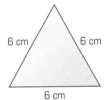

3 Accurately construct these nets of a tetrahedron.

a
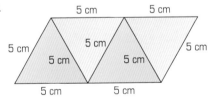

b
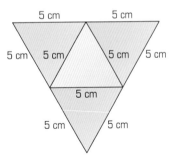

4 Accurately construct these quadrilaterals.
State the type of each quadrilateral.

a
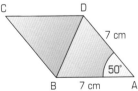

b
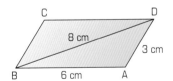

Hint: Triangles ABD and CDB are congruent.

This spread will show you how to:
⏩ Find simple loci to produce shapes and paths.
⏩ Construct the perpendicular bisector of a line.

KEYWORDS
Locus   Equidistant
Arc   Intersection
Bisect   Midpoint
Perpendicular bisector

The locus of an object is its path.

The locus of this ball is

a curve.

The locus of the swing is

an arc.

The locus of the train is

the path of the track.

You can find the locus of points that follow a rule.

The red counters are all the same distance from the blue counter.

The locus is a circle.

The red counters are the same distance from the two blue counters.

The locus is a straight line.
It bisects the line between the blue counters.

'Bisect' means cut exactly in half.

▶ A perpendicular bisector divides a straight line into two equal parts at right angles.

A ———————— B

This line bisects the length AB.

You use compasses to construct a perpendicular bisector.

Draw arcs from A ...

and equal arcs from B.

Join the intersections.

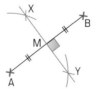

M is the midpoint of AB.

AXBY is a rhombus.

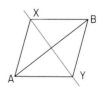

XY is the perpendicular bisector of AB.

The perpendicular bisector is the locus of all points that are equidistant from A and B.

Exercise S1.8

1 Draw the locus of each situation.
If possible, describe the path using mathematical terms.
  a A falling stone.
  b The tip of a hand on a clock.
  c A speck of dust on a CD as it rotates.
  d A point that is always 3 cm from a fixed point.
  e A point that is equidistant from two other points A and B.

2 The women's world record for the 4 kg shot is almost 23 metres.
Draw a scale drawing to show the region where the shot could
land. Use a scale of 1 mm for 1 m.

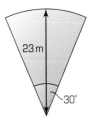

3 **a** Copy this diagram.

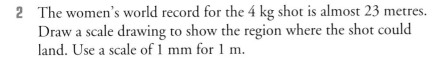

  b Construct the locus of the points that are equidistant from A and B.

4 **a** Draw a line AB, so that AB = 8 cm.
Construct the perpendicular bisector.
  b The perpendicular bisector crosses AB at M.
Measure AM.

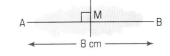

5 **a** Draw a 4 cm by 2 cm rectangle.

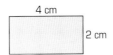

  b Construct the perpendicular bisectors of one long side
and one short side.

6 **a** Draw a line AB, so that AB = 6 cm.
Construct the perpendicular bisector.

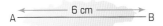

  b Mark the points of intersection of the arcs as X and Y.
Write down the name of the quadrilateral AXBY.
  c Explain why this construction method gives the perpendicular bisector of AB.

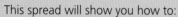

This spread will show you how to:
- ⏩ Construct the bisector of an angle.
- ⏩ Find simple loci to produce shapes and paths.

KEYWORDS

Locus   Compasses
Bisect   Arc
Angle bisector
Equidistant

Here are some more common loci:

The red counters are the same distance from the two blue lines.

The red counters are the same distance from the two blue lines.

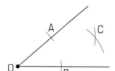

The locus is a straight line.
To construct this locus, you need to bisect the angle.

The locus is a straight line.

▶ An angle bisector divides an angle into two equal parts.
The bisector is equidistant from the arms of the angle.

This line bisects the angle.

You use compasses to construct an angle bisector:

| Use compasses to draw equal arcs on each arm. | Draw equal arcs from these arcs that intersect at C. | Join C to O, the vertex of the angle | OACB is a rhombus. |

The angle bisector is the locus of all points that are equidistant from OA and OB.

You can use LOGO to plot the path of a turtle.
You specify distance in mm and angles in degrees.

These commands ...   produce this path.

FORWARD 100
LEFT 90
FORWARD 100

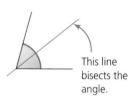

plan view is

10 cm

10 cm

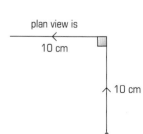

Exercise S1.9

1 **a** Use a protractor to draw an angle of 50°.
   b Construct the angle bisector.
      Measure and state the two new angles.

2 Copy these diagrams of walls:

a
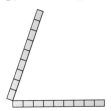

b
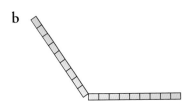

Construct the locus of the points that are equidistant from the walls.

3 What shapes are formed by these LOGO commands?

a		**b**		**c**	
FORWARD	100	FORWARD	150	FORWARD	100
RIGHT	120	RIGHT	90	RIGHT	72
FORWARD	100	FORWARD	50	FORWARD	100
RIGHT	120	RIGHT	90	RIGHT	72
FORWARD	100	FORWARD	150	FORWARD	100
		RIGHT	90	RIGHT	72
		FORWARD	50	FORWARD	100
				RIGHT	72
				FORWARD	100

4 Write the LOGO commands to draw these shapes:.

a
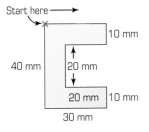

b
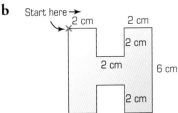

Hint: 1 cm = 10 mm

5 Draw a line AB, with AB = 5 cm.

Construct the locus of the points that are always 3 cm from the line.

6 **a** Construct this rhombus using compasses.
   b Measure the length of one of the sides of the rhombus.
   c Calculate the area of the rhombus.

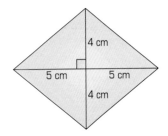

69

Summary

You should know how to ...

1 Identify alternate angles and corresponding angles.

2 Understand a proof that the sum of angles of a triangle is 180° and of a quadrilateral is 360°.

3 Use straight edge and compasses to construct perpendiculars and bisectors.

4 Identify the necessary information to solve a problem.

Check out

1 Give the angle that is:

   a alternate to d

   b corresponding to d

   c vertically opposite to d.

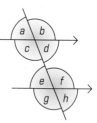

2 a Use this diagram to help you with the proof.

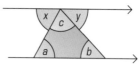

   $x + y + c = 180°$ (angles in a straight line)

   $x = a$ (alternate angles)

   $y = b$ (alternate angles)

   Copy and complete: $a + b + c = \_\_$

   What does this prove?

   b Use this diagram to help you with the proof.

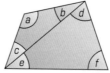

   $a + b + c = 180°$ (angles in a triangle)

   $d + e + f = 180°$ (angles in a triangle)

   Copy and complete:

   $a + b + c + d + e + f = \_\_$

   What does this prove?

3 a Draw a 5 cm square.

   b Construct the perpendicular bisector of each side.

   c Construct the angle bisector of each 90° angle.

5 cm
5 cm

4 A regular hexagon is divided into three congruent rhombuses.

   Calculate the interior angles of the rhombus.

This unit will show you how to:

▶▶ Decide which data to collect to answer a question, and the degree of accuracy needed.

▶▶ Identify possible sources.

▶▶ Collect data using a suitable method, such as observation, controlled experiment, including data logging using ICT, or questionnaire.

▶▶ Calculate statistics, including with a calculator.

▶▶ Recognise when it is appropriate to use the mean, median and mode and, for grouped data, the modal class.

▶▶ Interpret tables, graphs and diagrams for both discrete and continuous data, and draw inferences.

▶▶ Relate summarised data to the questions being explored.

▶▶ Construct on paper, and using ICT:
  ▶ pie charts for categorical data
  ▶ bar charts and frequency diagrams
  ▶ simple line graphs for time series
  ▶ simple scatter graphs

▶▶ Identify which are most useful in the context.

▶▶ Compare two distributions using the range and one or more of the mode, median and mean.

▶▶ Identify the necessary information to solve a problem.

▶▶ Represent problems and interpret solutions in algebraic, geometric or graphical form.

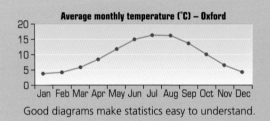

Good diagrams make statistics easy to understand.

Before you start

You should know how to ...

1 Order numbers and values.

2 Draw bar charts.

3 Interpret simple pie charts.

Check in

1 Put these values in order, smallest first:

3.2   9.7   ⁻1.6   ⁻12.9   5.6   15.3

2 Draw a bar chart for these results of a survey into pieces of fruit eaten per day.

Fruit eaten/day	1	2	3	4
Frequency	20	15	9	3

3 This pie chart shows the types of fruit eaten in one day by class 9C.

If there are 36 students in the class, how many ate an apple?

This spread will show you how to:
- ▶▶ Decide which data to collect to answer a question, and the degree of accuracy needed.
- ▶▶ Identify possible sources.
- ▶▶ Collect data using a suitable method.

KEYWORDS

Interpret	Secondary
Data	Primary
Average	Questionnaire

The handling data cycle shows the main stages in any statistical project.

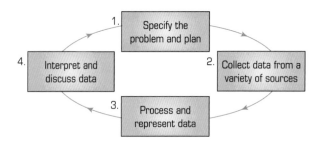

1. Specify the problem and plan
2. Collect data from a variety of sources
3. Process and represent data
4. Interpret and discuss data

Maxine follows these steps in her project about healthy eating.

1 HYPOTHESES

I want to investigate teenagers' eating habits. My hypothesis is that teenagers eat more high-fat fast food than adults! I'm going to use primary and secondary data.

2 DATA SHEET

I used a questionnaire to collect primary data, asking people in my class, their parents, and people at a burger bar. I found some good secondary data on the Internet.

4 CONCLUSIONS.

Teenagers seem to be eating more high-fat fast food than adults.
I also discovered that teenagers are taking less exercise than adults.

3

My Internet research showed that the average American eats about three hamburgers and four lots of chips every week. That's 90 grams of fat and 2520 calories. The average person needs about 2000 calories for a whole day. My survey showed that teenagers visited a burger bar on average 1.9 times a week but adults only visited 0.3 times on average.

Exercise D1.1

1 Shirley suggested that Maxine ask people the question:
'Do you eat healthy food?'

Maxine did not think that this was a good idea.
Explain why not.

2 Here is part of Maxine's questionnaire.

What is your age? (Tick a box)

☐ 0–10   ☐ 10–15   ☐ 15–20   ☐ 20+

   a Explain what is wrong with the question.
   b Write a better version of the question.

3 Explain whether each of these sets of data is primary or secondary.
   a The results of a survey you carry out in your class.
   b A table of data copied from a textbook.
   c The results of an experiment you do in a science lesson.
   d A set of data downloaded from the Internet.

4 Write what data Maxine needed to collect to investigate her hypothesis.
   Make two lists:
   ▶ one for the Primary data she collected in her questionnaire
   ▶ one for the Secondary data she found on the Internet.
   Remember to make sure you include all the information she needed.

5 Use the list you wrote for Primary data in question 4 to design a
   questionnaire Maxine could use for both teenagers and adults.
   ▶ Remember to make sure that all the data she will need is collected.
   ▶ Think about how accurate the data needs to be.
   ▶ Remember to give a range of options if they would make the
      question easier to answer.

6 Design a two-way table to help Maxine record her data.
   Here is an example:

Age and grams of fat eaten per day

	0–20	21–40	41–60	61–80	81–100	101+
0–10						
11–20						
21–30						
31+						

Calculating statistics

example

This spread will show you how to:

▶▶ Calculate statistics, including with a calculator.

▶▶ Recognise when it is appropriate to use the mean, median and mode and, for grouped data, the modal class.

KEYWORDS

Mean	Mode
Median	Range

The mean, median and mode are **averages**.

An average is one number that tries to give a fair picture of a whole set of data.

The **range** shows you how widely spread the data are.

Maxine asked 11 people how many burgers they ate last month. Their answers were: 4, 0, 2, 1, 0, 1, 12, 0, 3, 1, 0.

Work out the mean, median, mode and range.

Mean	Add all the numbers, and divide by how many values there are.	The total number of burgers is 24. The **mean** is 2.18.
Median	Put the numbers in order, and find the middle one.	0, 0, 0, 0, 1, **1**, 1, 2, 3, 4, 12. The **median** is 1.
Mode	Find the number that occurs most often.	There were more 1s in the data than any other number. The **mode** is 1.
Range	The difference between the maximum and the minimum numbers.	Maximum = 12, minimum = 0. The **range** = 12 − 0 = 12.

You should choose the best average for any set of data:

Advantages

▶ The **mean** is often the best average as it uses all of the data.
▶ The **median** is not affected by a single extreme value.
▶ The **mode** is usually easy to find.

Disadvantages

▶ One big value can increase the mean.
▶ You ignore most of the data values.
▶ It might not be very representative.

The table shows the time taken for 17 different taxi journeys. Find the modal class.

Time, t (minutes)	Frequency
$0 \leqslant t < 5$	2
$5 \leqslant t < 10$	7
$10 \leqslant t < 15$	5
$15 \leqslant t < 20$	3

The modal class is $5 \leqslant t < 10$, since this class has the highest frequency.

Exercise D1.2

1 A group of students was asked how many cats they owned:

> 0, 0, 0, 1, 3, 2, 0, 1, 1, 1, 0, 0, 1, 1, 2, 0, 1, 1, 1, 1, 1, 0, 1, 0, 0, 1

What was the mode of the number of cats owned?

2 A group of teenagers recorded how many text messages they received in a day:

> 4, 4, 3, 0, 1, 0, 7,
> 0, 3, 2, 8, 0, 1, 2,
> 4, 6, 3, 2, 0, 0, 2,
> 0, 1, 0, 2, 0, 1, 3, 0

a Draw a frequency table for this data.
b What was the mode of the number of calls?
c What was the range of the number of calls?

3 Sally and Baz both kept a record of how far (in miles) they drove each day.

	Mon	Tues	Wed	Thurs	Fri
Sally	21.5	32.6	41.8	9.7	11.6
Baz	33.8	36.7	36.5	91.2	3.2

a Work out the mean daily mileage for each person.
b Find the median distance driven by each person.
c Work out the range of the distances driven for each person.
d Explain why the mode would not be a useful average in this case.

4 Here are students' scores (out of 20) for a maths test.

> 15, 6, 2, 13, 14,
> 14, 9, 12, 20, 7,
> 17, 9, 11, 12, 17,
> 15, 18, 8, 9, 12, 17

a Work out the mean score.
b How many students got more than the mean score?

5 Find the median of each of these sets of data.
a 3, 7, 4, 2, 5, 8, 6
b 4, 7, 2, 4, 3, 2, 7, 9
c 2.1, 3.8, 2.6, 3.1, 4.2, 3.3, 2.5, 4.3

6 This frequency table shows the number of mistakes per page in a 20-page booklet.

Number of mistakes	0	1	2	3	4	5
Number of pages	7	4	3	3	2	1

a Find the modal number of mistakes per page.
b Find the total number of mistakes in the booklet.
c Calculate the mean number of mistakes per page.

7 Here are the distances in a welly-throwing competition.

> 5.2m 3.7m 2.7m
> 7.6m 5.4m 3.9m
> 1.5m 8.5m 7.9m
> 3.0m 6.2m 4.6m

a Copy and complete this tally chart.

Distance (m)	Tally	Frequency
$0 < d \leqslant 3$		
$3 < d \leqslant 6$		
$6 < d \leqslant 9$		

b Find the modal class.

Constructing pie charts

This spread will show you how to:
▶▶ Construct pie charts for categorical data.

▶ A pie chart uses a circle to represent data.
  It helps compare the size of a category with the whole.

To draw a pie chart, you need to work out the angle for each sector.

example

The table shows the eye colours of a group of 36 students.
Calculate the angle for each sector. Draw the pie chart.

Colour	Blue	Brown	Green
Frequency	12	18	6

Work out the angle for 1 person:
360° represents 36 people, so 1 person is represented by 10°.
The angles are: Blue, $12 \times 10° = 120°$
                   Brown, $18 \times 10° = 180°$
                   Green, $6 \times 10° = 60°$

▶ To find the angles in a pie chart:
  ▶ Work out the angle for one person.
  ▶ Multiply the angle for one person by the number of
    people in each category.

You may need to round the angle to the nearest degree.

example

A group of people was asked to taste three different types of ice cream,
and pick their favourite. Show the results in a pie chart.

Flavour	Kiwi	Cherry	Grape
People	14	9	6

First work out the angle for one person.
There are 29 people, so the angle for one person is $360° \div 29$.
The angle for each flavour of ice cream is:

    Kiwi: $360° \div 29 \times 14 = 174°$ (nearest 1°)
    Cherry: $360° \div 29 \times 9 = 112°$ (nearest 1°)
    Grape: $360° \div 29 \times 6 = 74°$ (nearest 1°)

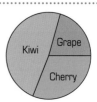

The total angle for all the sectors might not come to exactly 360° because of rounding.

Exercise D1.3

1 The pie chart shows the percentage of people who played different sports at a sports centre one Saturday morning.
  a Estimate the percentage of people who played squash.
  b 24 people played tennis. Estimate the total number of people represented by the pie chart.

2 There are 50 books on a shelf.
  Some of them are fiction, and the rest are non-fiction.
  a How many of the books are fiction?
  b What percentage of the books are non-fiction?

3 There are 30 students in a class. 12 of them are boys.
  This pie chart is not drawn accurately.
  What should the angles be?
  Show your working.

4 The table shows the colour of 12 cars parked in a school car park.

Colour	Red	Blue	Yellow	White
Number	5	4	1	2

Draw a pie chart for this data.

5 The table shows the number of trees of various types in a nature reserve.

Tree	Oak	Ash	Elm	Birch
Number	23	14	8	11

Draw a pie chart to show this data.

6 Two classes, 9A and 9B, took part in a survey about healthy eating.
  One of the questions was: 'What is your favourite fruit?'
  Here are the results from class 9A.

Favourite fruit	Apple	Banana	Orange	Pear
Number of children	5	12	4	3

  a Draw a pie chart to show class 9A's results.
  b In class 9B, 11 people chose bananas as their favourite fruit.
    When a pie chart was drawn for class 9B's results, the angle for the sector representing bananas was 132°.
    How many students are there in class 9B? Show your working.

Selecting and drawing charts

This spread will show you how to:

▶▶ Construct:
  ▶ Bar charts and frequency diagrams
  ▶ Simple line graphs for time series
  ▶ Simple scatter graphs.

▶▶ Identify which are most useful in the context.

KEYWORDS

Bar chart   Continuous
Discrete   Line graph
Category
Frequency diagram
Frequency table
Scatter graph

You use a pie chart to compare each category with the total.

To compare one category with another, you use:

a **bar chart**   or   a **frequency diagram**

Use a bar chart for discrete data (data that is collected by counting).

Use a frequency diagram for continuous data (data that is collected by measuring).

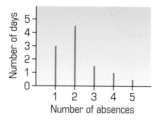

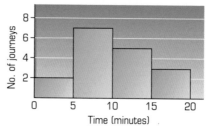

This bar-line chart uses lines for the bars. It shows the number of people absent from a class over a 4-week period.

This frequency diagram has no gaps between the bars. It shows the data for the taxi journeys from the example in D1.2.

Two other very useful types of diagram are:

scatter graphs   and   **line graphs**

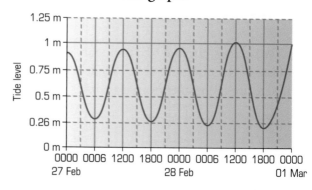

Scatter graphs show patterns in paired data. Each dot represents two measurements, like coordinates – in this case, the marks on two different tests.

Line graphs show how something changes over time. You plot time on the horizontal axis.

Exercise D1.4

1 Craig records the birds that he sees in his garden over a one-hour period.
He uses this code:

Code	T	S	M	P	B	W
Bird	Thrush	Sparrow	Magpie	Pigeon	Blackbird	Wren

Here are Craig's results:

S T T S M S S S P B B W S M S P S S M S S S S W B B S S T

a Draw a frequency table for the data.
b Draw a bar-line chart to show the data.

2 Some students counted the number of CDs they owned. Here are the results.

22, 14, 39, 34, 62, 17, 8, 22, 18, 34, 23, 18, 11, 42, 39, 42, 40, 32, 27, 29

a Record the results in a frequency table for grouped data.
Use groups like 0–9, 10–19, and so on.
b Draw a bar chart to show the data.

3 This table shows the time a sample of customers spent queuing
at a supermarket checkout.

Time, t (minutes)	Frequency
$0 \leqslant t < 5$	12
$5 \leqslant t < 10$	28
$10 \leqslant t < 15$	9
$15 \leqslant t < 20$	2

Draw a frequency diagram to represent this data.

4 Ten students took two different maths tests, each marked out of 20.
The table shows the marks for each student in the two tests.

	Andy	Bella	Dan	Ellie	Holly	Mandy	Ruta	Tim	Toni	Vinod
Test A	15	14	6	8	18	13	19	12	16	12
Test B	15	11	4	11	16	13	20	10	14	12

Draw a scatter graph for this set of data.

Hint: You need scales from 0 to 20 on each axis.

5 A group of students measured the depth of water in a stream.
They took measurements every 5 minutes, for 1 hour.

Time (minutes)	0	5	10	15	20	25	30	35	40	45	50	55	60
Depth (cm)	28	37	48	53	55	49	41	32	25	22	20	19	19

Hint: Plot time on the horizontal axis.

Draw a line graph for this set of data.

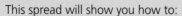

This spread will show you how to:
▶▶ Interpret tables, graphs and diagrams, and draw inferences that relate to the problem being discussed.
▶▶ Relate summarised data to the questions being explored.

KEYWORDS
Proportion
Bar chart
Pie chart

You need to interpret data presented in charts and tables.
Here are some examples.

This table shows the total distances travelled by bicycle in the UK.

Year	1955	1960	1965	1970	1975	1980	1985	1990	1995	2000
Billions of km	18.2	12.0	7.0	4.4	4.4	5.1	6.1	5.3	4.5	4.0

The table shows that people are travelling a smaller distance by bicycle than before.
There was a small increase in bicycle travel in the 1980s, but it has decreased since then.

These pie charts show the population of the UK by age group in 1901 and 1998.

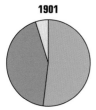
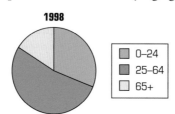

You can say that:

▶ In 1901, more than half the population was less than 25 years old.
  In 1998, it was closer to one third.
▶ There was a much greater proportion of people aged 65 or more in 1998 than there was in 1901.

You cannot say that:

▶ There were more people younger than 25 in 1901 than there were in 1998.
  The pie charts just show the **proportion** of the population in each category.
  The total population in 1998 was much larger than in 1901.

This **compound bar chart** shows that the average distance travelled by people in the UK has increased.
The bars show that the increase was completely due to the growth in the use of motor vehicles.
The use of other means of transport actually decreased.

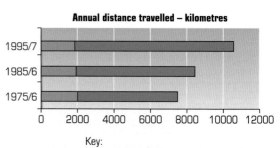

Exercise D1.5

1 This table shows how much sunshine (in minutes) there was each day for five days.

Day	Monday	Tuesday	Wednesday	Thursday	Friday
Minutes	242	115	210	165	42

    a Which day had least sunshine?
    b Which day had about 4 hours of sunshine?
    c There was more sunshine on Thursday than on Friday.
       How much more?

2 Roger is doing a survey about school meals. There are three choices of main meal.
He asks students in Years 7, 8 and 9 what they chose, and plots this chart.

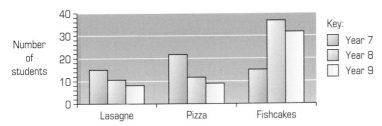

    a What was the most popular choice in each year group?
    b How many people chose lasagne altogether?

3 This pie chart shows information about the ages of people
in Belgium.

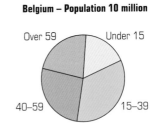

    a Use the chart to estimate the percentage of people in
       Belgium aged 40–59.
    b The population of Belgium is about 10 million people.
       Use your answer to part **a** to work out roughly how
       many people aged 40–59 there are in Belgium.

4 This chart shows the percentage of people
in different age groups in two villages.

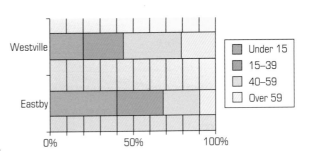

    a Roughly what percentage of the
       population in each village is under 15?
    b Which age group represents about the
       same percentage of the population in
       each village?
    c Why is it not fair to say that there must
       be more young people in Eastby than
       in Westville?

5 Using the data from question 2, produce a pie chart for each
year group, showing which meals the students chose.
Explain which features the different charts show best.

This spread will show you how to:
▶▶ Compare two distributions using the range and one or more of the
mode, median and mean.

KEYWORDS

Range   Mean
Distribution   Average

You can compare sets of data using an average and the range.

Stephanie obtained this information from the Internet as part of a
project comparing the climate in Oxford with that in Moscow.

Precipitation means the
amount of rain and snow.

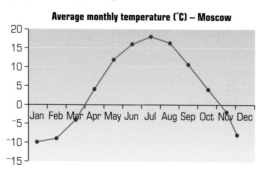

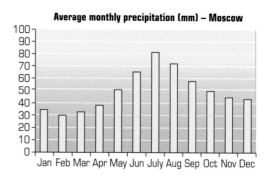

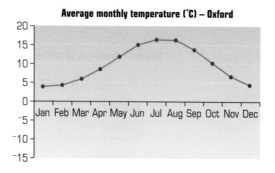

	Monthly temperatures (°C)			
	Mean	Max	Min	Range
Oxford	9.7	16.6	3.7	12.9
Moscow	4.1	18.5	⁻10.3	28.8

	Precipitation (mm)		
	Total	Mean	Range
Oxford	649.1	54.1	24.5
Moscow	600.6	50.1	52.5

Stephanie compares the distribution of the data for the two cities:

Temperature
The mean temperature for Moscow is
5.6°C lower than it is for Oxford.
However, the range of temperatures is
much greater in Moscow.
Moscow is a little warmer than Oxford
in the summer, and a lot colder in the
winter.

Precipitation
The means show that Oxford is
slightly wetter than Moscow.
The range for Moscow is more than
twice that for Oxford, showing that
the monthly precipitation is a lot
more varied in Moscow than it is in
Oxford.

Exercise D1.6

1 Karen and Judy compared the number of text messages they received each day for 10 days.

Day	1	2	3	4	5	6	7	8	9	10
Karen	3	2	3	2	2	4	3	2	3	4
Judy	7	2	1	8	5	0	2	1	1	5

   a Work out the mean number of text messages they each received.

   b Work out the range of the number of messages they each received.

   c Write a paragraph to compare the distribution of the number of messages they each received.

2 The table shows the mean and the range of the number of goals scored by two football teams in a season. Both teams played the same number of games.

Team	Mean number of goals	Range
Calthorpe FC	1.75	5
Holby Dynamo	2.5	6

Explain whether the following statements are definitely true, definitely false, or impossible to say.

   a Holby scored more goals in the season than Calthorpe.

   b Holby won more matches than Calthorpe.

   c Calthorpe scored 6 goals in one of their matches.

   d Holby lost one game 0–7, and won another one 7–0.

3 A teacher collects the number of absences for two of her classes for one week. There are 30 students in each class. For each class, work out:

Absences	Mon.	Tues.	Wed.	Thurs.	Fri.
Class 9A	3	3	2	1	4
Class 9B	5	3	0	0	1

   a the mean

   b the median

   c the range of the number of absences.

   d Use your answers to parts **a**–**c** to explain which class had the best attendance.

4 The tables show average monthly temperatures for Chicago (USA) and Madrid (Spain).

Temp (°C)	Jan	Feb	Mar	Apr	May	Jun	Jul	Aug	Sep	Oct	Nov	Dec	Yearly average
Chicago	4	2.5	2.6	8.9	15	20	23	23	19	13	5	1.4	10.1
Madrid	5.3	6.7	9.7	12	16	21	25	24	21	15	9.3	6	14.2

   a Draw line graphs and bar charts to show the average monthly temperatures for the two cities.

   b Find the range of the monthly temperatures for each city.

   c Write a paragraph comparing the temperatures of the two cities. Use charts and statistics to support your description.

D1 Summary

You should know how to …

1 Construct on paper, and using ICT:
- ▶ pie charts for categorical data
- ▶ bar charts and frequency diagrams
- ▶ simple line graphs for time series
- ▶ simple scatter graphs.

Identify which are most useful in the context of the problem.

2 Identify the necessary information to solve a problem.

3 Represent problems and interpret solutions in graphical form.

Check out

1 a For each of the types of chart listed:
- ▶ Draw a sketch to show its main features
- ▶ Give an example of data it could show.
  - **i** Pie chart
  - **ii** Bar chart
  - **iii** Line graph
  - **iv** Scatter graph

b Draw this data as:
- **i** a pie chart
- **ii** a bar chart.

Type of pet	Number owned
Cat	10
Dog	5
Rat	4
Lizard	1

c Explain which features of the data are shown best by each chart.

2 Tracey wants to find out which person in her class is best at estimating time. She decides to find out how well each person can estimate a time of 30 seconds.
Explain how Tracey could collect the data that she needs.

3 Christopher asked people in his class to record the number of hours they spend reading and watching television each evening for a week. The table shows his results.

Person	A	B	C	D	E	F	G	H	I	J
Hrs. reading	4	8	1	3	9	12	7	10	9	9
Hrs. T.V	25	23	29	24	18	19	25	20	21	20

Draw a suitable chart to represent these data. Explain the features of the data that your chart shows.

2

Perimeter, area and volume

This unit will show you how to:

- ▶▶ Find the midpoint of a line.
- ▶▶ Deduce and use the formula for the area of a triangle, parallelogram and trapezium.
- ▶▶ Calculate areas of compound shapes made from triangles and rectangles.
- ▶▶ Know the formula for the volume of a cuboid.
- ▶▶ Calculate volumes and surface areas of cuboids.
- ▶▶ Use units of measurement to estimate, calculate and solve problems.

- ▶▶ Know rough metric equivalents of imperial measures in daily use.
- ▶▶ Solve more demanding problems and investigate in a range of contexts.
- ▶▶ Identify the necessary information to solve a problem.
- ▶▶ Represent problems and interpret solutions in algebraic, geometric or graphical form.
- ▶▶ Identify exceptional cases or counter-examples.

It's useful to know equivalents of measures.

Before you start

You should know how to ...

1 Find the mean of two numbers.

2 Recognise and name triangles and quadrilaterals.

3 Recognise congruent shapes.

Check in

1 What is the mean of 3 and 7?

2 Copy this shape.
   Find and shade in:
   a an equilateral triangle
   b an isosceles triangle
   c a right-angled scalene triangle
   d a rhombus
   e an isosceles trapezium
   f a rectangle.

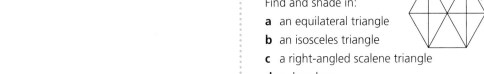

3 On your shape, colour in a shape that is congruent to each shape in question 2.

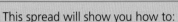

Coordinates

This spread will show you how to:
▶▶ Use coordinates in all four quadrants.
▶▶ Find the midpoint of a line.

You can plot coordinates on a grid.

▶ A grid has two perpendicular axes: the *x*-axis and the *y*-axis.

The axes split the grid into four quadrants.

The arrows on the axes show the positive direction.

The vertical line is the *y*-axis.

The horizontal line is the *x*-axis.

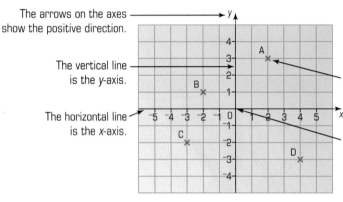

The coordinates are a pair of numbers (*x, y*) that fixes a point on a grid. (2, 3) means 2 along the *x*-axis and 3 up the *y*-axis.

The point of intersection of the axes is called the origin: (0, 0).

▶ Negative coordinates mean you go backwards or downwards.

B = (⁻2, 1) means
2 backwards along the *x*-axis and 1 up the *y*-axis.

C = (⁻3, ⁻2) means
3 backwards along the *x*-axis and 2 down the *y*-axis.

example

What are the coordinates of D?
....
You count 4 across, then 3 down.
The coordinates are (4, ⁻3).

The midpoint of a line is halfway along it.

A has coordinates (1, 2).   B has coordinates (5, 4).

The midpoint, M, has coordinates (3, 3).

You can find the midpoint from the coordinates without drawing.
You find the mean of the coordinates.

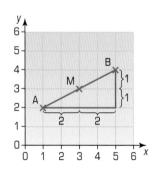

The *x*-coordinate is the mean of the *x*-coordinates:
$\frac{1+5}{2} = \frac{6}{2} = 3$

The *y*-coordinate is the mean of the *y*-coordinates:
$\frac{2+4}{2} = \frac{6}{2} = 3$

The midpoint, M, has coordinates (3, 3).

Exercise S2.1

1 Copy these axes.

Plot and join up the points.

Write down the letter that is formed by each set of coordinates.

a (3, 3) (2, ⁻1) (0, 1) (⁻2, ⁻1) (⁻3, 3)

b (⁻2, ⁻2) (⁻2, 2) (2, ⁻2) (2, 2)

c (0, 3) (⁻2, 3) (⁻2, 1) (⁻1, 1) (⁻2, 1) (⁻2, ⁻2)

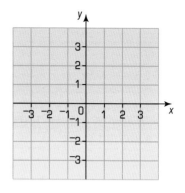

2 Copy these axes.

Plot and join up each set of coordinates on the same axes.

Name the shape for each set.

a (3, 3) (3, ⁻2) (⁻2, ⁻2) (⁻2, 3) (3, 3)

b (⁻2, ⁻2) (⁻3, ⁻1) (⁻3, 1) (⁻2, 3) (⁻2, ⁻2)

c (2, 2) (2, ⁻1) (⁻1, ⁻1) (⁻1, 2) (2, 2)

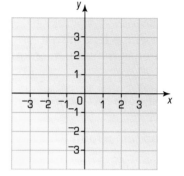

3 Copy these axes and plot the points as shown.

Write down, if possible, the coordinates of the extra vertex that will make:

a a square

b a kite

c an arrowhead (delta).

d a trapezium

e a rectangle.

Hint: A vertex is a point where two sides meet.

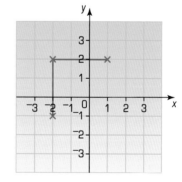

4 Copy these axes.

Plot these points and the midpoints of the lines joining:

a (1, 6) and (5, 6)

b (1, 2) and (1, 6)

c (2, 3) and (6, 5)

d (4, 4) and (6, 0)

e (⁻1, 2) and (3, 0)

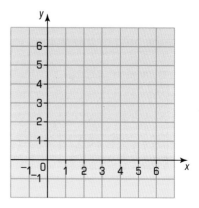

5 Check your answers to question 4 by finding the midpoints by calculation.

S2.2 Area of a triangle

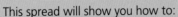

This spread will show you how to:
- ▶▶ Deduce and use the formula for the area of a triangle.
- ▶▶ Calculate areas of compound shapes.

KEYWORDS

Area   Perimeter

Triangle   Base

Height

The perimeter of a shape is the distance around it.

perimeter

Perimeter is a length so it is measured in mm, cm, m or km.

The area of a shape is the amount of space it covers.

area

Area is measured in square units: mm², cm², m² or km².

> ▶ Area of a rectangle = length × width

You can find a formula for the area of any triangle:

Split the triangle into two right-angled triangles.

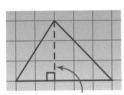

This is the perpendicular height.

Complete the rectangle for each triangle.

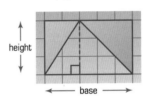

height

base

$\frac{1}{2}$ × **area of rectangle.**

> ▶ Area of triangle = $\frac{1}{2}$ × area of rectangle = $\frac{1}{2}$ × base × height

The height must be perpendicular to the base.

You can use these facts to find the area of this shape:

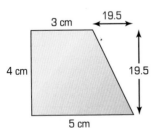

3 cm

19.5

4 cm   19.5

5 cm

Split it into a rectangle and a triangle:

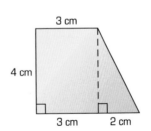

3 cm

4 cm

3 cm   2 cm

Find the area of each shape:

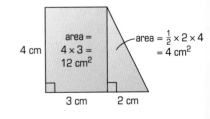

4 cm   area = 4 × 3 = 12 cm²

area = $\frac{1}{2}$ × 2 × 4 = 4 cm²

3 cm   2 cm

The total area is 12 cm² + 4 cm² = 16 cm²

Exercise S2.2

1 Find the perimeter and area of each of these shapes.

a
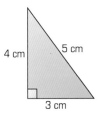
4 cm, 5 cm, 3 cm

b
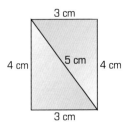
3 cm, 4 cm, 5 cm, 4 cm, 3 cm

c
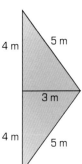
4 m, 5 m, 3 m, 4 m, 5 m

d
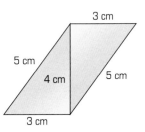
3 cm, 5 cm, 4 cm, 5 cm, 3 cm

e
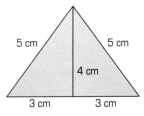
5 cm, 5 cm, 4 cm, 3 cm, 3 cm

2 Find the area of each of these triangles.

a
b
c
d

3 Calculate the area of each of these triangles.

a

8 cm, 10 cm

b

7 mm, 8 mm

c

4 cm, 4 cm

4 Draw a triangle with an area of 6 cm^2.
Label and mark the lengths of the base and perpendicular height.

5 Find the area of each of these shapes.

a
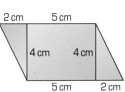
2 cm, 5 cm, 4 cm, 4 cm, 5 cm, 2 cm

b
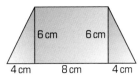
6 cm, 6 cm, 4 cm, 8 cm, 4 cm

c
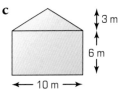
3 m, 6 m, 10 m

 **Area of a parallelogram and a trapezium**

This spread will show you how to:

▶▶ Deduce and use the formulae for the area of a parallelogram and trapezium.

A parallelogram is made up of two congruent triangles:

 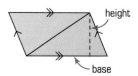 

The area of the parallelogram is double the area of the triangle.

▶ Area of triangle = $\frac{1}{2} \times$ base $\times$ height

▶ Area of parallelogram = base $\times$ height

The height must be perpendicular to the base.

A trapezium has one pair of parallel sides.

You can fit two congruent trapeziums together to make a parallelogram:

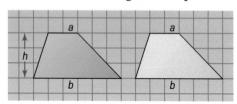 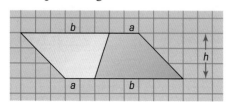

The base is $a + b$.
The height is h.

▶ Area of parallelogram = $(a + b) \times h$

▶ Area of trapezium = $\frac{1}{2} \times (a + b) \times h$

You can also split the shapes into triangles and rectangles.

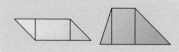

example

Calculate the area of each of these shapes.

a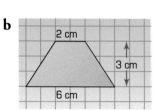

3 cm

4 cm

b

2 cm

3 cm

6 cm

....

a   Area = $4 \times 3 = 12$ cm^2

b   Area = $\frac{1}{2} \times (2 + 6) \times 3 = \frac{1}{2} \times 8 \times 3 = 12$ cm^2

Exercise S2.3

1 Calculate the area of each of these parallelograms.

a   **b** **c**

d 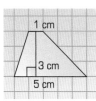 4 cm 10 cm

e 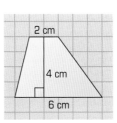 5 mm 8 mm

f 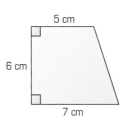 4 cm 5 cm 6 cm

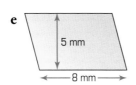

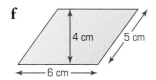

2 Calculate the area of each of these trapeziums.

a 1 cm 3 cm 5 cm

b 2 cm 4 cm 6 cm

c 5 cm 6 cm 7 cm

d 8 cm 10 cm 12 cm

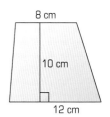

3 **a** Calculate the area of this trapezium using the trapezium area formula.

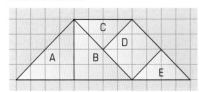

 b Calculate the area of each of the five shapes A, B, C, D and E.
 c Add your answers for the areas of A, B, C, D and E.
   Check that your answer matches your answer to part **a**.
 d On squared paper, make a copy of the diagram.
   Cut out the five shapes.
 e Rearrange all five shapes to make a rectangle.
   Calculate the area of your rectangle using the rectangle area formula.
 f Rearrange all five shapes to make an isosceles right-angled triangle.
   Calculate the area of your triangle using the triangle area formula.
 g What do you notice about your answers to **a**, **c**, **e** and **f**?

4 Use squared paper to answer these questions.
 a Draw two different rectangles with an area of 12 cm^2.
 b Draw two different triangles with an area of 12 cm^2.
 c Draw two different parallelograms with an area of 12 cm^2.
 d Draw two different trapeziums with an area of 12 cm^2.
 For each shape, write the calculation to show the area is 12 cm^2.

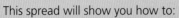# Measuring volume

This spread will show you how to:
- ▶▶ Find volumes by counting cubes.
- ▶▶ Know and use the formula for the volume of a cuboid.

KEYWORDS
Volume   3-D
Cuboid
cubic centimetres, cm^3
cubic metres, m^3

The volume of a 3-D shape is the amount of space it takes up.

You measure volume using cubes:

1 cm^3 is 1 cubic centimetre

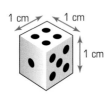

1 m^3 is 1 cubic metre

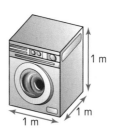

Most boxes have rectangular faces – they are cuboids.

You can find the volume of a cuboid by counting cubes:

There are 2 layers.

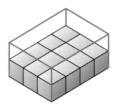

There are $3 \times 4 = 12$ cubes in each layer.

There are $2 \times 12 = 24$ cm^3 altogether.

▶ Volume of a cuboid = length × width × height

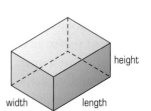

height

width   length

---

example

Find the volume of these shapes.
Shapes **a** and **b** are made from centimetre cubes.

a

b

c

1 m

1 m   3 m

....

a 7 cm^3 by counting   **b** $4 \times 2 \times 1 = 8$ cm^3 **c** $3 \times 1 \times 1 = 3$ m^3

Exercise S2.4

1 State the most suitable units, either cm³ or m³, to measure the volumes of these shapes.
   a A school dining room
   b A shoe box
   c A removal van
   d A calculator

2 State whether or not these shapes are cuboids.
   a Cereal packet   **b** Balloon   **c** CD case   **d** A container in a container ship

3 All these shapes are made from centimetre cubes. Find the volume of each shape.

a   **b**    **c**   **d**

4 All these cuboids are made from centimetre cubes.
   Write down the length, width and height of each cuboid.
   Find the volume of each cuboid.

a   **b**   **c**    **d**

5 Calculate the volumes of these cuboids.

a 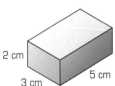   **b** 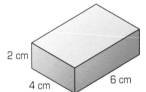   **c** 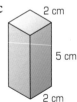   **d**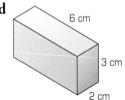

6 There are four different cuboids with a volume of 12 cm³.
   Use multilink cubes to find all four. Copy and complete this table with your results.

Length (*l*)	Width (*w*)	Height (*h*)	Volume (*V*)
4	3	1	12
			12
			12
			12

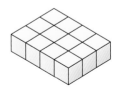

7 Find six different cuboids with a volume of 24 cm³.

This spread will show you how to:

Calculate volumes and surface areas of cuboids.

Most boxes are made up from flat shapes called nets.

This net ...

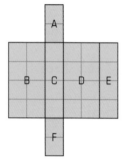

... folds to make a cuboid.

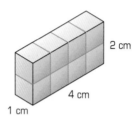

The dimensions of the cuboid are 1 cm, 2 cm and 4 cm.

The net has 6 rectangular parts.

The cuboid has 6 faces.

▶ **The area of the net is the surface area of the cuboid.**

The surface area of the cuboid is the sum of the areas of each surface:

A $1 \times 2 = 2$ F $1 \times 2 = 2$

B $2 \times 4 = 8$ D $2 \times 4 = 8$

C $1 \times 4 = 4$ E $1 \times 4 = 4$

The faces are in pairs that have the same area.
The pairs of faces are opposite each other.

Surface area $= 2 + 8 + 4 + 2 + 8 + 4 = 28$ cm^2

cm^2 are units of area.

The space inside the box is its volume or capacity.

▶ **Volume of a cuboid = length × width × height**

Volume $= 4 \times 1 \times 2 = 8$ cm^3

cm^3 are units of volume.

example

a Calculate the total surface area of the cuboid.
b Find the dimensions of the cuboid.
c Calculate the volume of the cuboid.
d Draw a net of the cuboid.

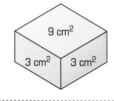

a Total surface area $= 3 + 3 + 9 + 3 + 3 + 9 = 30$ cm^2
b 3 cm, 3 cm, 1 cm
c Volume $= 3 \times 3 \times 1 = 9$ cm^3
d One possible net is:

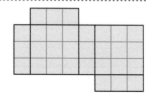

Exercise S2.5

1 Copy these nets onto squared paper and cut them out.

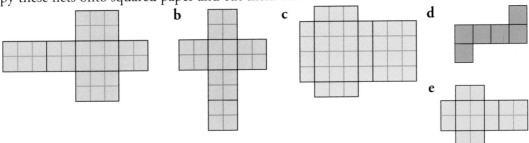

a   b   c   d

e

Fold each net into a 3-D shape. For each shape, find:
i the surface area   **ii** the dimensions   **iii** the volume.

2 Calculate the total surface area and the volume of each cuboid.

a

2 cm
4 cm
3 cm

b
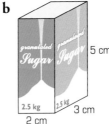
5 cm
2.5 kg 2.5 kg
3 cm
2 cm

c
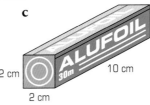
2 cm
10 cm
2 cm

d

10 cm
8 cm
3 cm

e

1 cm
5 cm
6 cm

f
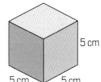
5 cm
5 cm
5 cm

3 There are three different cuboids with a volume of 8 cm³.
  a Find the dimensions of each cuboid (one is a cube).
  b Calculate the total surface area of each cuboid.
  c Draw a net of each cuboid.

4 For each of these cuboids:

a
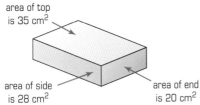
area of top
is 35 cm²
area of side
is 28 cm²
area of end
is 20 cm²

b
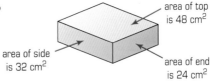
area of top
is 48 cm²
area of side
is 32 cm²
area of end
is 24 cm²

  i Calculate the surface area.
  ii Find the dimensions.
  iii Calculate the volume.

Units of measurement

This spread will show you how to:
▶▶ Use units of measurement.
▶▶ Know rough metric equivalents of imperial measures in daily use.

KEYWORDS

Metric	Imperial
Length	Capacity
Mass	Gram
Litre	Tonne
Metre	

Britain has used the metric system since 1971 but some imperial measures are still used regularly.

You need to know all of these measures:

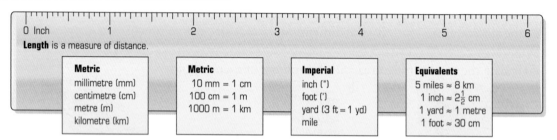

Length is a measure of distance.

Metric	Metric	Imperial	Equivalents
millimetre (mm)	10 mm = 1 cm	inch (")	5 miles ≈ 8 km
centimetre (cm)	100 cm = 1 m	foot (')	1 inch ≈ $2\frac{1}{2}$ cm
metre (m)	1000 m = 1 km	yard (3 ft = 1 yd)	1 yard ≈ 1 metre
kilometre (km)		mile	1 foot ≈ 30 cm

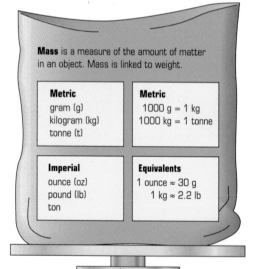

Mass is a measure of the amount of matter in an object. Mass is linked to weight.

Metric	Metric
gram (g)	1000 g = 1 kg
kilogram (kg)	1000 kg = 1 tonne
tonne (t)	

Imperial	Equivalents
ounce (oz)	1 ounce ≈ 30 g
pound (lb)	1 kg ≈ 2.2 lb
ton	

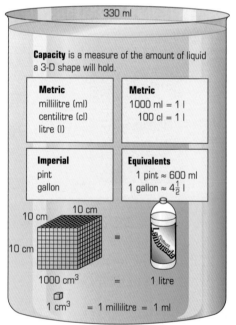

330 ml

Capacity is a measure of the amount of liquid a 3-D shape will hold.

Metric	Metric
millilitre (ml)	1000 ml = 1 l
centilitre (cl)	100 cl = 1 l
litre (l)	

Imperial	Equivalents
pint	1 pint ≈ 600 ml
gallon	1 gallon ≈ $4\frac{1}{2}$ l

10 cm
10 cm
10 cm

1000 cm³ = 1 litre

1 cm³ = 1 millilitre = 1 ml

---

example

Calculate the approximate length of a 12 inch ruler in:

a centimetres

b millimetres.

....

a $1" \approx 2\frac{1}{2}$ cm
   $12" \approx 2\frac{1}{2} \times 12 = 30$ cm

b 1 cm = 10 mm
   30 cm = 30 × 10 = 300 mm

Exercise S2.6

1 Suggest an appropriate metric unit **and** imperial unit to measure:
  a the height of a tree
  b the mass of an orange
  c the length of a small insect
  d the capacity of a jug
  e the distance from London to Paris
  f the mass of a bag of sugar.

2 Put these quantities in order of size, smallest first.
  a 1 pint, 1 litre
  b 1 kg, 1 lb

  c 1 mile, 1 kilometre
  d 1 inch, 1 centimetre

  e 1 gram, 1 ounce

3 A bottle holds 75 cl of wine. Change this capacity into:
  a litres   **b** millilitres.

4 **a** Measure the length and width of this page in centimetres.
  b Change these answers to millimetres.
  c Calculate the approximate length and width in inches.

5 It is 30 miles from Sheffield to Leeds.
  Calculate the approximate distance in kilometres.

6 A litre of petrol costs 80p.
  Calculate the approximate cost of a gallon of petrol.

7 I weigh 70 kg.
  What is my approximate mass in lb?

8 Calculate the approximate number of seconds from the
  21st June at midnight until midnight on Christmas Day.

9 If I pour this 500 ml bottle of liquid into this container,
  how high from the base will the level of the liquid be?

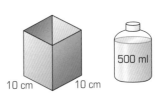

You should know how to ...

1 Deduce and use the formula for the area of a triangle, parallelogram and trapezium.

Check out

1 Find the area of each of these shapes.

a

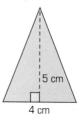

5 cm

4 cm

b

5 cm

4 cm

c

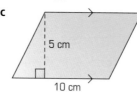

5 cm

10 cm

d

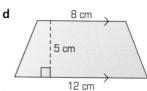

8 cm

5 cm

12 cm

2 Know and use the formula for the volume of a cuboid.

2 a Write down the formula for the volume of a cuboid.

b The volume of this cuboid is 40 cm^3.

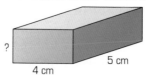

?

4 cm

5 cm

Calculate the height.

3 Calculate volumes and surface areas of cuboids.

3 a Calculate the volume of this cuboid.

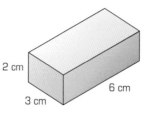

2 cm

3 cm

6 cm

b Calculate the surface area of the cuboid.

This unit will show you how to:

- ▶▶ Read and write positive integer powers of 10.
- ▶▶ Multiply and divide by 0.1 and 0.01.
- ▶▶ Order decimals.
- ▶▶ Round whole numbers to any power of 10.
- ▶▶ Round decimals to two decimal places.
- ▶▶ Use squares, square roots, cubes, cube roots and index notation for small integer powers.
- ▶▶ Add, subtract, multiply and divide integers.
- ▶▶ Use the laws of arithmetic and inverse operations.
- ▶▶ Use the order of operations.
- ▶▶ Recall known facts.
- ▶▶ Use known facts to derive unknown facts.
- ▶▶ Consolidate and extend mental methods of calculation.

- ▶▶ Solve word problems mentally.
- ▶▶ Make and justify estimates and approximations.
- ▶▶ Consolidate standard column procedures for addition and subtraction.
- ▶▶ Use standard column procedures for multiplication and division.
- ▶▶ Understand where to position the decimal point by considering equivalent calculations.
- ▶▶ Check a result by working backwards.
- ▶▶ Carry out more difficult calculations effectively.
- ▶▶ Use brackets and the memory on a calculator.
- ▶▶ Interpret the display on a calculator.
- ▶▶ Solve more demanding problems and investigate in a range of contexts.

19 tickets? That's £437, please.

How much is that each? £437 ÷ ? = 19

TONIGHT THE DAZE

Multiplying and dividing are everyday skills.

Before you start

You should know how to ...

1 Recall multiplication and division facts.

2 Use simple tests of divisibility.

Check in

1 Work out:

    a 7×6 **b** $49 \div 7$ **c** $64 \div 8$

    d 9×3 **e** 4×8 **f** $72 \div 9$

2 Here are five numbers:

    42   30   12   60   20

    Which of them can be divided by:

    a 2   **b** 4   **c** 3   **d** 5?

Powers and roots

This spread will show you how to:
▶▶ Use squares, square roots, cubes, cube roots and index notation for small integer powers.
▶▶ Make and justify estimates and approximations.

KEYWORDS

Index notation   Square
To the power of *n*
Square root   Cube root
Cube   Cubed

Multiplication is a short way of writing repeated additions:

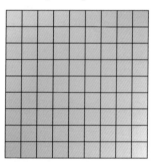

$3 + 3 + 3 + 3 + 3 = 5 \times 3$
You say '5 lots of 3'.

The two most common index numbers are:

Squares

$9^2 = 9 \times 9 = 81$
You say '9 squared is 81'.

Index notation is a short way of writing repeated multiplications:

$3 \times 3 \times 3 \times 3 \times 3 = 3^5$
You say '3 to the power of 5'.

Cubes

$7^3 = 7 \times 7 \times 7 = 343$
You say '7 cubed is 343'.

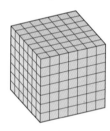

The inverse of a square or a cube is its root.

Square root

To find $\sqrt{16}$:
Think: what do I square to get 16?
$4^2 = 16$
$\sqrt{16} = 4$

Cube root

To find $\sqrt[3]{8}$:
Think: what do I cube to get 8?
$2^3 = 8$
$\sqrt[3]{8} = 2$

You can estimate square roots that are not whole numbers.

example

Estimate $\sqrt{53}$.

$\sqrt{53}$ is between $\sqrt{49}$ and $\sqrt{64}$.
$\sqrt{53}$ is between 7 and 8.
53 is nearer to 49 than 64.
$\sqrt{53}$ is approximately 7.3.

You can find the exact answer using a calculator.

Exercise N2.1

1 Write each of these multiplication expressions using index notation.
The first one is done for you.
  a $2 \times 2 \times 2 \times 2 = 2^4$ **b** 3×3 **c** $4 \times 4 \times 4$
  d $10 \times 10 \times 10 \times 10 \times 10$ **e** $6 \times 6 \times 6 \times 6 \times 6 \times 6$ **f** $1 \times 1 \times 1 \times 1 \times 1 \times 1 \times 1 \times 1$

2 Work out each of these in your head.
  a 2^2 **b** $\sqrt{16}$ **c** 5^2 **d** 10^2
  e $\sqrt{9}$ **f** $\sqrt{1}$ **g** 9^2 **h** 1^3

3 Copy and complete each of these questions, writing in the correct
less than (<) or greater than (>) or equals (=) sign.
The first one is done for you.
  a 2^3 < 3^2 **b** $5^2 \square 3^3$ **c** $\sqrt{1000} \square 4^2$ **d** $4^3 \square 7^2$
  e $\sqrt[3]{100} \square \sqrt{81}$ **f** $3^2 \square \sqrt[3]{125}$ **g** $1^3 \square 1^2$ **h** $4^3 \square 8^2$

4 Calculate each of these mentally.
  a $3^2 + 9$ **b** $29 - 5^2$ **c** $(4 + 2)^2$ **d** $\sqrt{(30 - 5)}$
  e $\sqrt{(23 - 18 + 31)}$ **f** $(23 - 7 - 8)^2$ **g** $(48 \div 12)^3$ **h** $(\sqrt{100})^3$

5 Archie says that 3^2 is bigger than 2^3 $(3^2 > 2^3)$ and this means
that 4^3 is bigger than 3^4.
Is Archie correct? Use calculations to justify your answer.

6 Copy and complete this square root table.
  a As in the example on page 100, find the two
     square roots that each number is between.
  b Estimate the answer to one decimal place.
  c Use a calculator to work out the actual answer
     then round this to one decimal place.

	Estimate	Actual
$\sqrt{34}$		
$\sqrt{18}$		
$\sqrt{98}$		
$\sqrt{6}$		
$\sqrt{69}$		

7 Investigation
Which numbers between 20 and 50 inclusive cannot be expressed
as either the sum of two squares or the difference of two squares?
For example: $5^2 - 2^2 = 21$ $3^2 + 5^2 = 34$

8 Investigation
1 and 64 are examples of integers that are both a square and a cube.
What is the next highest integer that is both a square and a cube?
Use your calculator to investigate.

Powers of 10

This spread will show you how to:
▶▶ Read and write positive integer powers of 10.
▶▶ Multiply and divide by 0.1 and 0.01.
▶▶ Order decimals.

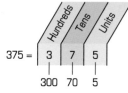

KEYWORDS

Decimal   Thousandth
Tenth   Place value
Hundredth

The size of a digit depends on its place value:

$$375 = \begin{array}{|c|c|c|} \hline 3 & 7 & 5 \\ \hline \end{array}$$

(Hundreds | Tens | Units)
300 70 5

You can use place value to help order numbers.

example

Which is bigger:
a 3705 or 3213

b 3.275 or 3.28?

a Use a place value table:

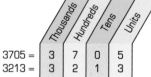

	Thousands	Hundreds	Tens	Units
3705 =	3	7	0	5
3213 =	3	2	1	3

Both numbers have 3 thousands.
3705 has more hundreds.
It is bigger than 3213.

b Use a place value table:

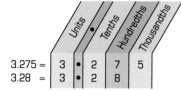

	Units	•	Tenths	Hundredths	Thousandths
3.275 =	3	•	2	7	5
3.28 =	3	•	2	8	

Both numbers have 3 units and 2 tenths.
3.28 has more hundredths.
It is bigger than 3.275.

A place value table uses powers of ten:

Each place is 10 times the previous place.

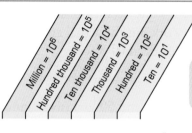

Million $= 10^6$
Hundred thousand $= 10^5$
Ten thousand $= 10^4$
Thousand $= 10^3$
Hundred $= 10^2$
Ten $= 10^1$

1 billion = 1000 million
          = 1 000 000 000
          = 10^9

You can use a place value table to help
multiply and divide by powers of 10.

example

Work out:

23.4×100

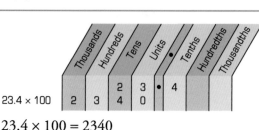

	Thousands	Hundreds	Tens	Units	•	Tenths	Hundredths	Thousandths
			2	3	•	4		
23.4×100	2	3	4	0				

$\times$ 100 means move two
columns to the left.

$23.4 \times 100 = 2340$

Exercise N2.2

1 Write each of these in figures.
  a Two hundred and thirty-seven
  c Twenty-one point eight five
  b Seven thousand and three
  d Two hundred point zero three nine

2 Write each of these in words.
  a 2.307   **b** 200 093   **c** 129.05   **d** 0.932

3 What is the value of:
  a the 9 in 293.5
  c the 2 in 38.832
  e the 5 in 3.5 litres
  b the 7 in 2.735
  d the 8 in 835 m
  f the 4 in 8.4 cm?

4 You have four number cards [2] [3] [7] [8] and a decimal point card [.].
  Use all five cards to make the following numbers.
  Write down your answers.
  a a number between 200 and 300
  c a number between 22.5 and 28.5
  b a number between 6 and 9
  d a number between 2.3 and 2.4

5 Look at these six numbers.
  Write them in order, starting with the smallest.

  37.2   2.95   3.75   3.652   2.915   37.17

6 Work out each of these.
  a $3.81 + 0.01$ **b** $2.7 - 0.01$ **c** $35 - 0.1$ **d** $2.573 + 0.001$
  e $3.292 - 0.001$ **f** $3.75 + 0.001$ **g** $23.05 - 0.001$ **h** $10.3 - 0.001$

7 Work out each of these.
  a $370 \div 10$ **b** 2.7×10 **c** $35 \div 100$ **d** $2.73 \div 100$
  e 0.057×10 **f** 1.057×1000 **g** $27.032 \div 1000$

8 Copy and complete each of these statements.
  a $0.5 \times 10 = \underline{}$ **b** $0.5 \div 10 = \underline{}$ **c** $\underline{} \div 100 = 0.05$
  d $\underline{} \times 100 = 50$ **e** $5 \div \underline{} = 0.05$ **f** $500 \div \underline{} = 0.5$

9 Investigate these statements. Use a calculator to help you.
  a Multiplying by 0.1 is the same as dividing by 10.
  b Dividing by 0.1 is the same as multiplying by __.
  c Multiplying by 0.01 is the same as dividing by __.
  d Dividing by 0.01 is the same as multiplying by __.

10 Work out each of these.
  a 56×0.1 **b** $3.5 \div 0.1$ **c** $6.35 \div 0.01$ **d** 200×0.01
  e 0.35×0.01 **f** $10.05 \div 0.01$ **g** $0.53 \div 0.1$ **h** 110.32×0.01

Rounding

This spread will show you how to:

▶▶ Round whole numbers to any power of 10.

▶▶ Round decimals to two decimal places.

KEYWORDS

Round   Decimal place

Approximate   Place value

Recurring decimal

Round numbers are easier to calculate with.

£49.37 × 2?

That's about £50 × 2 = £100.

A number line can help you round numbers.

▶ **To round to:**

  ▶ the nearest 10, use a number line that goes up in 10s

  ▶ the nearest 100, use a number line that goes up in 100s

  ▶ the nearest 1000, use a number line that goes up in 1000s.

example

a Round 375 to the nearest 100.

b Round 23 541 to the nearest 1000.

a 375 is between 300 and 400.
Draw a number line:

350 is exactly halfway.
375 is closer to 400.

375 is 400 to the nearest 100.

b 23 541 is between 23 000 and 24 000.
Draw a number line:

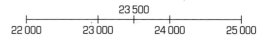

23 500 is exactly halfway.
23 541 is nearer to 24 000.

23 541 is 24 000 to the nearest 1000.

If a number is exactly halfway, you round up: 65 is 70 to the nearest 10.

You can round decimal numbers in the same way.

example

Round 3.2735 to two decimal places.

3.2735 is between 3.27 and 3.28.

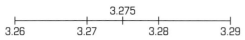

3.275 is exactly halfway.
3.2735 is closer to 3.27.
3.2735 is 3.27 to two decimal places.

You can use a place value table:

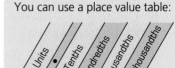

Units		Tenths	Hundredths	Thousandths	Ten thousandths
3	•	2	7	3	5
3	•	2	7		
3	•	2	8		
3	•	2	7	5	

Exercise N2.3

1 Round each of these numbers to the nearest 10.
  a 27   **b** 7   **c** 98   **d** 178

2 Round each of these numbers to the nearest 100.
  a 193   **b** 453   **c** 78   **d** 1920

3 Round each of these numbers to the nearest 1000.
  a 1700   **b** 7500   **c** 12 393   **d** 763

4 Look at this list of six best-selling books.

		Weekly sales
A	A Teacher's Life by Mark Knightly	28 172
B	The Wildlife of Australia by Carla Bare	8 909
C	Chicago by Wendy Sitty	8 524
D	A History of Bread by Finlay Sliced	7 588
E	Top Tips for Burglars by Patty O'Dawes	6 695
F	Trainspotters by Anna Rack	5 401

After these sales have been rounded they are not exact figures – they are an approximation.

Round the weekly sales to the nearest 1000, 100 and 10.
You can put your results in a table like this:

	Nearest 1000	Nearest 100	Nearest 10
A			
B			
C			

5 Round each of these prices to the nearest pound.

  a £29.75

  b £7.25

  c  £12.50

  d  £49.65

6 Round each of these numbers to:
  i the nearest whole number
  ii one decimal place
  iii two decimal places.
  a 7.527   **b** 2.103   **c** 15.9153
  d 6.0959   **e** 0.90915   **f** 2.5993

7 Use a calculator to do these calculations, then round the answer to:
  i 1 dp
  ii 2 dp.

Hint: '1 dp' means '1 decimal place'.

  a $(2.6 + 3.5) \times (9.7 - 8.3)$
  b $4.72^2 + 5 \times 3.9$

Addition and subtraction

This spread will show you how to:
- ▶▶ Add and subtract integers.
- ▶▶ Understand addition and subtraction of integers.
- ▶▶ Consolidate and extend mental methods of calculation.
- ▶▶ Consolidate standard column procedures.

KEYWORDS

Partition   Addition
Compensate   Subtraction
Integer
Negative number

To add, you count on.

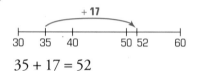

$35 + 17 = 52$

To subtract, you count back.

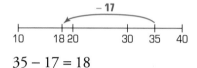

$35 - 17 = 18$

There are two main methods for calculating mentally:

Partitioning

Work in place value parts.

For example: $453 + 223$

Estimate first: $450 + 220 = 670$

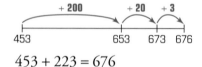

$453 + 223 = 676$

Compensation

Round and then compensate.

For example: $453 - 193$

Estimate first: $450 - 200 = 250$

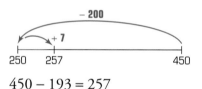

$450 - 193 = 257$

You can use a written method for harder calculations.
Remember to line up the units.

$643 + 272$

Estimate: $600 + 300 = 900$

$$\begin{array}{r} 643 \\ +272 \\ \hline 915 \\ \hline {\scriptstyle 1} \end{array}$$

$63.4 - 21.23$

Estimate: $60 - 20 = 40$

$$\begin{array}{r} 63.\overset{3}{4}\overset{1}{0} \\ -21.23 \\ \hline 42.17 \end{array}$$ ◀—— add a zero

You can add and subtract negative numbers:

▶ Adding a negative is the same as subtracting.

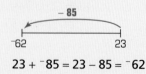

$23 + {}^-85 = 23 - 85 = {}^-62$

▶ Subtracting a negative is the same as adding.

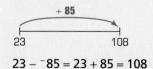

$23 - {}^-85 = 23 + 85 = 108$

Exercise N2.4

1 Calculate these using a mental method.
    a 153 + 29   **b** 483 − 291
    c 9.2 + 18.3   **d** 17.5 − 8.9

Remember to do an estimate first!

2 What number needs to be added or subtracted to change:
    a 63 into 243   **b** 429 into 191   **c** 35.7 into 63.5   **d** 4.96 into 2.57?

3 A farmer has a triangular-shaped field.
Calculate the length of fencing he would
need for the perimeter of the field.

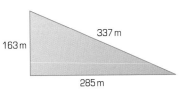

337 m
163 m
285 m

4 In a number wall, the two bricks next to each other add up to make the brick on top.
Copy and complete these number walls.

a

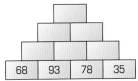

68   93   78   35

b

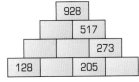

928
517
273
128   205

5 Use a mental or written method to work out these.
    a 32.75 + 29.63   **b** 6.95 − 4.78
    c 26.8 + 39.7   **d** 2563 − 777
    e 34.25 − 17.78   **f** 298 + 373 + 292

6 Mr Rogers has £25 in his bank account.
Mrs Rogers' account is £16 overdrawn.
Her account reads ⁻£16.
    a If they close their separate accounts and open a joint account,
        how much will be in it?

How much will they have in their joint account if they have
these amounts in their separate accounts?
    b Mr Rogers £23   Mrs Rogers ⁻£37
    c Mr Rogers ⁻£12   Mrs Rogers ⁻£19

7 Two numbers have a difference of 454.
The number exactly halfway between them is 512.
What are the two numbers?

8 What number needs to be added or subtracted to change:
    a 38.25 into 23.78   **b** 6.735 into 12.283
    c 3.615 into 12.4   **d** 7.1 into 2.537?

9 Use the digits 1, 2, 3, 4, 5 and 6 just once in each part to make the answer.
    a ☐.☐☐
      + ☐.☐☐
       5 . 8 8

    b ☐.☐☐
      − ☐.☐☐
       1 . 8 5

Mental multiplication and division

This spread will show you how to:
- ▶▶ Understand multiplication and division of integers.
- ▶▶ Recall known facts.
- ▶▶ Use known facts to derive unknown facts.
- ▶▶ Consolidate and extend mental methods of calculation.
- ▶▶ Solve word problems mentally.

KEYWORDS

Multiply	Compensate
Divide	Negative
Factor	Estimate
Partition	

Once you know your times tables ...   you can use them to work out other facts.

$1 \times 7 = 7$
$2 \times 7 = 14$
$3 \times 7 = 21...$

$0.7 \times 6 =$
$7 \times 0.1 \times 6 =$
$42 \times 0.1 =$
$4.2!$

There are three main methods for multiplying and dividing mentally:

Factors

Break the number into factors and calculate with one at a time.

3.3×30

Estimate: $3 \times 30 = 90$

3.3×30
$= 3.3 \times 10 \times 3$
$= 33 \times 3$
$= 99$

Partitioning

Break the number into separate parts then add them together.

5.4×12

Estimate: $5 \times 12 = 60$

5.4×12
$= 5.4 \times 10 + 5.4 \times 2$
$= 54 + 10.8$
$= 64.8$

Compensation

Round the number to a near 10 then compensate.

19×0.4

Estimate: $20 \times 0.5 = 10$

19×0.4
$= 20 \times 0.4 - 0.4$
$= 8 - 0.4$
$= 7.6$

You can multiply and divide with negative numbers.

$3 \times {}^-9$ means 3 lots of $^-9$.
$3 \times {}^-9 = {}^-27$

- ▶ positive × negative = negative   negative × positive = negative
- ▶ positive ÷ negative = negative   negative ÷ positive = negative

example

Work out:

a $^-8 \times 22$

b $126 \div {}^-18$.

a $8 \times 22 = 8 \times 20 + 8 \times 2$
            $= 160 + 16$
            $= 176$
   so $^-8 \times 22 = {}^-176$

b $126 \div 18 = 126 \div 2 \div 9$
               $= 63 \div 9$
               $= 7$
   so $126 \div {}^-18 = {}^-7$

Exercise N2.5

1 Copy and complete each of these calculation patterns.

    a $4 \times 20 = \underline{}$ **b** $3 \times 60 = \underline{}$

         $40 \times 20 = \underline{}$ $\underline{} \times 60 = 1800$

         $4 \times 200 = \underline{}$ $30 \times \underline{} = 18\,000$

         $40 \times 200 = \underline{}$ $300 \times 60 = \underline{}$

         $\underline{} \times 200 = 80\,000$ $3000 \times \underline{} = 18\,000\,000$

2 Use $\boxed{2.5 \times 3 = 7.5}$ to work out:

    a $7.5 \div 3$ **b** 3×2.5 **c** $7.5 \div 2.5$.

3 **a** Work out 11×42.

    Use your answer to part **a** to help you work out:

    b 11×4.2 **c** 1.1×42 **d** 11×420 **e** 1.1×420

4 Use a mental method to work out each of these.

    a 9×21 **b** $480 \div 20$ **c** 2.3×31

    d 17×23 **e** $672 \div 16$ **f** 0.38×19

5 **a** A shop sells pizzas for £2.95. Find the cost of 15 pizzas.

    b A piece of ribbon is cut in 12 equal lengths of 2.3 m.

       How long was the original piece of ribbon?

6 Copy and complete these number walls.

    Multiply two bricks next to each other to make the brick on top.

    a   **b**

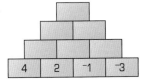
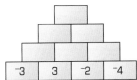

7 Work out the answers to each of these and place them in order, smallest first.

    a $3 \times {}^-4$ **b** ${}^-28 \div {}^-7$ **c** ${}^-4 \times 4$

    d ${}^-3 \times {}^-4$ **e** ${}^-24 \div 3$ **f** $10 \div {}^-2 \times {}^-4$

8 John records his own music onto CD.

    He posts fifteen of these CDs to a music store.

    At the Post Office they weighed 1.8 kg.

    How much did each CD weigh?

9 Puzzle

    Two numbers sum to 36. Their difference is 6. Their product is 315.

    a What are the two numbers?

    b Divide the larger number by the smaller. What answer do you get?

Written multiplication

This spread will show you how to:
▶▶ Use standard column procedures for multiplication.
▶▶ Understand where to position the decimal point by considering equivalent calculations.

When the numbers are more complex ...   it's better to use a written method.

42 × 24?
That's about
40 × 20 = 800

(40 × 24) + (2 × 24) =
960 + 48 =
1008

There are two main written methods for multiplication.
You break each of the numbers down into place value parts.

example

Work out 53 × 71.

Estimate: 50 × 70 = 3500

Find the place value parts: 53 = 50 + 3   71 = 70 + 1

Grid method
Find the values from the grid then add them.

	50	3
70	3500	210
1	50	3

```
3500
 210
  50
   3
----
3763
```

So 53 × 71 = 3763

Column method
Work out the values in a column then add them.

```
            53
          × 71
53 × 70   3710
53 × 1      53
          ----
          3763
```

So 53 × 71 = 3763

You can use these methods with decimal numbers too.
First you should turn the numbers into integers by multiplying.

example

Work out 3.2 × 4.5.

Estimate: 3 × 5 = 15
Multiply each number by 10:   3.2 × 10 = 32   4.5 × 10 = 45
Work out 32 × 45:   Adjust the answer by dividing:
                        1440 ÷ 10 = 144   144 ÷ 10 = 14.4

	30	2
40	1200	80
5	150	10

```
1200
 150
  80
  10
----
1440
```

You divide to undo each multiplication.

So 3.2 × 4.5 = 14.4

Exercise N2.6

1 Work out each of these.
   a 21 × 5   **b** 6 × 121   **c** 20 × 17   **d** 43 × 9

> Remember to do an estimate first!

2 Use your answers to question 1 to work out:
   a 2.1 × 5   **b** 12.1 × 6   **c** 20 × 1.7
   d 1.21 × 6   **e** 4.3 × 9   **f** 0.9 × 4.3

3 A bag of sweets costs 75p.
Work out how much 32 bags cost. Give your answer:
   a in pence   **b** in pounds.

4 The formula for working out the area of a rectangle is area = length × width.
Work out the area of each of these rectangles.

a
32 cm
52 cm

b
45 m
115 m

5 **Investigation**
You have five number cards:

What is the biggest 3 × 2 digit multiplication you can make?
For example:

6 Look at this calculation: 205 × 34.
Two statements can be made about it.
   i It ends in 5 × 4 so the answer will end in a zero.
   ii It is roughly 200 × 30 = 6000.
Write two similar statements for each of these calculations.
   a 192 × 28   **b** 73 × 283   **c** 571 × 81   **d** 269 × 63

7 **a** Henry works out 37 × 168 and gets 6214 as the answer. Is he correct?
     Give a reason for your answer by multiplying the last digits.
   b Tina works out 62 × 226 and gets 4012 as the answer. Is she correct?
     Again, give a reason for your answer using an estimate.

8 A 20 kg bag of dog food costs £7.23.
How much do 42 bags cost?

9 **Puzzle**
Find the missing digits in this calculation: 3__1 × 4__ = 13 161

10 Calculate each of these.
   a 6.5 × 72   **b** 31.5 × 2.3   **c** 0.187 × 22   **d** 3.05 × 0.29

This spread will show you how to:
- Understand division of integers.
- Use the laws of arithmetic and inverse operations.
- Use standard column procedures for division.
- Check a result by working the problem backwards.

KEYWORDS
Inverse   Division
Multiplication

The inverse of dividing is multiplying: $40 \times 9 = 360$ so $360 \div 9 = 40$

You can use this fact to help divide harder numbers.

a Find $1472 \div 23$.

b Find $1412 \div 17$.

a Estimate: $1400 \div 20 = 70$

Work out the answer roughly:
$50 \times 23 = 1150$
$60 \times 23 = 1380$
$70 \times 23 = 1610$

$$\begin{array}{ccc} \vdash & \vdash & \dashv \\ 1380 & 1472 & 1610 \end{array}$$

The answer is between 60 and 70.

$60 \times 23 = 1380$ so subtract this from 1472 to find what's left:
$$\begin{array}{r} 1472 \\ -1380 \\ \hline 92 \end{array}$$

Write out the 23 times table:
$1 \times 23 = 23 \quad 2 \times 23 = 46$
$3 \times 23 = 69 \quad 4 \times 23 = 92$

$1472 = 60 \times 23 + 4 \times 23$
$\quad = 64 \times 23$

$1472 \div 23 = 64$

b Estimate: $1400 \div 20 = 70$

Work out the answer roughly:
$60 \times 17 = 1020$
$70 \times 17 = 1190$
$80 \times 17 = 1360$
$90 \times 17 = 1530$

$$\begin{array}{ccc} \vdash & \vdash & \dashv \\ 1360 & 1412 & 1530 \end{array}$$

The answer is between 80 and 90.

$80 \times 17 = 1360$ so subtract this from 1412 to find what's left:
$$\begin{array}{r} 1412 \\ -1360 \\ \hline 52 \end{array}$$

Write out the 17 times table:
$1 \times 17 = 17 \quad 2 \times 17 = 34$
$3 \times 17 = 51 \quad 4 \times 17 = 68$

$1412 = 80 \times 17 + 3 \times 17 + 1$
$\quad = 83 \times 17 + 1$

$1412 \div 17 = 83$ remainder $1 = 83\frac{1}{17}$

You can divide decimals by making them into whole numbers then adjusting.

To find: $86.4 \div 16$
You know: $86.4 \times 10 = 864$
Work out: $864 \div 16 = 54$
Adjust by dividing: $86.4 \div 16 = 54 \div 10 = 5.4$

Exercise N2.7

1 Work out each of these.
   a $224 \div 7$ **b** $210 \div 5$ **c** $390 \div 6$ **d** $568 \div 8$
   e $351 \div 9$ **f** $742 \div 7$ **g** $1656 \div 8$ **h** $1092 \div 7$

2 A team of eight friends share the first prize of £744 in a quiz.
   How much do they each get?

3 Six identical pepperoni pizzas weigh a total of 1362 g.
   Work out the weight of each pizza.

4 Fourteen concert tickets cost £336.
   Work out the cost of one ticket.

5 Look at these numbers.

   512   787   848
   400   832   974   593

   a Without doing a calculation, which numbers can you tell do not divide exactly by 16?
   b You are told that 832 divides exactly by 16.
      Explain how you know that 848 does as well.
   c Show, using calculations, which other numbers divide exactly by 16.

6 Work out the missing digits in each of these questions.
   a $8\_4 \div 13 = 68$ **b** $792 \div 2\_ = 36$

7 Work out each of these by multiplying the decimal by 10 to make
   it an integer then adjusting the answer.
   a $80.5 \div 23$ **b** $91.8 \div 18$ **c** $122.2 \div 26$ **d** $151.9 \div 31$

8 Each of these calculations has a remainder.
   Which three calculations have remainders that sum to 10?
   a $422 \div 8$ **b** $463 \div 11$ **c** $653 \div 12$ **d** $407 \div 19$
   e $633 \div 15$

9 **a** Twenty-seven 3-inch nut and bolt sets cost a total of £34.29.
      Find the cost of one set.
   b Chunky Munch biscuits cost £28.35 for a box of 45 packets.
      How much does one packet cost?

10 A roll of ribbon is 5 m in length.
   a How many lengths of 35 cm can be cut from the roll?
   b What length of ribbon will be left over?

Calculator methods

This spread will show you how to:
- ▶▶ Use the order of operations.
- ▶▶ Carry out more difficult calculations effectively.
- ▶▶ Use brackets and the memory.
- ▶▶ Enter numbers and interpret the display.

KEYWORDS

Calculator   Decimal place
Brackets   Denominator
Indices   Memory
Sign change key
Order of operations

In some calculations you have more than one operation:

The standard order of operations is:
- ▶ Brackets first
- ▶ Indices next
- ▶ Division and Multiplication   (in any order)
- ▶ Addition and Subtraction   (in any order)

$$= 3^2 + 16 \div 1.6$$
$$= 9 + 16 \div 1.6$$
$$= 9 + 10$$
$$= 19$$

A scientific calculator will use this order.

example

Work out 3.715×4.3^2. Give your answer to 1 decimal place.

Input ③ · ⑦ ① ⑤ × ④ · ③ x^2 =
The output should be $68.69035 = 68.7$ to 1 decimal place.

You need to be able to input brackets and indices.
You can enter fractions on a calculator using: a^b/c

- ▶ To input $\frac{2}{5}$ press ② a^b/c ⑤ . It will show 2⌐5 .

- ▶ To convert 2⌐5 to a decimal, press a^b/c . It will show 0⌐4 .

- ▶ To simplify $\frac{16}{28}$ press ① ⑥ a^b/c ② ⑧ = . It will show 4⌐7 .

example

Calculate $\dfrac{31.5 \times 27.3}{61.3 - 43.5}$

Method 1

Using brackets $\dfrac{31.5 \times 27.3}{(61.3 - 43.5)}$

Input: $31.5 \times 27.3 \div (61.3 - 43.5) =$

The answer is 48.3 to 1 dp.

Method 2

Work out the denominator and keep it in the memory: $61.3 - 43.5 = \text{Min}$

Input: $31.5 \times 27.3 \div \text{MR} =$

Exercise N2.8

1 Use $\boxed{x^2}$ to find the squares of each of these numbers.
   a 9 **b** 3.5 **c** 12.1 **d** 305

2 Use $\boxed{\sqrt{}}$ to find the square roots of each of these numbers.
   a 144 **b** 1600 **c** 3.0625 **d** 1432.6225

3 Solve each of these using a calculator.
   a $(2.73 + 1.98) \times 5.2$ **b** $66.96 \div (8.3 - 2.9)$ **c** $322.5 \div 5^2$

4 For each question, decide whether you are going to use
   a mental, written or calculator method. Calculate:
   a $(7.2 + 2.8) \times 5.5$ **b** $(5^2 - 3^2) \times 2.5$ **c** $32 \times 11 - 4 \times 13$

   d $8 + (17.2 - 3.1)^2 \times 3$ **e** $\dfrac{252.75}{3.2 + 5.9 + 0.9}$ **f** $251.7 + 231.9 \times 3.2 - 750.78$

5 Work out each of these.
   a $\frac{1}{2} + \frac{1}{4} - \frac{1}{3}$ **b** $\frac{3}{5} - \frac{1}{6} + \frac{2}{15}$ **c** $\frac{1}{4} \times \frac{1}{2}$ **d** $\frac{1}{4} \div \frac{1}{2}$

6 To enter $^-3$ on a calculator you press either $\boxed{3}\,\boxed{+/-}$ or $\boxed{+/-}\,\boxed{3}$
   depending on your calculator.

   Check: $^-3 \times {}^-2 = 6$

   Use your calculator to work out:

   a $^-7 \times 3 \times {}^-5$ **b** $^-21.7 + 12.2 \times {}^-3.2$ **c** $\dfrac{^-10.5}{^-3.7 + 5.2}$

   d $\frac{^-1}{2} - \frac{1}{4} + \frac{1}{3}$ **e** $\frac{^-3}{5} \times \frac{2}{7}$ **f** $\frac{3}{4} - \frac{1}{2} \times \frac{^-1}{3}$

7 This formula converts temperatures in Celsius to Fahrenheit:
   $F = 1.8C + 32$
   a Convert these Celsius readings to Fahrenheit.
      i $^-10°C$ **ii** $^-5°C$ **iii** $^-7.5°C$ **iv** $^-43°C$
   b What temperature in °C is the same number in Fahrenheit (°F)?

8 Puzzle
   In each puzzle, you must get from the Start to the Finish by
   doing the calculations along the route.
   Only one route gives the correct answer.
   Use your calculator to help you find it.

   a
   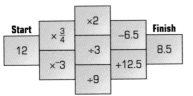

   b
   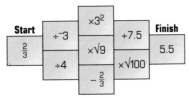

You should know how to ...

1 Add, subtract, multiply and divide integers.

2 Use standard column procedures for multiplication and division.

3 Understand where to position the decimal point by considering equivalent calculations.

Check out

1 Work out these:
  a 325 + 293
  b 927 − 263
  c John has £193. Terry has £209.
    How much do they have in total?
  d Toni has £173 more than Jim.
    Toni has £729.
    How much does Jim have?
  e 37 × 21
  f 840 ÷ 24
  g 34 × 213
  h A teacher buys a packet of crisps for each student on a school trip. Each packet weighs 25 g. How many students are on the trip if all the packets together weigh 1.575 kg?

2 Work out:
  a 63 × 2.9
  b 3.26 × 2.4
  c 68.4 ÷ 12
  d 29.21 ÷ 2.3
  e Football shirts cost £9.75 each.
    Jim buys 15 shirts for his new football team.
    How much does he pay?
  f Joel is making a fence.
    He needs 64 identical pieces of wood.
    These pieces measure 153.6 m in total.
    How long is each piece of wood?

3 You are told that 3.23 × 6.4 = 20.672
  Use this fact to help you work out:
  a 32.3 × 6.4
  b 323 × 64
  c 323 × 0.064
  d 20.672 ÷ 64
  e 206.72 ÷ 3.23

4 Graphs of functions

This unit will show you how to:

- ▶▶ Recognise and use multiples, factors (divisors), highest common factors, lowest common multiples and primes.
- ▶▶ Find and use the prime factor decomposition of a number.
- ▶▶ Use squares, positive and negative square roots, cubes and cube roots.
- ▶▶ Use the function key for square roots and powers.
- ▶▶ Use index notation for small positive integers.

- ▶▶ Generate points in all four quadrants and plot the graphs of linear functions, where y is given explicitly in terms of x.
- ▶▶ Recognise that equations of the form $y = mx + c$ correspond to straight-line graphs.
- ▶▶ Construct linear functions arising from real-life problems and plot their corresponding graphs.
- ▶▶ Discuss and interpret graphs arising from real situations, including distance–time graphs.
- ▶▶ Represent problems and interpret solutions in algebraic or graphical form.

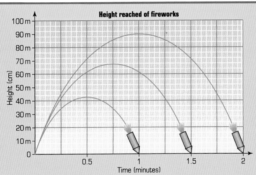

You can use graphs to describe many different functions.

Before you start

You should know how to ...

1 Recall multiplication and division facts.

2 Use simple tests of divisibility.

3 Find equivalent fractions.

4 Substitute values into simple formulae.

Check in

1 Work out:
   a $^-2 \times {}^-3$ b $^-5 \times 8$
   c $16 \div 2$ d $^-32 \div {}^-8$

2 Which of these numbers can be exactly divided by 5?
   35   90   125   37   141   150

3 Which of these fractions are equivalent?
   $\frac{12}{16}$ $\frac{75}{100}$ $\frac{3}{4}$ $\frac{32}{40}$

4 Find the value of y in these equations when $x = {}^-1$.
   a $y = 6x - 3$ b $2y = 4 - 2x$

This spread will show you how to:

▶▶ Recognise and use multiples, factors (divisors), highest common factors, lowest common multiples and primes.

▶▶ Know and use square numbers.

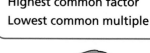

KEYWORDS

Multiple   Factor
Square number   Prime
Highest common factor
Lowest common multiple

You should know your times tables.

The 7 times table is:

7   14   21   28   35   42   49   56   63   70   77 ...

   ▶ The numbers in the 7 times tables are **multiples** of 7.

You can use your times tables to work out multiples of a number.

35 is a multiple of 5, 7 and 35 because:

35 appears in	the 5 times table	5, 10, 15, 20, 25, 30, ⟨35⟩, 40, ...
	the 7 times table	7, 14, 21, 28, ⟨35⟩, 42, 49, 56, ...
and	the 35 times table	⟨35⟩, 70, 105, 140, 175, 210, ...

example

Find the lowest common multiple (LCM) of 6 and 8.
....
Multiples of 6 = 6, 12, 18, ⟨24⟩, 30, 36, 42, 48, ...
Multiples of 8 = 8, 16, ⟨24⟩, 32, 40, 48, 56, 64, ...

24 is the lowest common multiple of 6 and 8.

6 and 8 are factors of 24.

To find all of the factors of a number, write them down in factor pairs:

$12 = 1 \times 12$
$12 = 2 \times 6$
$12 = 3 \times 4$
The factors of 12 are
1, 2, 3, 4, 6 and 12.

$13 = 1 \times 13$
The factors of 13 are
1 and 13.

Use a systematic method:
▶ start with $1 \times ...$
▶ then try $2 \times ...$
▶ then try $3 \times ...$

   ▶ A number with only two factors is a **prime** number, so 13 is a prime number.
   ▶ A number with an odd number of factors is a **square** number, for example, 9 (factors are 1, 3, 9) is a square number.

example

Find the highest common factor (HCF) of 24 and 36.
....
Factors of 24 = 1, 2, 3, 4, 6, 8, ⟨12⟩, 24
Factors of 36 = 1, 2, 3, 4, 6, 9, ⟨12⟩, 18, 36

12 is the highest common factor of 24 and 36.

Exercise A4.1

1 Find all the factor pairs of:
  - **a** 21
  - **b** 22
  - **c** 23
  - **d** 24
  - **e** 251
  - **f** 26
  - **g** 27

2 Which of the numbers in question 1 are square and which are prime?
Justify your answer.

3 **a** List the first four multiples of 16 and 24.
    Multiples of 16 = 16, 32, __, __, ...
    Multiples of 24 = 24, 48, __, __, ...
  b What is the LCM of 16 and 24?

4 **a** Find all the factors of 36.
  b Find all the factors of 81.
  c Use your answers to parts **a** and **b** to write down the HCF of 36 and 81.

5 Find the LCM and HCF of:
  - **a** 12 and 18
  - **b** 36 and 12
  - **c** 25, 50 and 75.

6 Challenge
You will need a 0–9 dice and each player needs a copy of this grid.

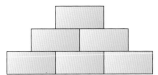

Take turns to roll the dice and write the number in one of the boxes of your grid. Once the boxes are full you will have a 1 digit, 2 digit and a 3 digit number. Work out all of the factors of your three numbers.
The winner is the player with the most factors.
Repeat the game.

7 **a** Find the lowest common multiple of 8 and 13.
  b Use your answer to part **a** to decide if $\frac{7}{8}$ is bigger than $\frac{11}{13}$.

This spread will show you how to:
▶▶ Find and use the prime factor decomposition of a number.
▶▶ Recognise and use the HCF and LCM.

KEYWORDS
Prime factor
Lowest common multiple
Highest common factor

You can write any number as a product of its prime factors.

Use a factor tree to find the prime factors.

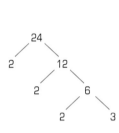

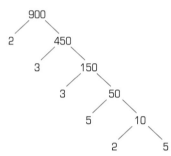

$24 = 2 \times 2 \times 2 \times 3$

$$900 = 2 \times 3 \times 3 \times 5 \times 2 \times 5$$
$$= 2 \times 2 \times 3 \times 3 \times 5 \times 5$$

The prime factors in common are 2, 2 and 3.

You can use prime factors to find the highest common factor (HCF) and lowest common multiple (LCM) of two numbers.

▶ The highest common factor (HCF) is the biggest number that divides into each of the numbers.

▶ The lowest common multiple (LCM) is the smallest number that each of the numbers divides into exactly.

example

Find the HCF and LCM of 24 and 900.

Draw two overlapping circles.

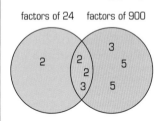

The factors that are common to both numbers go in the overlap.

The diagram is called a Venn diagram.

The rest of the numbers go in the appropriate circle.

The HCF is the product of the numbers in the overlap:
The HCF of 24 and 900 is $2 \times 2 \times 3 = 12$

The LCM is the product of all the numbers:
The LCM of 24 and 900 is
$2 \times 2 \times 2 \times 3 \times 3 \times 5 \times 5 = 1800$

Exercise A4.2

1 Find all the factor pairs of:
   a 100   **b** 72   **c** 56   **d** 880   **e** 1040

2 **a** Find the smallest number with exactly three factors.
    b Find the smallest number with exactly four factors.
    c Choose your own number of factors, say seven factors.
      Find the smallest number with that many factors.

3 These calculations have been worked out quickly using factors.

$$45 \times 16 = 5 \times 9 \times 2 \times 8 \qquad\qquad 300 \div 15 = \frac{3 \times 100}{3 \times 5}$$
$$= 5 \times 2 \times 9 \times 8 \qquad\qquad\qquad = \frac{100}{5}$$
$$= 10 \times 72 \qquad\qquad\qquad\qquad = 20$$
$$= 720$$

Work out these calculations using factors.
   a 35×18 **b** 64×75 **c** $600 \div 18$ **d** $210 \div 35$

4 **a** Two prime numbers are added. The answer is 44.
      What are the numbers? Can you find more than one pair?
    b Two other prime numbers are added. The answer is 45.
      What are the numbers?

5 Using factor trees, write these numbers as products of their prime factors.
   a 56   **b** 98   **c** 124   **d** 18
   e 99   **f** 1000   **g** 3200   **h** 8000

6 Using your workings in question 5, find the HCF and LCM
of each of these pairs of numbers.
   a 56 and 98   **b** 98 and 18   **c** 124 and 99   **d** 56 and 3200
   e 18 and 8000

7 To cancel a fraction you need to find the HCF of the numerator
and denominator.
Cancel these fractions.
   a $\frac{56}{98}$ **b** $\frac{18}{98}$ **c** $\frac{99}{124}$ **d** $\frac{56}{3200}$ **e** $\frac{18}{8000}$

8 To compare fractions, the fractions need common denominators.
Place < or > between these pairs of fractions.
   a $\frac{5}{6}\,\square\,\frac{7}{8}$ **b** $\frac{6}{9}\,\square\,\frac{12}{20}$ **c** $\frac{3}{5}\,\square\,\frac{22}{30}$ **d** $\frac{13}{14}\,\square\,\frac{9}{10}$ **e** $\frac{8}{11}\,\square\,\frac{11}{13}$

9 **What number am I?**
I am the smallest four-digit number that is a multiple of 21 and 35.
What am I?

This spread will show you how to:
▶▶ Use squares, positive and negative square roots, cubes and cube roots.
▶▶ Use index notation for small positive integers.
▶▶ Use the function key for square roots and powers.

KEYWORDS
Square number
Cube number
Square root   Cube root
Index   Power

You find a square number by multiplying an integer by itself.

The first five **square numbers** are:

$1^2 = 1 \times 1 = \mathbf{1}$ $2^2 = 2 \times 2 = \mathbf{4}$ $3^2 = 3 \times 3 = \mathbf{9}$ $4^2 = 4 \times 4 = \mathbf{16}$ $5^2 = 5 \times 5 = \mathbf{25}$

▶ The inverse of a square is a square root. $7^2 = 49$ so $\sqrt{49} = 7$

The **square roots** are:

$\sqrt{1} = 1$ $\sqrt{4} = 2$ $\sqrt{9} = 3$ $\sqrt{16} = 4$ $\sqrt{25} = 5$

You find a cube number by multiplying an integer by itself twice.

The first five **cube numbers** are:

$1^3 = 1 \times 1 \times 1$ $2^3 = 2 \times 2 \times 2$ $3^3 = 3 \times 3 \times 3$ $4^3 = 4 \times 4 \times 4$ $5^3 = 5 \times 5 \times 5$
$= \mathbf{1}$ $= \mathbf{8}$ $= \mathbf{27}$ $= \mathbf{64}$ $= \mathbf{125}$

▶ The inverse of a cube is a cube root. $7^3 = 343$ so $\sqrt[3]{343} = 7$

The **cube roots** are:

$\sqrt[3]{1} = 1$ $\sqrt[3]{8} = 2$ $\sqrt[3]{27} = 3$ $\sqrt[3]{64} = 4$ $\sqrt[3]{125} = 5$

You can use a scientific calculator to work out:

14^2 press [1] [4] [x^2] [=]   answer is 196.

$\sqrt{256}$ press [√] [2] [5] [6] [=]   answer is 16.

7^3 press [7] [x^3] [=]   answer is 343.

$\sqrt[3]{729}$ press [$\sqrt[3]{}$] [7] [2] [9] [=]   answer is 9.

Check you know how yours works.

If your calculator doesn't have a
[x^3] button, use the [x^y] button:
press [7] [x^y] [3] [=]

Exercise A4.3

1 Work out the value of these squares.

   a 20^2 **b** 13^2 **c** 100^2

   d 21^2 **e** 15^2 **f** 1000^2

2 Calculate:

   a 6^3 **b** 1.3^2 **c** 4.2^3

   d $\sqrt[3]{216}$ **e** 0.1^2 **f** $\sqrt{144}$

   g $(^-2)^3$ **h** 25^2 **i** $\sqrt[2]{121}$

   j 10^3 **k** $(^-9)^3$ **l** $(0.2)^3$

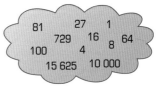

Hint:
To input $^-2$,
you press ⬚2 ⬚+/–

Square numbers	Cube numbers	Square and cube numbers

Cloud: 81   27   1   729   16   64   100   4   8   15 625   10 000

3 Copy this table and sort the numbers in the cloud into the three columns.

4 Write down the first 20 square numbers.
Describe the pattern formed by the last digits of the square numbers.
Do any numbers not appear as the last digit?
Could 523 be a square number? or 647?

5 Some numbers are equal to the sum of two squares.
For example, $10 = 1^2 + 3^2$.

Find all the numbers less than 100 that are equal to the sum of two squares.

6 Some numbers are equal to the difference of two squares.
For example, $20 = 6^2 - 4^2$.

Find the 20 numbers up to 30 that can be expressed as the difference of two squares.

7 **Investigation**
The outside of a $5 \times 5 \times 5$ cube is painted pink.
How many smaller cubes are in the $5 \times 5 \times 5$ cube?
How many of the smaller cubes have 0, 1, 2 or 3 faces painted pink?

Investigate 0, 1, 2 or 3 painted faces for cubes of different sizes.

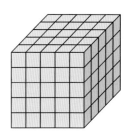

This spread will show you how to:
▶▶ Use squares, positive and negative square roots, cubes and cube roots.
▶▶ Use index notation for small positive integers.
▶▶ Use the function key for square roots and powers.

KEYWORDS

Odd   Powers
Even   Consecutive

Here are two useful methods to solve index problems without a calculator.

Using factors

You can use factors to help you find some square roots.

> **example**
>
> Find $\sqrt{196}$ using factors.
> ....
> You need to find factors of 196 that are square numbers:
> $\sqrt{196} = \sqrt{(4 \times 49)} = \sqrt{4} \times \sqrt{49} = 2 \times 7 = 14$

Trial and improvement

Most square roots do not have whole-number values.
You can estimate the square root.

> **example**
>
> Use trial and improvement to find $\sqrt{30}$ to 1 decimal place.
> ....
> You know $5^2 = 25$ and $6^2 = 36$ so $\sqrt{30}$ will be between 5 and 6.
> $\sqrt{25} = 5$ $\sqrt{36} = 6$
>
> Try $5.5^2 = 30.25$
> Try $5.4^2 = 29.16$
>
>
>
> You say 5.5 is the best estimate for $\sqrt{30}$.
>
> 30.25 is closer to 30 than 29.16 is.
> So $\sqrt{30} = 5.5$ to 1 dp.

You can use indices to show other powers.
$3^4 = 3 \times 3 \times 3 \times 3$
    $= 81$

You press   3 x^y 4   =   on a calculator.

The powers of 2 are: 2^0 2^1 2^2 2^3 2^4 2^5 2^6 ...

The values are: 1   2   4   8   16   32   64   ...

All of the numbers except 2^0 are even because
an even number × an even number = an even number

Exercise A4.4

1 Calculate:
   a 6^4
   b $\sqrt[3]{216}$
   c 0.1^3
   d $(^-3)^4$

   e 25^2
   f 10^7
   g $\sqrt{256}$
   h 0.3^3

   i $\sqrt[3]{0.125}$
   j 18^2
   k 1^0
   l $(^-5)^5$

2 Find the value of these by using factors.
   a $\sqrt{400}$
   b $\sqrt{1600}$
   c $\sqrt{250\ 000}$

   d $\sqrt{225}$
   e $\sqrt{441}$
   f $\sqrt{256}$

3 Without using a calculator, find a number that when multiplied by itself gives:

> **Hint:** Find the square root of each number.

   a 324
   b 784
   c 2025

4 Copy and complete this table for powers of 10.

Power of 10	Value	Name
10^1		ten
10^2		hundred
10^3		
10^4		
10^5		
10^6		

5 Use trial and improvement to find each of these numbers to one decimal place.
   a $\sqrt{70}$
   b $\sqrt{95}$
   c $\sqrt{7}$
   d $\sqrt{120}$
   Use the square root key on your calculator to check your answer.

6 Using a calculator, find two consecutive numbers that have a product of 7482.
Explain your method for solving this problem.

7 **a** Calculate these without a calculator:
      4^2 4^3 4^4 4^5 4^6
   b What digit does 4^{25} end in?
   c What digit does 4^{26} end in?
   d Will 4^n ever be an odd number? Explain your answer.

8 Use your calculator to work out the value of x in each of these equations.
   a $2^x = 64$
   b $5^x = 625$
   c $3^x = 59\ 049$

   d $6^x = 1$
   e $5^9 = x$
   f $x^{10} = 1024$

   g $x^3 = 512$
   h $x^2 = 361$
   i $x^5 = 3125$
   j $y^1 = x$

> You don't need to work out y!

Plotting linear graphs

This spread will show you how to:

▶▶ Generate points in all four quadrants and plot the graphs of linear functions, where y is given explicitly in terms of x.

▶▶ Recognise that equations of the form $y = mx + c$ correspond to straight-line graphs.

KEYWORDS

Linear function

Straight-line graph

x-axis y-axis

A function is an equation that links two variables:

$y = 3x - 2$ links the variables x and y.

You can substitute a value for one variable and work out the value of the other variable.

When $x = 2$,

$$y = 3 \times 2 - 2$$
$$= 6 - 2$$
$$= 4$$

You draw a graph of a function by finding pairs of values in this way.

To draw the graph of $y = 3x - 2$

▶ Choose the x-values:

▶ Work out the y-values:

x	⁻2	⁻1	0	1	2
	$3 \times ⁻2 - 2$	$3 \times ⁻1 - 2$	$3 \times 0 - 2$	$3 \times 1 - 2$	$3 \times 2 - 2$
	⁻6 − 2	⁻3 − 2	0 − 2	3 − 2	6 − 2
y	⁻8	⁻5	⁻2	1	4

The coordinate pairs are: (⁻2, ⁻8)   (⁻1, ⁻5)   (0, ⁻2)   (1, 1)   (2, 4)

Draw a suitable grid.

▶ The x-axis needs to go from ⁻2 to 2.
▶ The y-axis needs to go from ⁻8 to 4.

Plot the points and join them up.

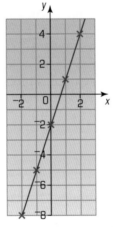

The graph of $y = 3x - 2$ is a straight line.

▶ **The graph of a linear function is a straight line.**

You can read other values from a graph:
The point (1.5, 2.5) lies on the straight line.
When $x = 1.5$, $y = 2.5$.

You can also work this out from the function:

$$y = 3 \times 1.5 - 2$$
$$= 4.5 - 2$$
$$= 2.5$$

Exercise A4.5

1 The points (⁻2, 1) and (1, 2) are two of the four vertices of a rectangle.
Plot these two points on a suitable size grid.
Suggest coordinates for the other two vertices.

2 **a** Copy and complete the table of values for the function $y = x + 3$.

x	⁻3	⁻2	⁻1	0	1	2	3
y							

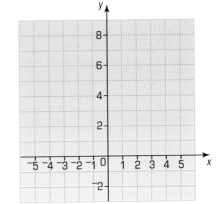

  b Write down the coordinate pairs.
  c Copy the grid and plot the coordinate pairs. Join the coordinate pairs and extend the line to the edges of the grid.
  d Choose a point on the line that is not plotted and write down its coordinates.
  Check that these coordinates fit the function.
  e Choose points on the line that include:

  i a fraction   **ii** a negative value.

  Write down the coordinates of both points and check that they fit the function.

3 **a** Copy and complete the table of values for the linear function $y = 3x - 4$.

x	⁻3	⁻2	⁻1	0	1	2	3
y		⁻10					

  b Plot the points on a coordinate grid.
  Choose a suitable size grid.
  c These coordinates lie on the straight line $y = 3x - 4$.

  $(a, \frac{1}{2})$ $(2\frac{1}{2}, b)$ $(⁻\frac{1}{2}, c)$

  Use your graph to find the values of a, b and c.
  d Use the rule $y = 3x - 4$ to check that the coordinates in part **c** fit the function.

4 **a** Complete a table of values for the graph $y = 4x - 3$ for x-values ⁻3 to 3.
  b Plot the graph on a suitable size grid.
  c Read off two pairs of coordinates from the line and check that they fit the function.

5 **a** Draw the graphs of $y = 2x + 2$ and $y = 3x - 4$ for x-values ⁻3 to 3 on a suitable size grid.
  b Write down the coordinates of the point where the two lines cross. Check that these coordinates fit both functions.

Straight-line graphs

This spread will show you how to:

▶▶ Generate points in all four quadrants and plot the graphs of linear functions, where *y* is given explicitly in terms of *x*.

▶▶ Recognise that equations of the form $y = mx + c$ correspond to straight-line graphs.

KEYWORDS

Equation   Horizontal
Diagonal   Intercept
Function   Vertical
Gradient

There are three different types of straight-line graph:

Horizontal graph   Vertical graph   Diagonal graph

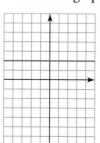   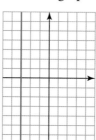   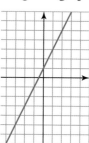

Here is the function for each graph:

$y = 2$ $x = {}^-3$ $y = 2x + 1$
All the *y*-coordinates are 2.   All the *x*-coordinates are ⁻3.   The *y*-value depends on the *x*-value.

▶ The equation of a horizontal line is $y =$ something
▶ The equation of a vertical line is $x =$ something

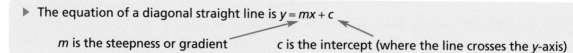

▶ The equation of a diagonal straight line is $y = mx + c$

m is the steepness or gradient   *c* is the intercept (where the line crosses the *y*-axis)

The steeper the graph, the bigger the value of *m*.

A straight-line graph is made up of an infinite number of points.
You only need to plot four!

example

Plot the graph of the function $y = 2x - 2$.
Write down the *y*-intercept of the graph.

Choose four *x*-values and work out the *y*-values:

x	⁻1	0	1	2
y	⁻4	⁻2	0	2

The graph cuts the *y*-axis at ⁻2 so the *y*-intercept is ⁻2.

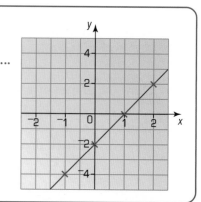

Exercise A4.6

1 Sort these equation cards into three piles:
horizontal graphs, vertical graphs and diagonal graphs.

$y = 2x$ $y = {}^-5$ $y = x + 1$ $x = 4$ $y = 0$

$y = x$ $y = 2x + 4$ $x = {}^-3$ $y = 6$ $y = 3x - 4$

2 **a** Complete a table of values for each of these graphs:

$y = x$, $y = 2x$, $y = 3x$ and $y = 4x$

Use x-values $^-2$, 0, 2, 4.

b Plot all the graphs on a copy of this grid.
Not all of your points will fit on the grid.

c Describe the similarities and differences between the
four graphs.

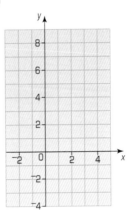

3 **a** Construct tables of values for each of these graphs. Use x-values $^-2$, 0, 2, 4.

$y = 3x$ $y = 3x - 1$ $y = 3x + 4$ $y = 3x + 2$ $y = 3x - 4$

b Plot the graphs on the same axes using a suitable size grid.

c Describe the similarities and differences between the five
graphs.

Hint: Look for the smallest
and largest y-values in your
five tables.

4 Arrange these equation
cards into order of steepness,
starting with the steepest.
Explain how you sorted the cards.

$y = 2x + 1$ $y = 3x - 2$ $y = x + 2$ $y = 7x - 9$ $y = 5x + 10$

5 On separate grids, sketch the graphs in question 4.

Hint: If you are unsure, plot the
graph using your grid and
counters.

6 Match each equation with its correct graph.
Explain how you decided.

a 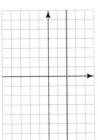   **b** 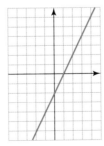   **c** 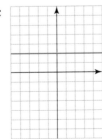   **d**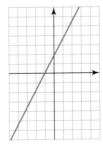

i $y = 2x - 2$ **ii** $y = 2$ **iii** $y = 2x + 2$ **iv** $x = 2$

This spread will show you how to:

▶▶ Generate points in all four quadrants and plot the graphs of linear functions, where y is given explicitly in terms of x.

▶▶ Recognise that equations of the form $y = mx + c$ correspond to straight-line graphs.

KEYWORDS
Intercept
Gradient
Steepness

Manjit has some equations and graphs playing cards.
The cards are all jumbled up.
She sorts them into pairs to make sure she has all of the cards.

 $y = 3x$

 $y = 2x - 4$

 $x = {}^{-}3$

$y = 3x - 1$

 $y = {}^{-}2x - 1$

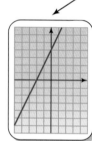

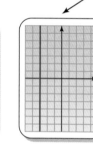

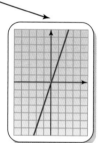

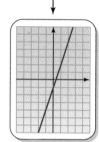

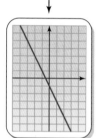

Manjit worked out the pairs in two stages.

First she looked at the steepness:

Diagonal	Vertical	These are parallel	Slopes downwards
	The function is $x = {}^{-}3$	The functions are $y = 3x$ and $y = 3x - 1$	The function is $y = {}^{-}3x - 1$

Then she wrote down the intercept:

intercept = 4	intercept = none	intercept = 0	intercept = ⁻1	intercept = ⁻1

This gave her the exact functions:

$y = 2x - 4$	$x = {}^{-}3$	$y = 3x$	$y = 3x - 1$	$y = {}^{-}2x - 1$

▶ $y = mx + c$ is the equation of a straight-line graph.
   m is the gradient and c is the intercept.

A downward-sloping graph has a negative gradient.

Exercise A4.7

1 Match these graphs to the correct function:

a 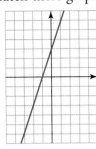   b 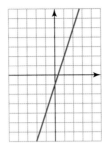   c 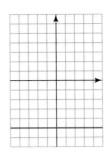   d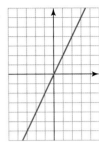

   i $y = 3x - 1$ **ii** $y = 2x$ **iii** $y = {}^-5$ **iv** $y = 3x + 3$

2 a 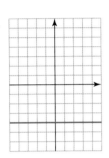   b 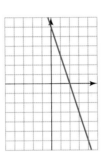   c 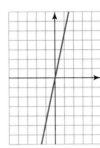   d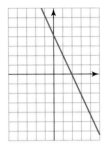

   i $y = 6 - 3x$ **ii** $y = 5x$ **iii** $y = {}^-4$ **iv** $y = 4 - 2x$

3 Here are some equations:

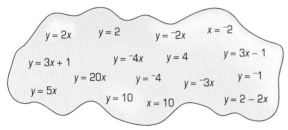

     $y = 2x$ $y = 2$ $y = {}^-2x$ $x = {}^-2$

   $y = 3x + 1$ $y = {}^-4x$ $y = 4$ $y = 3x - 1$

     $y = 20x$ $y = {}^-4$ $y = {}^-3x$ $y = {}^-1$

   $y = 5x$ $y = 10$ $x = 10$ $y = 2 - 2x$

Without drawing the graphs, sort the equations into one of the four columns in a copy of this table:

Vertical graph	Horizontal graph	Positive gradient	Negative gradient
$x = 4$		$y = x$	

A4.8 Using graphs

This spread will show you how to:
- ▶▶ Construct linear functions arising from real-life problems and plot their corresponding graphs.
- ▶▶ Discuss and interpret graphs arising from real situations.

KEYWORDS
Slope
Axes
Interpret

Graphs can help you understand real-life situations.

This graph shows the depth of water in the sink when David is doing the dishes.

Look at the slope of each part of the graph.

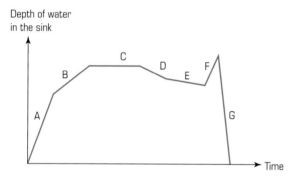

The graph shows:

A   Hot and cold taps on
B   Dishes put into the sink
C   Dishes washed in the sink
D   Some dishes taken out of the sink
E   Rest of the dishes taken out of the sink
F   Cold water tap put on to rinse dishes
G   Plug taken out and water draining out.

Graphs are useful for showing patterns.

example

Some students are recording how long an ice cube takes to melt.
They record the mass of the ice cube at different times.
Which of these graphs shows the likely pattern?

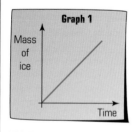
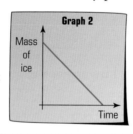
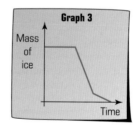
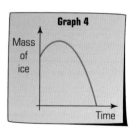

Ice will start to melt as soon as it is taken out of the freezer.

It couldn't be graph 1 as this shows the mass increasing over time.
It could be graph 2 as this shows the mass decreasing over time.
It couldn't be graph 3 as this shows the mass staying the same at the beginning.
It couldn't be graph 4 because this shows the mass increasing at the beginning.

The only suitable graph is graph 2 which shows the likely pattern.

Exercise A4.8

1 Explain what each of these graphs show.

a

Drinking water

Volume of water in glass / Time

b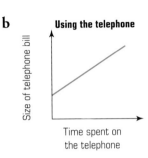

Using the telephone

Size of telephone bill / Time spent on the telephone

2 Which of these graphs correctly represents a lift travelling up through three floors?
Give reasons for your choice and explain why you have not chosen the other two graphs.

a

Height / Time

b

Height / Time

c

Height / Time

3 On one set of axes for both, sketch line graphs to show the depth of water against time when water runs steadily from a tap into these jars:

Jar 1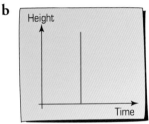

Jar 2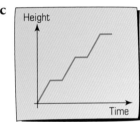

Hint: Imagine the depth of water in each jar after a few seconds.

4 Three mugs of coffee are made at the same time and the temperature of the coffee is recorded over time.

Coffee mug 1 is left on the table.

Coffee mug 2 is left outside in the cold weather.

Coffee mug 3 is wrapped in insulation.

Sketch the temperature graph for each mug of coffee.

5 Sketch the graph of:
   a temperature during a summer's day
   c the amount of fuel left in a car during a long journey
   b hours of daylight during the year
   d speed of running during a 800 m race.

 **Interpreting distance–time graphs**

<table>
<tr><td colspan="2">

This spread will show you how to:

▶▶ Construct linear functions arising from real-life problems and plot their corresponding graphs.

▶▶ Discuss and interpret graphs arising from real situations, including distance–time graphs.

</td><td>

KEYWORDS

Distance–time graph

Steepness

Interpret

</td></tr>
</table>

The graph shows Miss Warner's day from getting up in the morning to arriving at school.

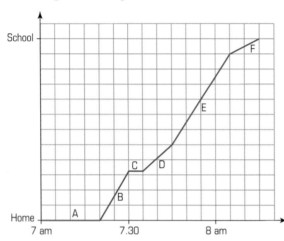

The journey:

A: Shower and eat breakfast
B: Start of the journey by car
C: Stuck in a traffic jam
D: Travelling in slow traffic
E: Travelling at normal speed
F: Travelling in slow traffic again near school.

> The vertical axis shows distance away from home.

A horizontal line shows there is no movement – she is in the same place.

A sloping line shows movement – the steeper the line the faster the movement.

You can draw a distance–time graph for any journey.

example

Sanjiv and Claire went to the cinema. This is the timetable for their evening:

6.00   Left home by car
6.30   Dropped off outside the cinema
8.30   Picked up outside the cinema
9.00   Arrived back at home

a Draw a distance–time graph to show the information.
b How did you show the time at the cinema?

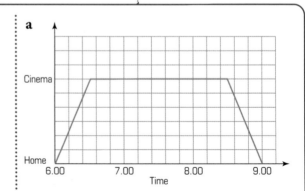

b To show the time at the cinema you draw a horizontal line, as this shows no movement.

Exercise A4.9

1 This graph shows a train journey from Penzance to Birmingham.

   a What time did the train leave Penzance?

   b Which stations did the train stop at?

   c How long did the train stop at these stations?

   d How long did the journey take from Penzance to Birmingham?

   e During which part of the journey was the train travelling the slowest?

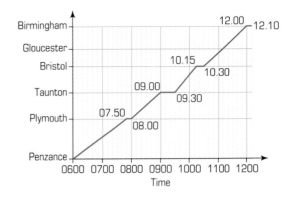

2 This graph show's Manjit's journey to the park on her new bike.

   a These statements explain each stage of her journey. Match the correct statement with the stage on the graph.

   i   At the park for 25 minutes

   ii Cycling to the park the first time

   iii Cycling to the park the second time

   iv Cycling back home the first time

   v   Cycling back home the second time

   vi Back at home

   b What happened at the beginning of her journey to the park?

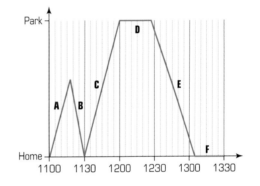

3 David and Teresa drive to visit their daughter. This is the order of events:

   9.00   Leave the house by car
   10.00 Arrive at their daughter's house
   12.00 Start the return journey
   12.30 Stop at the shops
   1.30   Leave the shops
   2.00   Arrive at home

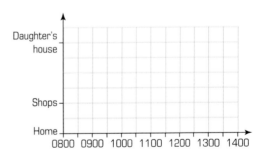

Copy and complete the distance–time graph to show this information

4 Draw a distance–time graph to illustrate a journey you have made recently, for example: a day out shopping, a trip to relatives, a night out at a disco, the journey home from school.

Include a timetable of events as in question 3.

You should know how to ...

1 Recognise and use multiples, factors (divisors), highest common factors, lowest common multiples and primes.

2 Plot the graphs of linear functions.

3 Represent problems and interpret solutions.

Check out

1 a What are the lowest common multiples of:

   i   6 and 24

   ii 9 and 12

   iii 5 and 20

   iv 13 and 14?

 b What are the highest common factors of:

   i   72 and 96

   ii 45 and 27

   iii 120 and 66

   iv 32 and 30?

 c Simplify these fractions:

   i $\frac{36}{78}$

   ii $\frac{18}{36}$

2 Plot the graphs of $y = 3x + 1$ and $y = 3x - 1$. Copy and complete this table of values to help you:

x	$^-2$	$^-1$	0	1	2
y					

Describe the similarities and differences between the graphs.

3 a Draw a distance–time graph for this journey:

David leaves home at 8.00 am.

He cycles 2 km to school and arrives at 8.30 am.

He leaves school at 12.30 pm and goes home on the train, which takes 45 minutes.

 b How long in total did David spend travelling?

2 Probability

This unit will show you how to:

▶▶ Use the vocabulary of probability when interpreting the results of an experiment.

▶▶ Know that if the probability of an event occurring is p, then the probability of it not occurring is $1 - p$.

▶▶ Find and record all possible mutually exclusive outcomes for single events and two successive events in a systematic way.

▶▶ Appreciate that random processes are unpredictable.

▶▶ Compare experimental and theoretical probabilities in different contexts.

▶▶ Estimate probabilities from experimental data; understand that:

  ▶ If an experiment is repeated there may be, and usually will be, different outcomes.

  ▶ Increasing the number of times an experiment is repeated generally leads to better estimates of probability.

▶▶ Solve more demanding problems and investigate in a range of contexts.

▶▶ Identify the necessary information to solve a problem.

The chance of winning a lottery is quite small, but someone wins most weeks.

Before you start

You should know how to ...

1 Find and justify probabilities based on equally likely outcomes.

2 Express an amount as a decimal, fraction and percentage. For example,

    3 out of 8 is $\frac{3}{8}$ as a fraction

and

    $3 \div 8 = 0.375$ as a decimal

and

    $0.375 \times 100\% = 37.5\%$ as a percentage.

Check in

1 When a fair dice is rolled, what is the probability that the score is:

  a 5 **b** even **c** a prime number?

2 a Write these amounts as decimals:

    i $\frac{3}{5}$ **ii** $\frac{12}{16}$ **iii** 62%

  b Write these amounts as percentages:

    i 0.35 **ii** $\frac{11}{20}$ **iii** $\frac{9}{15}$

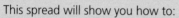

This spread will show you how to:

▶▶ Understand and use the probability scale from 0 to 1.

▶▶ Identify the mutually exclusive outcomes of an event.

▶▶ Use the vocabulary of probability when interpreting the results of an experiment.

KEYWORDS

Probability   Trial

Outcome   Estimate

Experiment

You use a probability scale to explain how likely a result is.

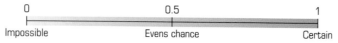

Probabilities can be given as fractions, decimals or percentages.
An 'evens chance' is a probability of $\frac{1}{2}$ or 0.5 or 50%.

There are two ways to work out probabilities.

If all the **outcomes** of an experiment are equally likely, you work out the theoretical probability.

$$\text{Theoretical probability of an event} = \frac{\text{Number of favourable outcomes}}{\text{Total number of outcomes}}$$

The favourable outcomes are the results you are looking for.

The **outcomes** of an experiment are the different results that could happen.

example

An ordinary dice is rolled.
What is the probability of getting a score bigger than 4?

....

There are 6 equally likely outcomes.
There are two favourable outcomes: 5 and 6.
Probability of getting a score bigger than $4 = \frac{2}{6} = \frac{1}{3}$.

If you do not know that the outcomes are equally likely, you can estimate the probability, using an experiment.

$$\text{Experimental probability} = \frac{\text{Number of successful trials}}{\text{Total number of trials}}$$

An **experiment** is a series of **trials**.

This spinner is an irregular quadrilateral, so you cannot say that all the outcomes are equally likely.

In 50 trials, a score of 3 happened 18 times.
Estimated probability of getting a score of 3
$= 18 \div 50 = 0.36$.

Exercise D2.1

1 Sarah has this set of cards. She picks one of the cards without looking.

    a Sarah says: 'I am more likely to get a card with a cross than one with a heart.' Explain why Sarah is wrong.

    b Find the probability that Sarah gets:

        i   a card with an even number

        ii   a card with an odd number

        iii   a card with the number 4

        iv   a card with a number less than 9.

    c Draw a probability scale, and mark the probabilities from part **b** on it. Explain how likely each event is.

2 These boxes contain some red and some blue counters. Ella chooses a box, shakes it, and picks a counter without looking.
Explain which box Ella chooses if:

    a It is certain that she will get a blue counter.

    b It is impossible that she will get a blue counter.

    c There is an evens chance that she will get a red counter.

    d It is very unlikely that Ella will get a blue counter.

    e The probability of getting a red counter is $\frac{1}{3}$.

3 A bag contains seven green cubes and three yellow cubes.
Louis says: 'There are two colours – green and yellow.
This means that the probability of getting a yellow cube is $\frac{1}{2}$.'
Explain why Louis is wrong.

4 This fair spinner is marked with numbers.

    a Find the probability that the spinner lands on 6.

    b Find the probability that the spinner lands on an even number.

    c This fair spinner has eight equal sections.
Every section needs to be marked with a 1, a 2 or a 3.
The probability of getting a 1 is 50%, and the probability of getting a 2 is 25%.
Copy the diagram, and mark each section with the correct number.

5 Karen, Huw and Sophie are testing this spinner to estimate the probability of getting each score. The table shows their results.

    a Whose data should give the most reliable estimate for the probability of each score? Explain your answer.

	Score		
	1	2	3
Karen	38	45	17
Huw	14	8	8
Sophie	23	21	16

    b Combine all three sets of data together, and use the combined data to estimate the probability of each score.

This spread will show you how to:
▶▶ Know that if the probability of an event occurring is p, then the probability of it not occurring is $1 - p$.

KEYWORDS
Occur   Event
Probability

You can find the probability of an event not occurring if you know the probability that it will occur.

example

A counter is picked at random from this box.

a   What is the probability that it will be green?
b   What is the probability that it will **not** be green?

....

There are 10 counters in the box.
a   There are 3 favourable outcomes for the event 'the counter picked is green', so the probability will be $\frac{3}{10}$.
b   There are 7 favourable outcomes for the event 'the counter picked is not green', so the probability will be $\frac{7}{10}$.

▶ If you know that the probability of an event occurring is p, then the probability that it will not occur is $1 - p$.

You can work out the probability of an event not occurring, whether the probability is given as a fraction, a decimal or a percentage.

example

a   The probability of an event occurring is $\frac{2}{7}$.
    What is the probability that the event does not occur?
b   The probability of winning a game is 0.35.
    What is the probability of not winning the game?
c   The probability of passing a test is 45%.
    What is the probability of not passing the test?

....

a   You need to work out $1 - p$, with $p = \frac{2}{7}$.
    $$1 - \tfrac{2}{7} = \tfrac{7}{7} - \tfrac{2}{7} = \tfrac{5}{7}$$
    The probability that the event does not occur is $\frac{5}{7}$.
b   You need to work out $1 - p$, with $p = 0.35$.
    $$1 - 0.35 = 0.65$$
    The probability of not winning the game is 0.65.
c   You need to work out $1 - p$, with $p = 45\%$.
    $$1 - 45\% = 100\% - 45\% = 55\%$$
    The probability of not passing the test is 55%.

Exercise D2.2

1 In a competition, the probability of winning a prize is $\frac{1}{8}$.
Work out the probability of not winning a prize.

2 The probability of Robin getting to school on time is 94%.
Work out the probability that Robin will not get to school on time.

3 The probability that Mrs Kaur's car will start first time is 0.84.
Find the probability that it will not start first time.

4 This table shows the probability, p, of
some events. Copy the table, and complete
it to show the probability, $1 - p$, that each
event does **not** occur.

p	0.77	$\frac{3}{16}$	52%	0.015	31%	0.99
$1-p$						

5 A bag contains red and green counters only.
A counter is chosen at random.
The probability of getting a red counter is 0.3.
What is the probability of getting a green counter?

6 A box contains 4 blue counters, 5 red counters and 1 yellow
counter. Wendy is going to pick a counter at random from the box.
  a What is the probability that she does not get a yellow counter?
  b Wendy actually gets a red counter. She does not put it back,
     and she picks another counter from the box at random.
     What is the probability that she does not get a yellow counter this time?

7 This fair spinner has sections
coloured red, yellow and blue.
Copy and complete the table to
show the probability of getting
each colour, and the probability
of not getting each colour.

Colour	Probability of getting the colour	Probability of not getting the colour
Red		
Yellow		
Blue		

8 Some students made a biased dice from a cuboid. They rolled
the dice 200 times to estimate the probability of each score.
The table shows the results.

Score	1	2	3	4	5	6
Frequency	8	30	64	56	35	7
Probability of getting this score						
Probability of **not** getting this score						

Copy the table, and complete it to show the estimated
probability of getting each score, and the estimated probability
of not getting each score. Give your answers as decimals.

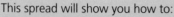

This spread will show you how to:

▶▶ Find and record all possible mutually exclusive outcomes for single events and two successive events in a systematic way, using diagrams and tables.

You need to know all the outcomes of an event to use the formula:

▶ Theoretical probability of an event $= \dfrac{\text{Number of favourable outcomes}}{\text{Total number of outcomes}}$

A sample space diagram helps you find all the outcomes in a systematic way, so that outcomes are not left out or repeated.

example

Two coins are tossed.
What is the probability of getting one head and one tail?

....

The sample space diagram shows all the possible outcomes.

There are 2 favourable outcomes for the event 'one head and one tail'; these are (H, T) and (T, H).

There are 4 outcomes altogether, so the probability of getting one head and one tail is $\frac{2}{4} = \frac{1}{2}$.

		Coin 2	
		Head	Tail
Coin 1	Head	(H, H)	(H, T)
	Tail	(T, H)	(T, T)

The way you record your results depends on the information you want.

example

A blue dice and a red dice are rolled, and the scores are added.
What is the probability of getting a score of 7?

....

The sample space diagram shows all the possible outcomes. You record the total score, since that is what you need to know.

There are 6 favourable outcomes, which are coloured green.

There are 36 possible outcomes altogether, so the probability of getting a total score of 7 is $\frac{6}{36} = \frac{1}{6}$.

Totals		Red dice score					
		1	2	3	4	5	6
Blue dice score	1	2	3	4	5	6	7
	2	3	4	5	6	7	8
	3	4	5	6	7	8	9
	4	5	6	7	8	9	10
	5	6	7	8	9	10	11
	6	7	8	9	10	11	12

Exercise D2.3

1 An ordinary pack of playing cards contains Hearts, Diamonds, Clubs and Spades. Colin picks a card, puts it back in the pack, and then picks another card.
One possible outcome is a Club on the first pick, and a Spade on the second pick. You could write this as (C, S).

> Try to be systematic – list all the combinations with Hearts first, then Diamonds, Clubs and Spades in order.

   a Write all of the possible outcomes in this way.
   b Draw a sample space diagram to show your answers.

2 A dice is rolled and a coin is tossed.

   a Copy and complete this sample space diagram to show the possible outcomes.

		\multicolumn{6}{c}{Dice}
		1	2	3	4	5	6
Coin	Heads	(H, 1)					
	Tails						

Use your sample space diagram to work out the probability that:

   b The coin will show Heads.
   c The dice will show a 3.
   d The coin will show heads and the dice will show an even number.

3 A red dice and a blue dice are rolled, and the scores are multiplied together.
Draw a sample space diagram to show the possible outcomes.
Use your diagram to work out the probability that the product of the numbers on the two dice will be:

   a exactly 12   b more than 10   c less than 15
   d a prime number   e an odd number.

4 To decide who does the washing up, Simon, Denise, Rita and Jon put their names in a hat and pick two out, without looking. The first person picked will wash up, and the second person will dry.

The table will show the possible outcomes.

		\multicolumn{4}{c}{Drying the dishes}
		Simon	Denise	Rita	Jon
Washing the dishes	Simon		(S, D)		
	Denise				
	Rita				
	Jon				

(S, D) means Simon washes, Denise dries.

   a Copy and complete the diagram to show all the possible outcomes.
   b Explain why four of the spaces in the diagram are blanked out.

Use your diagram to find the probability that:

   c Rita washes up and Jon dries.
   d Rita washes up.
   e Jon is not given a job to do.
   f Simon and Denise do the two jobs.

This spread will show you how to:
▶▶ Appreciate that random processes are unpredictable.
▶▶ Compare experimental and theoretical probabilities in different contexts.
▶▶ Estimate probabilities from experimental data.

KEYWORDS
Experiment   Vary
Expect   Biased
Reliable   Estimate
Fair
Experimental probability

Probability tells you what to expect when an experiment is carried out.
However, you would not expect to get exactly the same results every time you carried out the experiment.

Six students tested a coin to see if it was fair.
Each person tossed the coin 10 times.
Here are their results:

Student	A	B	C	D	E	F
Heads	4	3	3	6	6	6
Tails	6	7	7	4	4	4

Martin says:
'If the coin was fair, you would expect to get 5 heads and 5 tails.
Nobody did! The coin must be biased.'
Explain why Martin is wrong.

It is normal for the results to vary.
If you put all of the data together, there were 28 heads and 32 tails, which is very close to what you would expect.

If all six students had got more heads than tails, this **may** have shown bias.

Carrying out an experiment more often gives more reliable results.

Ten students tested this biased spinner, to find the probability of getting each result. Each person spun the spinner 20 times.
Here are the results.

Student	A	B	C	D	E	F	G	H	I	J
Star	3	2	4	2	1	2	4	3	5	3
Moon	10	2	5	8	7	4	6	4	5	4
Sun	7	16	11	10	12	14	10	13	10	13

Use these results to estimate the probability of each outcome.

The results from each student vary a lot.
The best estimate will come from combining all of the data.
Altogether there were 200 outcomes: 29 stars, 55 moons and 116 suns.
The estimated probabilities are 0.145 for star, 0.275 for moon and 0.58 for sun.

Exercise D2.4

1 Nina spins a coin 20 times. She gets 12 heads and 8 tails. She says:
'This coin must be biased. A fair coin should give 10 heads and 10 tails.'
Explain why this is not correct.

2 Gordon tosses a coin 3 times. He gets heads every time. He says:
'I'm certain to get tails next time.'
Explain why Gordon is wrong.

3 Sandra is testing a coin. She thinks the coin is biased.
Sandra spins the coin 10 times, and she gets these results:

Heads	Tails
7	3

  a Estimate the experimental probability of getting heads,
     based on this data.
  b How reliable do you think your estimate in part **a** is?
  c What could Sandra do to get a more reliable estimate of
     the probability for heads?

4 Samir carried out an experiment to test a
trick dice. The dice was designed to land on
6 more often than the other numbers.
The table shows the results of the experiment.

Score	1	2	3	4	5	6
Frequency	1	0	3	2	2	42

  a How many times did Samir roll the dice?
  b Estimate the probability of getting a 6 with this dice.
  c How good do you think this trick dice is? Explain your answer.

5 Five students tested a dice to see if it was fair.
They each rolled the dice 100 times.
The table shows their results.

Student	\multicolumn{6}{}{Score}

Student	1	2	3	4	5	6
Sally	20	15	20	16	14	15
Karis	20	18	19	18	16	9
David	22	11	18	18	20	11
Judy	14	22	23	16	14	11
Ben	14	22	13	24	15	12
Total						

  a Copy the table, and add the frequencies to
     find the total frequency for each score.
  b Use this combined set of data to estimate the
     experimental probability of each score.
  c Use your answer to part **b** to explain whether
     or not you think the dice is fair.

6 Karen and Jayne tested this spinner. The table shows their results.

	Face	Rainbow	Lightning
Karen	16	48	36
Jayne	44	75	81

  a How many times did each person spin the spinner?
  b Estimate the probability of each result, based on Karen's data.
  c Now estimate the probability of each result using Jayne's data.
  d Whose results should be most reliable? Explain your answer.
  e Now combine both sets of results, and estimate the probability
     of each result based on the combined data.

You should know how to ...

1 Find and record all possible mutually exclusive outcomes for single events and two successive events in a systematic way, using diagrams and tables.

2 Identify the necessary information to solve a problem.

Check out

1 Jenny has these two spinners:

She spins the two spinners together and adds the results to get the total score.
Draw a sample space diagram to show all the possible outcomes.

2 Dara has these sets of cards:

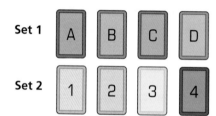

Dara chooses one card from each set.
He wants to be able to answer questions like, 'What is the probability of getting a vowel and an even number?' or 'What is the probability of getting a D and a number bigger than 2?'

Explain how Dara could use a sample space diagram to answer questions like these.

Transformations

This unit will show you how to:

▶▶ Use bearings to specify direction.

▶▶ Transform 2-D shapes by simple combinations of rotations, reflections and translations.

▶▶ Identify all the symmetries of 2-D shapes.

▶▶ Enlarge 2-D shapes given a centre of enlargement and a positive whole-number scale factor.

▶▶ Understand and use the language and notation associated with enlargement.

▶▶ Make simple scale drawings.

▶▶ Represent problems and interpret solutions in algebraic, geometric or graphical form.

▶▶ Suggest extensions to problems, conjecture and generalise.

Buildings can be symmetrical or have no symmetry.

Before you start

You should know how to ...

1 Use a protractor.

2 Recognise congruent shapes.

3 Simplify ratios.

Check in

1 Measure these angles:

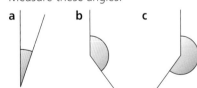

a   b   c

2 State which shapes are congruent.

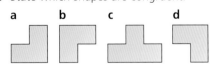

a   b   c   d

3 Express these ratios in their simplest form.

a 4 : 10   b 15 : 18   c 12 : 8

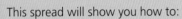

This spread will show you how to:

▶▶ Use bearings to specify direction.

KEYWORDS
Bearing   Direction
Three-figure bearing

This is the view from the top of a mountain called
The Old Man of Coniston in the Lake District.

In the distance is a mountain called Scafell Pike which
is the highest in England.

The direction of Scafell Pike
from The Old Man of
Coniston is 328°.

The angle is called a bearing.

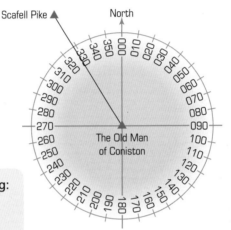

▶ To give an accurate bearing:
  ▶ Use the 360° scale.
  ▶ Measure from North.
  ▶ Measure clockwise.
  ▶ Always give three figures.

example

On a map, a mountain is marked with
a triangle: ▲

a Write down the mountains that are
on these bearings from The Old
Man of Coniston.
  i 034°
  ii 230°
  iii 328°
b What is the bearing of The Old
Man of Coniston from Scafell Pike?

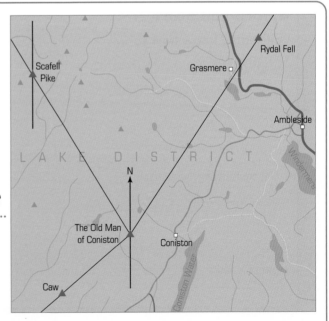

- -

a i Rydal Fell
  ii Caw
  iii Scafell Pike
b Bearing of The Old Man is 148°.

Note: 328° − 180° = 148°

Exercise S3.1

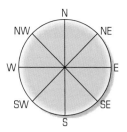

1 a Copy the diagram accurately.
 b Copy and complete this table.

Direction	N					SW	W	NW
Bearing	000°	045°	090°	135°	180°			

2 Write down the three-figure bearings of these places from Burton Fleming.

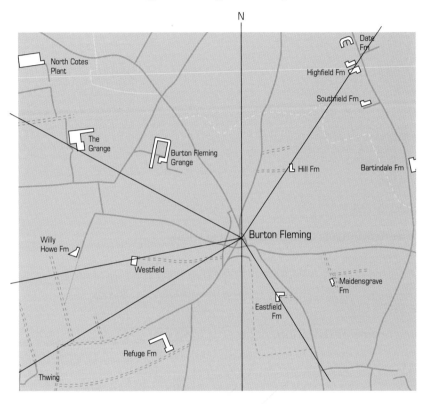

a Highfield Farm   **b** Eastfield Farm   **c** Westfield
d The Grange   **e** Thwing

3 Put a cross in the middle of your page for each question.
 Plot the points and join them up in order to form a shape.
 Name each shape and then draw the lines of symmetry.

a

Bearing from cross	000°	072°	144°	216°	288°
Distance from cross	5 cm	5 cm	5 cm	5 cm	5 cm

b

Bearing from cross	000°	050°	180°	310°
Distance from cross	5 cm	5 cm	3 cm	5 cm

c

Bearing from cross	090°	220°	270°	320°
Distance from cross	5 cm	5 cm	1 cm	5 cm

Describing transformations

This spread will show you how to:

▶▶ Recognise and visualise transformations.

All the shapes in this diagram are congruent.

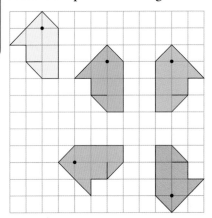

The original shape or object is red.

You can move the object onto an image using a **transformation**.

Reflection

▶ A reflection flips the object over.

You specify the mirror line or line of reflection.

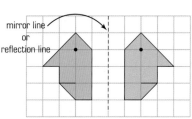

Rotation

▶ A rotation turns the object.

You specify:
▶ The centre of rotation
   – the point about which it turns.
▶ The angle of turn.
▶ The direction of turn
   – clockwise or anticlockwise.

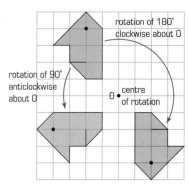

Translation

▶ A translation slides the object.

You specify the distance moved left or right, then the distance moved up or down.

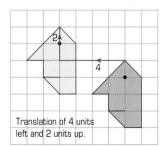

Exercise S3.2

For each question, copy the shapes onto squared paper.

1 On the same grid, translate each shape.

A $\begin{pmatrix} 7 \text{ right} \\ 5 \text{ up} \end{pmatrix}$ B $\begin{pmatrix} 3 \text{ right} \\ 9 \text{ up} \end{pmatrix}$

C $\begin{pmatrix} 0 \text{ across} \\ 5 \text{ up} \end{pmatrix}$ D $\begin{pmatrix} 1 \text{ left} \\ 5 \text{ up} \end{pmatrix}$

E $\begin{pmatrix} 2 \text{ right} \\ 5 \text{ down} \end{pmatrix}$ F $\begin{pmatrix} 2 \text{ right} \\ 6 \text{ down} \end{pmatrix}$

G $\begin{pmatrix} 10 \text{ left} \\ 7 \text{ down} \end{pmatrix}$

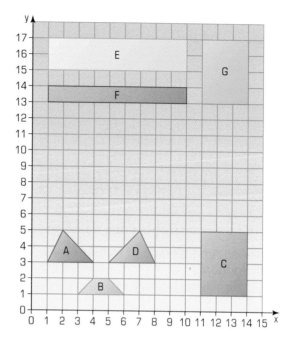

2 Reflect each shape in the mirror line.
Name the new shape you have made.
Mark the equal angles and equal sides on the new shape.

a   **b**   **c**   **d**   **e**

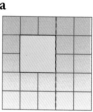 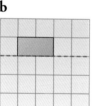 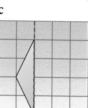 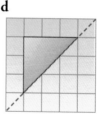 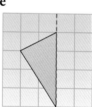

f Explain why it is impossible to draw a parallelogram using this method.

3 Rotate each shape about the dot through 180°.
Name the new shape you have made.
Mark the equal angles and equal sides on the new shape.

a   **b**   **c**   **d**   **e**

  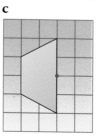  

f Explain why it is impossible to draw a kite using this method.

Combining transformations

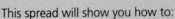

> This spread will show you how to:
> ▶▶ Transform 2-D shapes by simple combinations of rotations, reflections and translations.

KEYWORDS

Transformation   Rotation
Tessellation   Translation
Reflection

A tessellation is a tiling pattern with no gaps or overlaps.

You can tessellate shapes using transformations.

This tessellation is made of translated parallelograms.

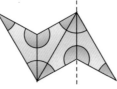

This tessellation is made from kites rotated about the midpoint of a side.

This tessellation is made from a combination of reflections and rotations of a triangle.

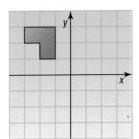

You can often use a single transformation to describe a combination of transformations.

example

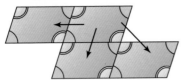

a Reflect the red shape in the *y*-axis. Label the new shape A.
b Reflect shape A in the *x*-axis. Label the new shape B.
c What single transformation moves the red shape to B?

a, b

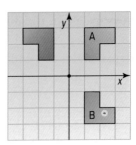

c A rotation of 180° about the origin.

Exercise S3.3

1 **a** Make a copy of this pattern on squared paper.
   b Reflect the pattern in the horizontal mirror line.
   c Reflect both patterns in the vertical mirror line.
   d Repeat this process for your own pattern on squared paper.

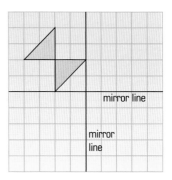

2 **a** Draw a 4 by 2 rectangle on squared paper.

   b Remove the top triangle and slide it down the rectangle.

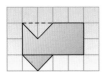

   c Remove the triangle on the right and slide it across the rectangle.

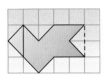

   d Cut out your shape and tessellate it using repeated translations.

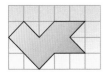

3 Copy this diagram onto squared paper.
   a Reflect the orange shape in mirror line A.
       Label the new shape A.
   b Reflect shape A in mirror line B.
       Label the new shape B.
   c What single transformation moves the orange shape
       directly to shape B?

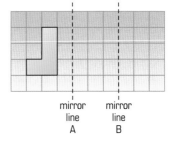

4 Copy this triangle on squared paper.
   Colour in the angles as shown. Cut it out.
   a Tessellate the triangle by rotating it through 180°
       about the midpoints of the sides.
   b Colour the angles in all the triangles.
       Describe any angle properties that you can see.

Symmetries of polygons

This spread will show you how to:
▶▶ Identify all the symmetries of 2-D shapes.

KEYWORDS
Reflection symmetry
Order of rotational symmetry
Polygon   Regular

This sign has reflection symmetry:
The dotted line is a line of symmetry.

> ▶ A shape has reflection symmetry if you can fold it so that one half fits exactly on top of the other half.

A kite has reflection symmetry:

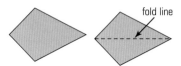

fold line

You can mark equal angles and lengths:

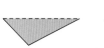

> ▶ A shape has rotational symmetry if it rotates onto itself more than once during a full turn.
>
> ▶ The order of rotational symmetry is the number of times the shape rotates onto itself during a full turn.

A rectangle has rotational symmetry of order 2:

Start

> ▶ A regular polygon has equal sides and equal angles.

A regular triangle has 3 equal sides and 3 equal angles.
It is called an equilateral triangle.

It has 3 lines of symmetry ...

and rotational symmetry of order 3.

Start

Exercise S3.4

1 a Copy these regular polygons and draw in all the lines of symmetry.

pentagon   hexagon   heptagon   octagon

b Give the order of rotational symmetry for each polygon.
c Describe a rule to calculate the number of lines of symmetry
and the order of rotational symmetry for regular polygons.

2 Copy and complete this table.
Draw each shape and mark the lines of symmetry.
Give the order of rotational symmetry.

	Shape	Lines of symmetry	Order of rotational symmetry
a	square		4
b	rectangle		
c	parallelogram		
d	rhombus		
e	kite		
f	arrowhead (delta)		
g	isosceles trapezium		
h	equilateral triangle		
i	isosceles triangle		

3 Put these shapes through this flow chart.

> square, rectangle, rhombus, parallelogram,
> kite, arrowhead (delta), isosceles trapezium

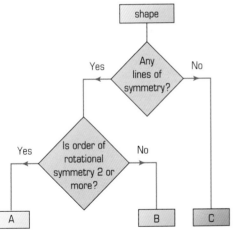

Write where each shape finishes.

4 Draw an isosceles triangle and cut it out.
Fold it along its line of symmetry.
What geometrical properties does this show?

5 A parallelogram has rotational symmetry of order 2.
What geometrical properties does this show?

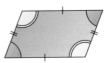

Enlargements

This spread will show you how to:

▶▶ Understand and use the language and notation associated with enlargement.

▶▶ Enlarge 2-D shapes given a centre of enlargement and a positive whole-number scale factor.

KEYWORDS

Enlargement   Ratio
Scale factor
Centre of enlargement

This photo has been enlarged:

 2 times larger

All the lengths have been multiplied by 2.
This is an enlargement, scale factor 2.
The two photos are similar. They are the same shape but a different size.

You can show an enlargement on a grid:

example

Enlarge this shape by a scale factor of 3.

All the lengths must be 3 times longer:

The centre of enlargement is the point where the lines joining the vertices of the original and the enlargement meet.

You can enlarge a shape from a centre on a grid.

You multiply each distance from the centre of enlargement by the scale factor.

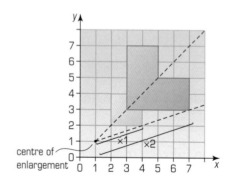

▶ An enlargement changes the size of a shape. The lengths remain in the same ratio.
You specify:
  ▶ The scale factor of the enlargement.
  ▶ The centre of enlargement.

Exercise S3.5

1 Find the scale factor of these enlargements.

a 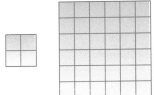 **b** 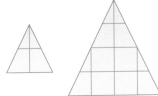 **c**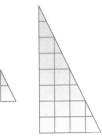

2 Copy these shapes onto squared paper. Enlarge each shape by scale factor 2.

a **b** **c** **d** **e**

3 **a** Copy this grid onto squared paper.
b Plot and join these points to make a face:
(2, 0) (1, 1) (1, 4) (2, 5) (3, 5) (4, 4) (4, 3) (5, 2)
(4, 2) (4, 1) (3, 1) (3, 0).
c Multiply every coordinate by 2,
for example (4, 0) (2, 2) (2, 8) (4, 10) ...
d On the same grid, plot these new points
to make a new face.
e What are the new coordinates of the eye?
f State the scale factor of the enlargement.
g Find the centre of enlargement.
h Copy and complete this table.

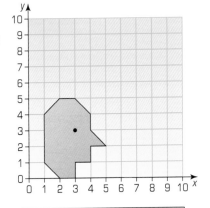

	Original shape	Enlarged shape
Width of neck (cm)		
Length of head (cm)		
Width of head (cm)		

4 You need three copies of this grid.
On your grids, enlarge the shape using:
a scale factor 2, centre (0, 4)
b scale factor 3, centre (1, 3).
c scale factor 4, centre (1, 2).

Hint: You cannot multiply
the coordinates in this
question.

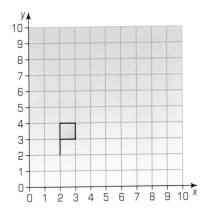

Scale drawings

This spread will show you how to:
▶▶ Make simple scale drawings.

KEYWORDS
Scale drawing Enlargement
Scale   Ratio
Simplify

These coins are full size:

A full size postbox will not fit on the page.

A scale drawing will fit.

All the lengths in real life have been divided by 30.

The scale is   2 cm represents 60 cm.

You can write the scale as a ratio   2 cm : 60 cm or 1 : 30.

▶ In a scale drawing, corresponding lengths are in the same ratio.

Enlargements are scale drawings.

You can simplify ratios if the parts have a common factor.

example

Express these ratios in their simplest form.

a 4 cm : 10 cm   **b** 8 kg : 20 kg   **c** 10 cm : 1 m   **d** 25 cl : 1 l

-----

a 4 cm : 10 cm   **b** 8 kg : 20 kg   **c** 10 cm : 1 m   **d** 25 cl : 1 l
    4 : 10   8 : 20   10 cm : 100 cm   25 cl : 100 cl
    2 : 5   2 : 5   10 : 100   25 : 100
                                          1 : 10   1 : 4

You can use ratios to help you find a scale.

example

Find the scale of this drawing.

2 cm

20 m

2 cm represents 20 m.
The ratio of heights is 2 cm : 20 m
                      2 cm : 2000 cm
                      1 cm : 1000 cm
                        1 : 1000

The lengths in the scale drawing are 1000 times smaller than in real life.

Exercise S3.6

1 A model car is built using a scale of 1 : 10. Copy and complete this table.

Measurement	Model car	Real car
Length		350 cm
Width		150 cm
Number of wheels		4

2 Write these ratios in their simplest form.
  a 10 cm : 20 cm   **b** 10 cm : 50 cm   **c** 10 cm : 1 m
  d 5 cm : 25 cm   **e** 5 cm : 1 m   **f** 1 cm : 1 m
  g 1 cm : 5 m   **h** 2 cm : 1 m   **i** 1 cm : 10 m
  j 1 cm : 1 km

3 In this scale drawing, 1 cm represents 4 m.
  a Calculate the width of the real house.
  b Calculate the height of the real house.
  c Express the scale as a ratio in its simplest form.

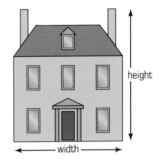

4 The ratio of the height of the person to the height of the tree is 1 : 6.
Estimate the height of the tree in metres.

5 The scale for this drawing of a classroom is 1 cm represents 1 metre.
  a Express this scale as a ratio.
  b Calculate the lengths of the window and the whiteboard.
  c What is the length and width of the classroom?
  d Calculate the area of the classroom.
  e Make an accurate copy of this scale drawing.
    Draw desks or tables to scale in the classroom to decide how many students can be seated in the classroom.

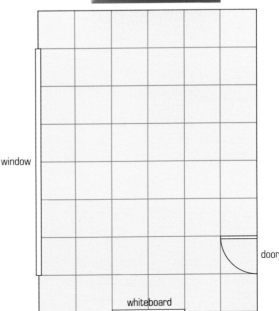

You should know how to ...

1 Enlarge 2-D shapes given a centre of enlargement and a positive whole-number scale factor.

2 Represent problems and interpret solutions in geometric form.

Check out

1 Copy this diagram onto squared paper.
Enlarge the shape by scale factor 2 using the dot as the centre of enlargement.

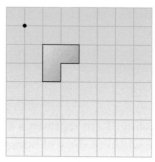

2 a Describe the single transformation in this diagram that moves:
   i A to B
   ii A to C
   iii A to D
   iv A to E.

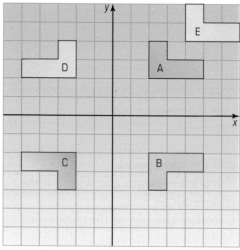

b Describe a combination of two transformations that moves:
   i D to E
   ii B to E
   iii C to E.

Problem solving and revision

This unit will show you how to:

▶▶ Solve more demanding problems.
▶▶ Identify the necessary information to solve a problem.
▶▶ Represent problems and interpret solutions in algebraic, graphical or geometric form.
▶▶ Use the unitary method to solve simple problems.

▶▶ Solve more complex problems by breaking them into smaller steps or tasks, choosing efficient techniques.
▶▶ Give solutions to an appropriate degree of accuracy.
▶▶ Check results using appropriate methods.

You will use four stages in an exam question to maximise your marks:

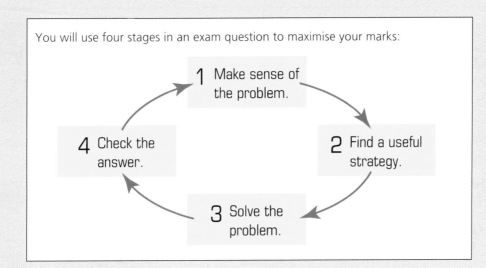

1 Make sense of the problem.

2 Find a useful strategy.

3 Solve the problem.

4 Check the answer.

Before you start

You should know how to ...

▶ Round numbers.
▶ Add, subtract, multiply and divide integers.
▶ Use division to convert a fraction to a decimal.
▶ Add and subtract fractions by writing them with a common denominator.
▶ Use the equivalence of fractions, decimals and percentages.
▶ Use the order of operations.
▶ Generate and describe sequences.

▶ Use letter symbols.
▶ Solve simple equations.
▶ Solve geometrical problems using side and angle properties.
▶ Use units of measurement.
▶ Know and use formulae for perimeter and area.
▶ Interpret graphs and diagrams.
▶ Use probabilities.

Making sense of the problem

This spread will show you how to:
- ►► Solve more demanding problems.
- ►► Identify the necessary information to solve a problem.
- ►► Represent problems and interpret solutions.

KEYWORDS
Interpret
Units
Total

Before you answer a question you need to work out:
- ► what the question is about
- ► what it is asking you to find out
- ► what information it gives to help you find the answer.

Start by identifying the units needed in the answer.

> Exam questions include a space for your answer. The **units** may be given here as a clue.

example

The sign shows the cost of entrance into a local art gallery.
a 530 people paid the entrance fee on Saturday.
   How much did they pay altogether?
b £490 was paid in entrance fees last Wednesday.
   How many people visited the gallery that day?

> *art gallery*
> *£1.40 admission*

a You want to find **how much they paid**.
   Your answer will be **in £**.

   1 person pays £1.40
   530 people will pay 530 × £1.40

   530 × £1.40 = 53 × 10 × 1.4
             = 53 × 14
             = 53 × 10 + 53 × 4
             = 530 + 212
             = 742

   They paid £742 altogether.

> Write down the facts you know.

> Use an appropriate method.

> You need to interpret your answer.

b You want to find the **number of people**.
   Your answer will be **a number**.

   100 people pay £140
   300 people pay £420
   400 people pay £560   The answer is between 300 and 400 people.
                    300 × £1.40 = £420 which leaves £70

   40 people pay £56 and 50 people pay £70
                    50 × £1.40 = £70

   The answer is 350 people.

Exercise P1.1

1 a Jenny and her boyfriend each had a set meal at the cafe.
   Jenny paid with two ten-pound notes.
   How much change did she get?
   b A party of 12 people each had the set meal at the cafe.
   What was the total amount to be paid?

CAFÉ
Set meal
£6.20

2 Copy and complete this spider diagram
   so that the answer is always 36.

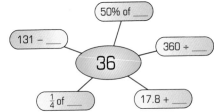

50% of ____

131 – ____

360 ÷ ____

36

$\frac{1}{4}$ of ____

17.8 + ____

3 Copy and complete this magic square.
   Each row, column and diagonal add up
   to the same total.

38		
9		35
19		

4 This is a house pattern made with
   matchsticks:
   a How many matchsticks will there be
   in the sixth picture in the pattern?

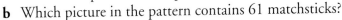

   b Which picture in the pattern contains 61 matchsticks?
   c Which of these rules is the rule for this
   matchstick pattern?
   where m = the number of matchsticks
   h = the number of houses

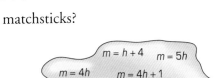

$m = h + 4$ $m = 5h$
$m = 4h$ $m = 4h + 1$
$m = 5h - 1$ $m = h + 5$

5 This diagram shows a rectangle 16 cm long by
   12 cm wide.
   It has been split up into four smaller rectangles.
   a Work out the areas of sections A, B and C.
   b What is the area of the whole rectangle?
   c What is 16 × 12?

11 cm   5 cm

?

A   B

5 cm   C   25 cm²

6 a A car travels 220 miles at an average speed of 40 mph.
   How many hours does the journey take?
   b An aeroplane travels 1520 miles in four hours.
   Find its average speed.
   c A cyclist travels at an average speed of 14 mph for $3\frac{1}{2}$ hours.
   How far does she go?

Reading tables and diagrams

This spread will show you how to:
▶▶ Identify the necessary information to solve a problem.
▶▶ Represent problems and interpret solutions.

KEYWORDS
Diagram   Pie chart
Interpret
Two-way table

You often need to find information from tables and diagrams, then interpret the solution.

You may also be asked to explain or justify your answer.

Students often lose marks by forgetting to explain answers.

example

Twelve students each measured two angles.
Here are their results:

Angle x

Angle measured	Number of students
25°	1
26°	2
27°	8
28°	1

Angle y

Angle measured	Number of students
26°	4
153°	2
154°	4
155°	2

Use the results to decide what each angle is likely to be.
Give reasons for your answers.

. . . .

a   You are asked for an **angle**.
Your answer will be **25°**, **26°**, **27°** or **28°**.
You must give a **reason** for your answer.

Highlight key words to help you identify the information you need.

8 students measured the angle as 27°.

The angle is likely to be 27° because most students measured it as 27°.

b   You are asked for an **angle**.
Your answer will be **26°**, **153°**, **154°** or **155°**.
You must give a **reason** for your answer.

4 students measured the angle as 26°.

Less than 90°

8 students measured the angle as 153°, 154° or 155°.

4 students measured the angle as 154°.

More than 90°

The angle is likely to be 154° because most of the students have measured an angle bigger than 90° and of those, most have measured 154°.

Exercise P1.2

1 This table shows the distances in miles
from Crosschester to other towns on the same railway.

Crosschester   Valleytown   Bowmer   Stapletown
                Boscombe   Downcastle

	Miles from Crosschester
Valleytown	30 miles
Boscombe	47 miles
Bowmer	63 miles
Downcastle	72 miles
Stapletown	91 miles

What is the distance between:
a Valleytown and Boscombe
b Bowmer and Downcastle
c Boscombe and Stapleton?

2 Kelly has two spinners.
She spins them both and adds the scores.
a Copy and complete this two-way table of
possible scores.

What is the probability that Kelly's score is:
b an even number
c an odd number
d less than five
e a prime number?

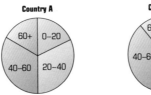
Spinner 1   Spinner 2

		Spinner 1		
		1	2	3
Spinner 2	1	2	3	4
	2	3	4	
	3			

3 Look at these pie charts of the age of the
population of two countries.
Joey says there are more people under the age
of 20 in country B than in country A.
Do you agree?
Explain your answer.

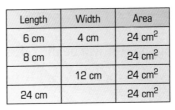

4 a Copy and complete this table for rectangles that
have an area of 24 cm².
b Barry says:
'Long thin rectangles have greater perimeters than
more "square-like" rectangles.'
Do you agree?
Give examples to illustrate your decision.

Length	Width	Area
6 cm	4 cm	24 cm²
8 cm		24 cm²
	12 cm	24 cm²
24 cm		24 cm²

5 This graph shows how to convert from miles to km:
▶   5 miles = 8 km
Use it to find out:
a 3 miles in km   b 7 miles in km
c 3 km in miles   d 10 km in miles.

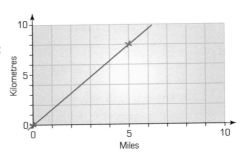

Using a strategy

This spread will show you how to:

▶▶ Solve complex problems by breaking them down into smaller steps or tasks, choosing and using efficient techniques.

KEYWORDS

Strategy   Total
Fraction   Ratio
Percentage   Probability

In exams you always get some questions that have more than one step to get to the answer.

You need to break these problems into steps.

These questions usually have 3 marks.

---

example

Find the missing number:
$\frac{3}{4}$ of $80 = \frac{1}{2}$ of ___

....

Your answer will be **a number.**

First you have to work out $\frac{3}{4}$ of 80.

You know that $\frac{1}{4}$ of 80 is 20.
So $\frac{3}{4}$ of 80 is 60.

$\frac{1}{2}$ of ___ is 60.
$\frac{1}{2}$ of 120 is 60.

The missing number is 120.

Choose an appropriate method – a mental method is easiest here.

Another strategy is to try out a few examples.

---

example

Put brackets into this calculation to make the answer 40:
$4 \times 4 + 5 + 1$

....

Your answer will be the **calculation with brackets in**.

Try: $4 \times (4 + 5) + 1 = 4 \times 9 + 1$
                            $= 36 + 1$
                            $= 37$

You know that × comes before + so you don't need to try $(4 \times 4) + 5 + 1$

$4 \times 10 = 40$ so try to make 10.

Try: $4 \times (4 + 5 + 1) = 4 \times 10$
                              $= 40$

The answer is $4 \times (4 + 5 + 1)$

Exercise P1.3

1 Copy and complete each 0–200 number line by filling in the missing numbers.

    a Four equal steps:

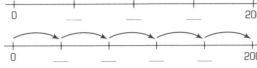

    b Five equal steps:

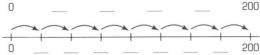

    c Eight equal steps:

2 Copy the calculation and fill in the gaps to make the answer 44.
Use any of the signs: $+ - \times \div$

26 ☐ 2 ☐ 31 = 44

3 John is 1.3 m tall.
Ravindha is 38 cm shorter than John.
How tall is Ravindha?

4 Copy and complete these statements:
    a The number 5 is halfway between 1.7 and __
    b The number 5 is halfway between ⁻7 and __
    c The number 5 is halfway between ⁻1.35 and __

5 Sophie buys some CDs on the Internet.
The CDs all cost exactly the same.
In total she spent £70 including postage and packaging of £2.
How much did each CD cost if the postage and packaging was 25p per CD?

6 This table shows some information about students in Year 9 at a school.

	Girls	Boys
Wears glasses	20	14
Doesn't wear glasses	30	56

    a What fraction of boys don't wear glasses?
    b What is the ratio of boys to girls?
       Give your answer in its simplest form.
    c What percentage of girls wear glasses?
    d A student from Year 9 is chosen at random to read in the school assembly.
       What is the probability that the student is a girl who wears glasses?

7 Work out this problem:
$\frac{3}{4}$ of 124 = __ % of 60.

Proportional reasoning

example

This spread will show you how to:
- ▶▶ Solve more complex problems by breaking them into smaller steps or tasks, choosing efficient techniques.
- ▶▶ Use the unitary method to solve simple problems.

KEYWORDS

Proportion
Unitary method
Common denominator

Many questions are based on the idea of a proportion.

You can express a proportion as a fraction, decimal or percentage.

The diagram shows a fair spinner.
  a   What is the probability of it landing on blue?
       Give your answer as a percentage.
  b   The probability of it landing on yellow is $\frac{1}{3}$.
       Find the fraction of the spinner that is red.

- -

a   You are asked to find **a probability**.
    Your answer will be a percentage between 0% and 100%.

One quarter of the spinner is coloured blue. $\frac{1}{4} = 25\%$

The probability of it landing on blue is 25%.

b   You are asked to find the fraction that is red.
    Your answer will be **a fraction** between 0 and 1.

$\frac{1}{4}$ is blue and $\frac{1}{3}$ is yellow.
The rest of the spinner is red.

The fraction that is not red is $\frac{1}{4} + \frac{1}{3}$
The lowest common denominator is 12: $\frac{1}{4} = \frac{3}{12}$ $\frac{1}{3} = \frac{4}{12}$

$\frac{1}{4} + \frac{1}{3} = \frac{3}{12} + \frac{4}{12} = \frac{7}{12}$

The rest is red. So $\frac{5}{12}$ is red.

$1 - \frac{7}{12} = \frac{12}{12} - \frac{7}{12} = \frac{5}{12}$

You can use proportional reasoning to help solve problems.

example

10 bars of chocolate cost £4.30. How much do 13 bars cost?

- -

10 bars cost £4.30 so 1 bar costs 43p.
3 bars cost 3 × 43p = 129p
so 13 bars cost £4.30 + £1.29 = £5.59

This is the **unitary method**.
First find the cost of **one** bar.

Exercise P1.4

1 Tony and Joanne share a packet containing 24 sweets.
   a Tony eats 12 of the sweets.
   What fraction of the sweets does he eat?
   b Joanne eats a quarter of the packet of sweets.
   How many sweets does she eat?
   c How many sweets are left?
   d What percentage of the packet of sweets is left?

2 Philippa is making beef stew for six people.
   She is following this recipe:
   How much of each ingredient does Philippa need to use?

> Beef Stew – serves 4
> 600 g beef
> 400 g potatoes
> 300 g carrots
> 2 onions
> 200 ml beef stock

3 The ratio of Tom's weight to his father's weight is 1 : 4.
   These scales show Tom's weight.

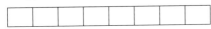

   How much does his father weigh?

4 Copy this diagram twice:

   a Shade in $\frac{1}{4}$ of the bar.
   b Shade in $37\frac{1}{2}\%$ of the bar.

5 Ayesha is an expert bubble blower.
   She uses these two mixes to blow her bubbles.

Small bubbles
Mix 1 part washing-up liquid with 9 parts of water

Big bubbles
Mix 1 part washing-up liquid with 4 parts of water

   a To blow big bubbles, how much water should Ayesha mix
   with 150 ml of washing-up liquid?
   b For small bubbles, how much washing-up liquid should
   Ayesha mix with 360 ml of water?
   c Ayesha says that one-ninth of the small bubble mixture is
   washing-up liquid. Is she correct?
   Explain your answer.

6 A bottle of salad cream has this nutritional information:
   How many grams of fat does 45 g of salad cream provide?
   Show your working.

Each 100 g provides	
Energy	317 kcal
Protein	1.5 g
Carbohydrate	17.0 g
Fat	27.0 g

Geometrical reasoning

This spread will show you how to:
▶▶ Represent problems and interpret solutions in geometric form.

KEYWORDS
Angle   Strategy
Length   Area

There are always some geometry questions in exams.
The answer may be:

an angle   a length   an area   the name of a shape   a drawing.

Some useful strategies are:

▶ Write down the facts you know.
▶ Give letters to unknown values you need to find.
▶ Make a sketch if there is no drawing.
▶ Show all your working.
▶ Use trial and error.

Make sure you know which
facts are given in your exam.

example

Find the missing angle in this triangle.

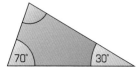

Your answer will be **an angle**. Give the angle a letter – call it a.

You know that angles in a triangle add to 180°.
$$a + 30° + 70° = 180°$$
$$a + 100° = 180°$$
$$a = 80°$$

You need to know the labelling conventions for shapes.

example

In this diagram:
a   Which side is opposite BC?
b   Which side is parallel to DC?
c   What type of angle is A?
d   If you fold AB onto DC, what shape will you have?

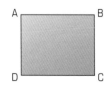

a   You need a side. Your answer will be two letters.
    AD is opposite BC.
b   You need a side. Your answer will be two letters.
    AB is parallel to DC.
c   You want the name of an angle. Your answer will be a word.
    A is a right angle.
d   You want the name of a shape. Your answer will be a word.
    It will be a rectangle.

Exercise P1.5

1 Look at these angles.
Which angle is:
a a right angle
b an acute angle?
c What is the name given to angle D?

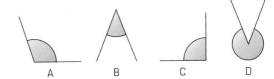

2 For each of these descriptions, name the shape:
a Four straight sides and four right angles. All four sides are the same.
b Four straight sides and four right angles. Two lines of reflection symmetry.
c Four straight sides. No lines of reflection symmetry. Two pairs of equal sides.

3 Name each of these triangles: a   b   c

4 Look at these five shapes:

A   B   C   D   E

Copy and complete this table with the number of
lines of symmetry and order of rotational symmetry
of each shape.
One has been done for you.

Lines of symmetry

		0	1	2	3	4
	0					
Order of	1					
rotational	2					
symmetry	3					
	4					D

5 Draw a net of this cuboid.

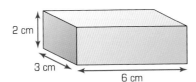

2 cm
3 cm
6 cm

6 Construct a triangle with three sides of lengths 9 cm, 8 cm and 6 cm.
Remember to leave in your construction marks.

7 Calculate the areas of these shapes.

a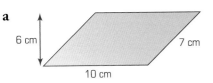
6 cm
7 cm
10 cm

b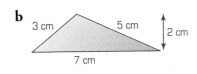
3 cm   5 cm
2 cm
7 cm

Checking results

This spread will show you how to:

▶▶ Give solutions to an appropriate degree of accuracy.

▶▶ Check results using appropriate methods.

KEYWORDS

Estimate

Investigate

Rounded

To gain better marks in exams you must always show all your working.

You can minimise errors by checking your answers.

Here are some useful strategies:

▶ Always estimate before calculating.

---

example

Find 283 × 38.

This is a calculation – your answer will be **a number**.
$283 \times 38 \approx 300 \times 40 = 12\ 000$
The answer will be less than 12 000
(both numbers were rounded up).

	200	80	3
30	6000	2400	90
8	1600	640	24

$283 \times 38 =$

```
    6 000
    2 400
    1 600
      640
       90
       24
  -------
   10 754
```

A last-digit check can help:
10 754 ends in a 4.
$3 \times 8 = 24$

So 283 × 38 = 10 754

▶ You can check an answer by working backwards.

---

example

Find x when $7x - 5 = 37$.

The answer will be **a number**.

Imagine the function machine:

Work backwards.
So $x = 6$

$x \longrightarrow \boxed{\times 7} \Longrightarrow \boxed{-5} \longrightarrow 37$

$6 \longleftarrow \boxed{\div 7} \Longleftarrow \boxed{+5} \longleftarrow 37$

▶ You can check a result by substituting.

In the example above $7 \times 6 - 5 = 42 - 5 = 37$.

Exercise P1.6

1 Copy these questions and fill in what the missing numbers could be.

   a __ + __ + __ = 45   **b** __ × __ = 45

   c __ ÷ __ = 45   **d** __ + __ × __ = 45

2 Salika works out 34 × 127.
This grid shows her method:
Her answer of 1618 is wrong.

×	100	20	7
30	300	600	210
4	400	80	28

   a Show where Salika went wrong in her calculation.

   b Find an estimate of the result. How is this different from Salika's answer?

3 **a** Andy says that when you multiply odd numbers together the
     answer is always odd. For example, 3 × 9 = 27.
     Investigate by multiplying other pairs of odd numbers together.

   b Copy and complete this table for other multiplications.

   c Use your table to say which of these calculations cannot be
     correct. Give a reason for your answer.

odd × odd	=
odd × even	=
even × odd	=
even × even	=

     i 33 × 28 = 924   **ii** 37 × 46 = 1701

     iii 17 × 29 = 494   **iv** 32 × 26 = 835

4 Dervla measures the height of her bedroom door.
Which of these values is the most appropriate for her measurement?
0.63 m   2.14723 m   2.1 m   2920 cm
Explain why you chose your answer.

5 Malcolm sets this puzzle for his friends:
Work out his original number by working backwards and
doing the opposite calculation. Show your working.

6 **a** These four cards have a mean of seven.
     Find the value of the missing card.

   b These three cards have a range of four.
     Find the possible mean values of the three cards.

7 This formula shows the cost of buying apple trees from
Conny Fur Trees Ltd.
$c = 22t + 15$ where c is the cost in pounds
                             t is the number of trees.

   a Adam buys 12 trees. How much do they cost him?

   b Kwame's bill comes to £785.
     How many trees does he buy?

You should know how to ...

1 Identify the necessary information to solve a problem.

Check out

1 a Copy and complete this spider diagram:

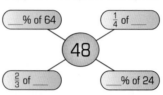

b 27 people bought a total of 36 CDs between them. Each CD cost £14. How much did they spend in total?

c Copy and complete this area and perimeter table for rectangles.

Rectangle length	Rectangle width	Area	Perimeter
4 cm	3 cm		
	3 cm	24 cm²	
25 cm			60 cm

2 Represent problems and interpret solutions in algebraic, graphical or geometric form.

2 a Calculate the missing angles in these shapes.

i 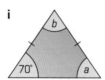   **ii**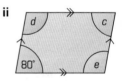

b Which of these rules is the rule for the sequences below?

i 3, 6, 9, 12, 15, ...

ii 2, 6, 10, 14, 18, ...

$2n + 2$ $4n - 2$
$4n + 1$ $2n$
$3n - 1$ $3n$

3 Use the unitary method to solve simple problems.

3 A 500 g jar of coffee costs £3.55.
A 300 g jar of coffee costs £2.19.

a How much does 100 g of coffee cost from:

i the 500 g jar

ii the 300 g jar?

b Which jar is better value?

This unit will show you how to:

▶▶ Distinguish the roles played by letters.

▶▶ Simplify or transform linear expressions by collecting like terms.

▶▶ Multiply a single term over a bracket.

▶▶ Construct and solve linear equations.

▶▶ Use formulae from mathematics and other subjects.

▶▶ Substitute integers into simple formulae and positive integers into expressions involving small powers.

▶▶ Derive simple formulae.

▶▶ Check results using appropriate methods.

▶▶ Plot the graphs of linear functions.

▶▶ Solve more demanding problems and investigate in a range of contexts.

▶▶ Compare and evaluate solutions.

▶▶ Represent problems and interpret solutions in algebraic and graphical form.

▶▶ Suggest extensions to problems, conjecture and generalise.

We go round Earth in 90 minutes. That's an average speed of 17 500 miles an hour!

You can calculate many measures using a formula.

Before you start

You should know how to ...

1 Use letters to stand for unknown numbers.

2 Use the grid method of multiplication.

▶ 29 × 35

×	30	5
20	600	100
9	270	45

60
100
270
45
―――
1015

29 × 35 = 1015

3 Solve simple equations.

Check in

1 Write these sentences using algebra:

a 3 less than x then double

b 9 more than y then halve.

2 Work out these using the grid method:

a 5 × 23   b 32 × 81

c 34 × 120   d 46 × 275

3 Solve these equations to find the value of x:

a $3x - 2 = 1$ b $3 - 6x = 15$

c $\dfrac{x}{2} + 1 = 7$ d $\dfrac{x - 3}{3} = 4$

A5.1 Equations, formulae and functions

This spread will show you how to:
- ▶▶ Distinguish the roles played by letters.
- ▶▶ Construct and solve linear equations.
- ▶▶ Substitute numbers into formulae and expressions.

KEYWORDS

Equation	Variable
Identity	Formula
Substitute	Function
Expression	

In algebra you use letters in different ways.

In an equation	$3x - 7 = 5$	... x has a particular value.
In a function	$y = 7 - 5x$	... you can find a unique value of y for any value of x.
In a formula	$V = IR$	... V, I and R are variables. When you know two of the values you can find the third.
In an identity	$4(x + 3) \equiv 4x + 12$	... this is true for all values of x.

To solve an equation you can use:

inverse function machines   or   inverse operations

$2x + 5 = 10$

Input is x Output is 10

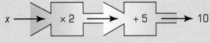

Go backwards using the inverse function machine.

$x = 2.5$

$2x + 5 = 10$

Subtraction is the inverse of addition:

$$2x = 10 - 5$$
$$2x = 5$$

Division is the inverse of multiplication:

$$x = 5 \div 2$$
$$x = 2.5$$

You can also use the balance method – keep the equation balanced.
You can substitute into formulae to find unknown values.

---

example

Use the balance method to solve $3x + 5 = 5x - 1$

$$3x + 5 = 5x - 1$$

Subtract $3x$ from each side:	$5 = 2x - 1$
Add 1 to both sides:	$6 = 2x$
Divide both sides by 2:	$3 = x$
So $x = 3$	

Check by substitution:
LHS: $3x + 5$
   $= 3 \times 3 + 5$
   $= 9 + 5 = 14$
RHS: $5x - 1$
   $= 5 \times 3 - 1$
   $= 15 - 1 = 14$
Both sides are equal, so $x = 3$ is correct.

Exercise A5.1

1 Solve these equations:

    a $2x = 10$ **b** $x + 3 = 16$ **c** $10 - x = 8$ **d** $2x = 15$

    e $3x + 1 = 10$ **f** $5x - 2 = 1$ **g** $4x - 10 = 6$ **h** $2x + 4 = 16$

2 Write an equation for each of these problems.

    a Jamie thinks of a number, multiplies it by four and gets twelve.

    b Sonia thinks of a number, multiplies it by three and adds nine and gets thirty-nine.

    c Balbir thinks of a number, divides it by two, then adds four and gets nine.

    d Calvin thinks of a number, adds four, then multiplies it by three and gets twenty-one.

3 Solve each of the equations in question 2.

4 Solve these equations:

    a $2x + 1 = x + 5$ **b** $4x + 3 = 3x + 6$ **c** $6x - 3 = 5x + 2$

    d $4x + 1 = 6x - 1$ **e** $2x + 3 = 4x - 7$ **f** $2x - 1 = 3x - 3$

5 Work out the value of x in each of these problems.

    a   **b**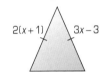

6 Substitute the values $a = 2$, $b = 3$ and $c = \frac{1}{2}$ to work out the value of each expression.
The first one is done for you.

    a $2a + b$ $2a + b = 2 \times 2 + 3$
                                  $= 4 + 3$
                                  $= 7$

    b $ab + 1$ **c** $2c - a$ **d** $3b + 2c$

    e $2(a + b) + c$ **f** $3c + 2(a + b)$ **g** $\frac{2c + 3b}{a}$

    h $a^2 + b^2$ **i** $(a + b)^2$ **j** c^2

7 Use the area formulae given to find the area of each shape.
All lengths are in centimetres.

> Use $\pi = 3.14$ or the $\boxed{\pi}$ on a scientific calculator.

    a $\frac{1}{2}(a + b)h$ **b** $\frac{1}{2}bh$ **c** πr^2

    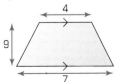   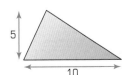

This spread will show you how to:

▶▶ Simplify or transform linear expressions by collecting like terms.

▶▶ Multiply a single term over a bracket.

Teresa has a bag of sweets.
She says there are n sweets in her bag.

The total number of sweets is **n**.

She doesn't know how many sweets are in her bag exactly.

Teresa has another identical bag of sweets.
She has two bags with n sweets in each.

The total number of sweets is **$n + n$** or **$2n$**.

$n + n$ simplifies to $2n$.

Teresa adds three sweets to each bag.
She now has two bags with $n + 3$ in each.

The total number of sweets is
$2(n + 3)$ or **$2n + 6$**.

2 bags of $n + 3$ = $2(n + 3)$
or
2 bags of n plus 6 = $2n + 6$

You can use a multiplication grid to expand brackets.

example

Multiply out these expressions:

a $4(3a + 5)$ **b** $6a(a - 3)$ **c** $^-5(4 + 2a)$

....

a   Use the grid:

×	3a	+5
4	12a	+20

$4(3a + 5) = 12a + 20$

b   Use the grid:

×	a	−3
6a	6a²	−18a

$6a(a - 3) = 6a^2 - 18a$

c   Use the grid:

×	4	+2a
⁻5	⁻20	−10a

$^-5(4 + 2a) = {}^-20 - 10a$

▶ To expand brackets, you multiply each term inside the brackets by the term outside.

$a(b + c) = ab + ac$

$a(b - c) = ab - ac$

Multiplication is **distributive**,
$a(b + c) = ab + ac$

Exercise A5.2

1 Work out these multiplications.
  a $2 \times a$ **b** $^-3 \times a$ **c** $4 \times ^-5$ **d** $2a \times ^-2$ **e** $^-5 \times 6$
  f $^-2a \times 3$ **g** $10 \times ^-4$ **h** $2b \times 3c$ **i** $2a \times 2a$ **j** $^-3a \times 2b$

2 Copy and complete the grids to expand these brackets.
  a $2(x+3)$ **b** $5(y-2)$ **c** $3(w-3)$

×	x	+3
2		

×	y	-2
5		

×	w	-3
3		

  d $10(p+3)$ **e** $^-2(n+3)$ **f** $^-4(a+3)$

×	p	+?
10		

×	?	+3
¯2		

×	a	+?
¯?		

3 Expand these brackets, using a grid if necessary.
  a $3(x+5)$ **b** $2(b-2)$ **c** $4(a-1)$ **d** $^-2(a+2)$ **e** $3(x+3)$
  f $^-4(y+3)$ **g** $^-3(p+1)$ **h** $10(w+2)$ **i** $12(q-2)$ **j** $^-4(f+3)$

4 Simplify these expressions.
  a $3a+3a+1$ **b** $4(p+3)+4p$ **c** $3r-3x+3(r-3)$
  d $5(x-3)+15+2x$ **e** $3d+4(e-2)-4e$ **f** $5(a+2b)-3(2a+3b)$

5 The area of the shaded part of this shape is: $8 \times 10 - 3 \times a$
                                                       $= 80 - 3a$

  a Show that these two expressions for the area are
     equivalent to $80 - 3a$.

     ▶ $8(10-a)+5a$
     ▶ $50+3(10-a)$

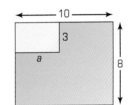

  b Find all the different expressions for the area of the shaded
     region in these shapes and show that they are all equivalent.

  i 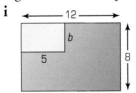   **ii**   **iii**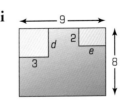

6 Sanjeet has expanded these expressions.
   Use the grids to work out the original expression.

  a

×	?	?
?	2a	+14

  b

×	?	?
?	3c	+9

  c

×	?	?
?	6e	-12

  d

×	?	?
?	8p	+12

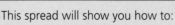

This spread will show you how to:
▶▶ Construct and solve linear equations.
▶▶ Multiply a single term over a bracket.
▶▶ Check results using appropriate methods.

You can solve equations containing brackets.
You expand the brackets first.

example

Solve $2(x + 4) = 14$.

First multiply out the brackets: $\quad 2x + 8 = 14$

×	x	+4
2	2x	+8

Use either:
Inverse function machines ...

For $2x + 8 = 14$:

$x \longrightarrow \boxed{\times 2} \Longrightarrow \boxed{+ 8} \longrightarrow 14$

$3 \longleftarrow \boxed{\div 2} \longleftarrow \boxed{- 8} \longleftarrow 14$

So $x = 3$

or inverse operations.

$$2x + 8 = 14$$

Subtract 8 from both sides: $\quad 2x + 8 - 8 = 14 - 8$

$$2x = 6$$

Divide both sides by 2: $\qquad 2x \div 2 = 6 \div 2$

$$x = 3$$

When there is more than one bracket, you expand each of them in turn.

example

Solve these equations.

a $\quad 4(c - 1) + 5(c + 1) = 100$ **b** $\quad 4(y + 3) = 6(y - 1)$

a Expand brackets
$$4c - 4 + 5c + 5 = 100$$

Simplify: $\qquad\qquad 9c + 1 = 100$

Solve the equation:
-1 from both sides: $\quad 9c + 1 - 1 = 100 - 1$
$$9c = 99$$

$\div 9$ to both sides: $\qquad 9c \div 9 = 99 \div 9$
$$c = 11$$

b Expand the brackets:
$$4y + 12 = 6y - 6$$

$(-4y) \quad 4y - 4y + 12 = 6y - 4y - 6$
$$12 = 2y - 6$$

$(+6) \qquad 12 + 6 = 2y - 6 + 6$
$$18 = 2y$$

$(\div 2) \qquad 18 \div 2 = 2y \div 2$
$$9 = y$$
$$y = 9$$

Exercise A5.3

1 The number in each cell is the result of adding the numbers
in the two cells beneath it.
By writing equations, find the unknown letter in each wall.

a

10

$x+2$	$2+x$

x	2	x

b

22

14	$4+p$

10	4	p

c

18

?	?

5	a	4

2 Solve these equations.

a $4(a+3) = 20$ **b** $3(b-1) = 12$ **c** $5(c+5) = 50$ **d** $2(d-2) = 16$

e $^-2(e+4) = {}^-26$ **f** $3(f-9) = 3$ **g** $4(g+1) = 4$ **h** $^-3(h+4) = {}^-15$

3 There are 100 stones in three piles. The number of stones in Pile 1 is s.
Pile 2 has 12 more stones than Pile 1.
Pile 3 has twice as many stones as Pile 2.

Pile 1	Pile 2	Pile 3	Total
s			100

a Write an expression for the number of stones in Pile 2.
b Write an expression for the number of stones in Pile 3.
c Write an equation for the total number of stones.
d Solve your equation to find out exactly how many stones are in each pile.

4 In these flow diagrams, you can take either route from s to finish at the same number f.
Write and solve an equation to find s in each case. The first one has been started.

a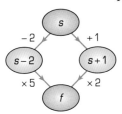

$5(s-2) = 2(s+1)$

b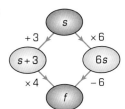

c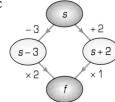

d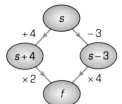

e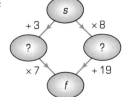

f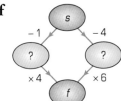

Equations involving fractions

This spread will show you how to:

▶▶ Construct and solve linear equations.

A fraction means you divide by the denominator.

▶ $\frac{3}{4}$ means $3 \div 4$

▶ $\frac{5}{6}$ means $5 \div 6$

▶ $\frac{a}{4}$ means $a \div 4$

▶ $\frac{5}{b}$ means $5 \div b$

You can solve equations involving fractions using inverse operations.

▶ The inverse of multiplication is division.

▶ The inverse of division is multiplication.

---

example

Solve $\frac{2a}{5} = 3$ to find the value of a.

Using inverse function machines:

$$a \rightarrow \boxed{\times 2} \rightarrow \boxed{\div 5} \rightarrow 3$$

$$7.5 \leftarrow \boxed{\div 2} \leftarrow \boxed{\times 5} \leftarrow 3$$

Using inverse operations:

Multiply both sides by 5: $\quad \frac{2a}{5} \times 5 = 3 \times 5$

so $\qquad\qquad\qquad\qquad\quad 2a = 15$

Divide both sides by 2: $\quad 2a \div 2 = 15 \div 2$

$$a = 7.5$$

You can use brackets for more complicated fractions: $\frac{a+3}{2} = \frac{(a+3)}{2} = (a+3) \div 2$

---

example

Solve $\frac{2b+4}{5} = 2$ to find the value of b.

Using inverse function machines:

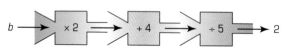

$$b \rightarrow \boxed{\times 2} \rightarrow \boxed{+ 4} \rightarrow \boxed{\div 5} \rightarrow 2$$

$$3 \leftarrow \boxed{\div 2} \leftarrow \boxed{- 4} \leftarrow \boxed{\times 5} \leftarrow 2$$

Using inverse operations:

Multiply both sides by 5:

$$\frac{(2b+4)}{5} \times 5 = 2 \times 5$$
$$2b + 4 = 10$$

Subtract 4 from both sides:

$$2b + 4 - 4 = 10 - 4$$
$$2b = 6$$

Divide both sides by 2: $\quad 2b \div 2 = 6 \div 2$

$$b = 3$$

So $b = 3$

Exercise A5.4

1 Solve these equations.

a $\frac{x}{3} = 4$ **b** $\frac{10}{x} = 5$ **c** $\frac{x}{3} = 9$ **d** $\frac{x}{2} = 2$

e $\frac{15}{x} = 5$ **f** $\frac{9}{x} = 4.5$ **g** $\frac{3}{x} = 0$ **h** $\frac{x}{3} = 1$

2 Solve these equations.

a $\frac{x+3}{2} = 4$ **b** $\frac{x+2}{4} = 3$ **c** $\frac{x-4}{2} = 3$ **d** $\frac{2x+1}{3} = 3$

3 Solve each equation and use this code to change your answers to letters.

A	B	C	D	E	F	G	H	I	J	K	L	M	N	O	P	Q	R	S	T	U	V	W	X	Y	Z
1	2	3	4	5	6	7	8	9	10	11	12	13	14	15	16	17	18	19	20	21	22	23	24	25	26

a $\frac{y+2}{2} = 5$ **b** $\frac{y}{10} = 0.5$ **c** $\frac{y+4}{2} = 8$ **d** $\frac{14-y}{2} = 1$ **e** $\frac{30}{y} = 2$

What word do the answers make?

4 Amanda has p sweets.

She shares them into two piles, with the same number on each pile.

a Write an expression for the number of sweets in one pile.

b Amanda counts the sweets and finds she has 18 in each pile.
Use this and your answer to part **a** to write an equation for
the number of sweets in each pile.

c Solve your equation to find the total number of sweets, p.

5 Kurt has r sweets, divided into four equal piles.
There are 8 sweets in each pile
Form and solve an equation to find the value of r.

6 In these flow charts, you can take either route from s and you will get the same f value.
Find the value of s in each diagram.
The first one has been started for you.

a

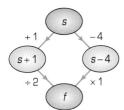

$$\frac{s+1}{2} = s-4$$

$$\frac{s+1}{2} \times 2 = (s-4) \times 2$$

$$s+1 = 2(s-4)$$

b

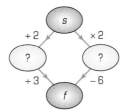

c

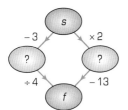

d

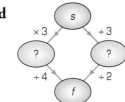

183

This spread will show you how to:
- ▶▶ Use formulae from mathematics and other subjects.
- ▶▶ Substitute integers into simple formulae and positive integers into expressions involving small powers.

Mr Hussain is travelling from Coventry to Cornwall.

The distance is 240 miles.
He will travel at approximately 60 miles per hour.

He wants to know how long the journey will take.

He knows that $\quad$ Speed $= \frac{\text{Distance}}{\text{Time}} \quad$ or $\quad S = \frac{D}{S}$

He can rearrange the formula using a triangle:

To find S, cover up S leaving D over T.

To find D, cover up D leaving S next to T.

To find T, cover up T leaving D over S.

Speed $= \frac{\text{Distance}}{\text{Time}}$

Distance $=$ Speed $\times$ Time

Time $= \frac{\text{Distance}}{\text{Speed}}$

To work out how long the journey will take, use the formula:

Time $= \frac{\text{Distance}}{\text{Speed}}$

Time $= \frac{240 \text{ miles}}{60 \text{ miles per hour}}$

Time $= 4$ hours

You can use formulae to find unknown values.

The formula for the perimeter of a rectangle of length l and width w is $P = 2(l + w)$.

a If $l = 3$ and $w = 4$, find the perimeter of the rectangle.

b If $P = 30$ and $w = 5$, find l.

....

a $\quad P = 2(l + w)$
$\quad\quad P = 2 \times (3 + 4)$
$\quad\quad P = 2 \times 7$
$\quad\quad P = 14$ cm

b $\quad P = 2(l + w)$ $\quad$ (substitute values into the formula)
$\quad\quad 30 = 2(l + 5)$ $\quad$ (divide both sides by 2)
$\quad\quad 15 = l + 5$ $\quad$ (subtract 5 from both sides)
$\quad\quad l = 10$ cm

Exercise A5.5

1 The formula for converting centimetres c into metres m is:

$m = c \div 100$

Use this formula to work out how many metres there are in:

a 300 cm   **b** 1000 cm   **c** 25 cm   **d** 50 000 cm

2 The formula for the area A of a rectangle of length l and width w is: $A = lw$

Use the formula to work out the area of a rectangle with:

a $l = 2$ cm, $w = 3$ cm   **b** $l = 5$ cm, $w = 4$ cm

c $l = 45$ mm, $w = 20$ mm.

d   Find the length, l, when $A = 50$ cm^2 and $w = 5$ cm.

3 The voltage V in an electrical circuit, with current I and resistance R, is given by the formula: $V = IR$

a   What is V when $I = 6$ and $R = 8$?

b   What is R when $V = 56$ and $I = 8$?

4 The formula for the volume V of a cuboid is: $V = lwh$ where $l =$ length, $w =$ width and $h =$ height.

a   Find the volume of a cuboid with $l = 5$ cm, $w = 2$ cm, $h = 3$ cm.

b   Which of these cuboids has the largest volume?

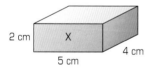 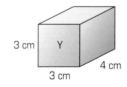 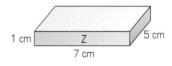

5 Copy and complete this table.

a   Find a formula for the sum of the angles in an n-sided polygon.

b   Use your formula to find the sum of the angles in:

    i   a 12-sided polygon

    ii   a 20-sided polygon

    iii a 25-sided polygon.

Name of polygon	Number of triangles	Sum of angles in polygon
Triangle 3 sides	1	$1 \times 180° = \mathbf{180°}$
Quadrilateral 4 sides	2	$2 \times 180° = \mathbf{360°}$
Pentagon 5 sides	3	
Hexagon 6 sides		

This spread will show you how to:
▶▶ Plot the graphs of linear functions.
▶▶ Derive simple formulae.

KEYWORDS
Intersection
Formula
Linear function

Samera wants to hire a car. There are two tariffs:

Cars R Us
Cost £15
plus £3 per mile

Yellow Cars
Cost £50
plus £2 per mile

She needs to work out which is cheaper for different journeys.

First she writes the information as formulae.

She uses C = cost in pounds   and m = number of miles.

     Cars R Us: $C = 15 + 3m$ Yellow Cars: $C = 50 + 2m$

            £15 plus £3 per mile   £50 plus £2 per mile

She works out the cost of different journeys.

Cars R Us: $C = 15 + 3m$ Yellow Cars: $C = 50 + 2m$

m	0	10	20	30	40	50	60	70
C	15	45	75	105	135	165	195	225

m	0	10	20	30	40	50	60	70
C	50	70	90	110	130	150	170	190

She plots a graph to show these results.

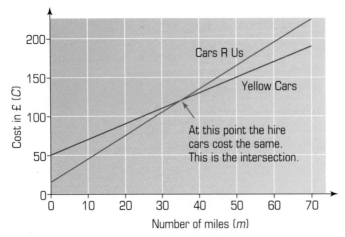

Samera is going to drive to Hull from Leeds which is about 60 miles.
She decides to use Yellow Cars because it will be cheaper.

Exercise A5.6

1 Write formulae for each of these advertisements. The first two have been started.

a
> **Car hire**
> Cost £40
> plus £2 per mile

$C = $ ___ $+ 2m$
(C = cost, m = miles)

b
> **Rent a house**
> Deposit £400
> plus £200 per month

$C = $ ___ $+$ ___ m
(C = cost, m = months)

c
> **Buy a new car**
> Deposit £1000
> plus £200 per month

d
> **Buy a new sofa**
> Deposit £100
> plus £15 per month

e
> **Hire a bike**
> Cost £10
> plus £1.50 per hour

f
> **Hire a car**
> Cost £30
> plus 10p a mile

> **Hint:** Change both to pounds or both to pence.

2 Jerry wants to find out which washing machine to hire.

> **Washer World**
> £20 deposit
> then £5 per month

> **Washers R Us**
> £15 deposit
> then £6 per month

a Copy and complete the formulae:

Washer World: $C = $ ___ $+$ ___ m **Washers R Us:** $C = $ ___ $+$ ___ m

b Copy and complete the tables of values:

Washer World:

m	0	1	2	3	4	5	6	7
C								

Washers R Us:

m	0	1	2	3	4	5	6	7
C								

c Draw a graph with both lines plotted on the same graph.
d When do both washing machines cost the same amount to hire?
e If you wanted to hire a washing machine for 3 months, would you use Washer World or Washers R Us? Why?
f If you wanted to hire a washing machine for 10 months, which would you use? Why?

> Use axes like these.
>
>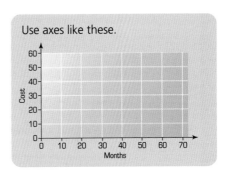

3 Write a report for a magazine comparing these two adverts for hiring a van.

Include in your report, formulae, tables of results and graphs as in question 2.

> **Book a van**
> £90 deposit
> plus £6 per mile

> **Van hire shop**
> £30 deposit
> plus £8 per mile

You should know how to ...

1 Simplify or transform linear expressions by collecting like terms.

2 Multiply a single term over a bracket.

3 Substitute integers into simple formulae.

4 Plot the graphs of linear functions.

5 Represent problems and interpret solutions in algebraic form.

Check out

1 In a magic square, the sum of the expressions in each row, column and diagonal is the same. Show that this is a magic square:

$x+y$	$x-y+z$	$x-z$
$x-y-z$	x	$x+y+z$
$x+z$	$x+y-z$	$x-y$

2 Solve these equations by first removing the brackets:

a $3(x-2)=5(x-4)$

b $4(a+2)=3(2a-4)$

3 Substitute $x=3$ to find the value of y in these equations:

a $y=2x+3$

b $2y=6x-2$

c $3-y=x-3$

4 Copy and complete the table and plot a graph from this data:

$y=3x+2$

x	0	1	2	3
$y=3x+2$	2			

5 Write an expression using algebra for the cost of a phone on this tariff per month:

Mobile phone tariff

▶ £5 per month then 3p per minute.

3 Statistical reports

This unit will show you how to:

▶▶ Discuss a problem that can be addressed by statistical methods.

▶▶ Decide which data to collect to answer a question, and the degree of accuracy needed.

▶▶ Identify possible sources.

▶▶ Plan how to collect the data.

▶▶ Construct frequency tables with given equal class intervals for sets of continuous data.

▶▶ Calculate statistics, including with a calculator.

▶▶ Recognise when to use the mean, median and mode and the modal class.

▶▶ Calculate a mean using an assumed mean.

▶▶ Construct stem-and-leaf diagrams.

▶▶ Construct simple line graphs for time series.

▶▶ Construct simple scatter graphs.

▶▶ Identify which diagrams are most useful in the context of the problem.

▶▶ Interpret diagrams and draw inferences that relate to the problem being discussed.

▶▶ Communicate orally and on paper the results of a statistical enquiry and the methods used, justifying the choice of what is presented.

▶▶ Represent problems and interpret solutions in algebraic, geometric or graphical form.

▶▶ Suggest extensions to problems, conjecture and generalise.

You have to think carefully before you start to research.

Before you start

You should know how to ...

1 Find the average and range of a set of data.

2 Draw and interpret bar charts and pie charts.

3 Add and subtract negative numbers.

Check in

1 24 people were asked how many items of post they received one morning. Their answers were:

7, 4, 3, 2, 6, 2, 3, 3, 6, 4, 5, 2,
5, 5, 4, 7, 2, 5, 3, 4, 1, 0, 4, 6.

Find the mean and range of this data.

2 Group the data in question 1 into four groups (0–2, 3–5, 6–8, 8 and above) and draw a bar chart to represent the data.

3 Work out:

a ⁻3 – ⁻6   b 6 – ⁻4

This spread will show you how to:
▶▶ Decide which data to collect to answer a question, and the degree of accuracy needed.
▶▶ Identify possible sources.
▶▶ Plan how to collect the data, including sample size.
▶▶ Construct frequency tables with given equal class intervals for sets of continuous data.

KEYWORDS
Accuracy
Sample size
Secondary data
Frequency table
Primary data
Data logging

Sharon wants to investigate the heights of people of different ages. Her hypothesis is that the older a person is, the taller they are.

She could collect primary data.

Sharon needs to decide how much data to collect, and the degree of accuracy needed – how accurate her measurements need to be.

Sharon only has time to collect 30 measurements in each year group. She is responsible for the accuracy of the data.

Sharon organises her primary data for Year 9 into a frequency table.

She looks for secondary data.

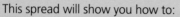

She can quickly download lots of data from the Census at School website. This gives a larger sample size but she has to assume the results are accurate.

Height, h cm	Tally	Frequency
$130 \leqslant h < 140$	I	1
$140 \leqslant h < 150$	II	2
$150 \leqslant h < 160$	ЖН ЖН III	13
$160 \leqslant h < 170$	ЖН III	8
$170 \leqslant h < 180$	III	3
$180 \leqslant h < 190$	II	2
$190 \leqslant h < 200$	I	1

The first row is for any height from 130 cm up to (but not including) 140 cm.

All the heights in this range go in the first category.

130   140

Because Sharon is grouping her data, she will need to be quite careful when recording a height that is close to a multiple of 10 cm.

Exercise D3.1

1 Here are some sets of data that a group of students used in their data projects. Explain whether each set is primary data or secondary data. Give a reason for your answer.

  a Reuben carried out a survey about school dinners in the canteen one lunchtime.

  b Karyn went to the library to find out how school students in the UK travel to school.

  c Byron used the Internet to find out how much different countries spent on education.

2 Sandra asked a group of her friends to record how many telephone calls they made one evening. Here are her results:

> 1, 1, 0, 4, 3, 0, 2, 4, 8, 6, 3, 2, 0,
> 0, 1, 7, 3, 2, 1, 0, 1, 1, 1, 0, 2

She organises her results as grouped discrete data like this:

Number of calls	Frequency
0–1	

Copy and complete the table.

3 As part of a geography project, Ben collected and measured a set of rocks from the bed of a stream. He measured the length of each rock in centimetres, to 1 dp. Here are the results:

> 9.7, 3.6, 10.0, 2.7, 5.8, 6.9, 16.3,
> 18.9, 7.4, 6.4, 4.9, 8.3, 11.1, 6.3,
> 5.2, 14.0, 13.2, 14.9, 12.8, 8.3

Ben organises his results into a table that starts like this:
Copy and complete the table to show Ben's data.

Length, x cm	Frequency
$0 \leqslant x < 5$	

4 As part of a science project, Cassie measured the lengths of 20 leaves from a tree. The lengths, in centimetres to 1 dp, are shown.

> 17.3, 5.8, 8.7, 17.5, 25.8, 13.4, 15.3,
> 23.7, 25.1, 15.9, 15.2, 10.1, 16.4,
> 18.0, 14.6, 12.6, 20.0, 19.5, 22.4, 18.4

Organise the data into a frequency table.
The first row of the table should include lengths from 5 cm up to (but not including) 10 cm.

5 A gym instructor uses data logging to record the number of km different people cover on the running machine.
Here are the distances to 2 dp:
Organise the data into a frequency table. The first row should be for distances from 0 up to but not including 3 km.

> 3.65, 4.22, 0.75, 5.10, 2.67, 8.51, 2.79,
> 7.62, 4.31, 3.26, 0.96, 10.31

Data logging is when data are collected automatically by instruments.

This spread will show you how to:

⏩ Calculate statistics, including with a calculator.

⏩ Recognise when it is appropriate to use the mean, median and mode and, for grouped data, the modal class.

KEYWORDS

Grouped data	Median
Modal class	Discrete
Mean	Continuous

You can summarise your data using statistics.
There are some useful methods when the data is in a table.

example

Zoë asked some people how many televisions they had in their homes. Here are the results:

Number of televisions	1	2	3	4	5
Number of people	6	9	4	3	1

Find the mean number of televisions per person.

Mean = total number of televisions ÷ total number of people

Find the total number of televisions like this:

▶ There were 6 people with 1 television, making 6 televisions.
▶ There were 9 people with 2 televisions, making $2 \times 9 = 18$ televisions.

The total number of televisions is: $(1 \times 6) + (2 \times 9) + (3 \times 4) + (4 \times 3) + (5 \times 1)$
$$= 6 + 18 + 12 + 12 + 5 = 53$$

The total number of people is: $6 + 9 + 4 + 3 + 1 = 23$
The mean number of televisions per person is $53 \div 23 = 2.3$ to 1 dp.

You use **grouped** data if you have:

▶ Discrete data with many different values, or
▶ Continuous data.

When you have grouped data, the easiest average to work out is the **modal class**.

example

Emily was doing a project about school transport. For 20 days, she recorded some data about her bus journey home:

Find the modal class of each set of data.

Passengers	Frequency
0–4	1
5–9	1
10–14	3
15–19	5
20–24	8
25–29	2

Time, T minutes	Frequency
$18 \leqslant T < 20$	1
$20 \leqslant T < 22$	3
$22 \leqslant T < 24$	9
$24 \leqslant T < 26$	4
$26 \leqslant T < 28$	2
$28 \leqslant T < 30$	1

▶ The modal class of the number of passengers is 20–24.
  (This is grouped discrete data.)
▶ The modal class of journey times is T minutes, where $22 \leqslant T < 24$.
  (This is continuous data.)

Exercise D3.2

1 Find the mean, median, mode and range of these sets of numbers.
   a 7, 3, 4, 2, 8, 7, 3, 2, 7, 9
   b 3.2, 2.9, 3.0, 3.3, 3.1, 3.0, 3.4, 3.0

2 A scientist recorded the number of eggs in 21 birds' nests in this table.

Number of eggs	0	1	2	3	4
Frequency	4	7	5	3	2

   a Write the modal number of eggs in a nest.
   b The scientist inspected 21 nests. Explain how you would find the median number of eggs in a nest, and write down the median.
   c Work out the total number of eggs in all 21 nests.
   d Use your answer to part **c** to work out the mean number of eggs in a nest.
   e Write the range of the number of eggs in the nests.

3 The scientist who collected the data in question 2 then found another 3 nests.
   Each of these nests contained 2 eggs.
   She decided to add this data to the data she had already collected.
   a Make a table to show the new, combined set of data.
   b Find the modal number of eggs in a nest, using the new set of data.
   c Find the median of the new set of data.
   d Use the new set of data to work out the mean number of eggs in a nest.

4 Ken played 30 games of snooker. The number of points he scored in each game are shown below.

23	17	48	91	2	89	38	25	28	39	92	44	8	16	52
33	41	28	36	61	52	48	42	36	44	30	47	39	30	36

   a Organise the data into groups (0–9 points, 10–19 and so on), and draw a frequency table.
   b Draw a bar chart to represent the data, and state the modal class.

5 The heights of 20 students in a class are shown in the table.
   a Identify the modal class, and explain in words the range of heights that belong in this class.
   b Five students were out at a basketball competition. Their heights were 166, 168, 169, 170 and 172 cm. Make a new frequency table for the complete set of data, and use this to find the modal class for all 25 students.

Height, h cm	Frequency
$150 \leqslant h < 155$	2
$155 \leqslant h < 160$	4
$160 \leqslant h < 165$	7
$165 \leqslant h < 170$	5
$170 \leqslant h < 175$	2

This spread will show you how to:

▶▶ Calculate a mean using an assumed mean.

Calculating the mean can be complicated with large sets of data.
You can use an assumed mean to make it easier.

> ▶ To find the mean using an assumed mean:
>   ▶ Choose a value to be the assumed mean.
>   ▶ Find the difference of the assumed mean from each data value.
>   ▶ Find the mean of the differences.
>   ▶ Add the assumed mean back on.
>
> You can use the formula:
>
> $$\text{Mean} = \text{Assumed mean} + \frac{\text{Total of differences}}{\text{Number of items}}$$

example

Nina recorded the number of minutes it took her to get to school for 10 days:

   23, 29, 22, 34, 28, 22, 27, 40, 39, 30

Find the mean of these times.

....

All of the times are 'more than 20'. Use 20 as an assumed mean.
Work out the differences from 20:
3, 9, 2, 14, 8, 2, 7, 20, 19 and 10.
The total of the differences is 92.
The mean of the differences is $92 \div 10 = 9.2$.
The mean time is $20 + 9.2 = 29.2$.

If the assumed mean is in the middle of the data, some differences will be negative.

example

Find the mean of this data, using an assumed mean of 60.

| 68 | 49 | 70 | 63 | 65 | 52 | 66 | 58 | 43 | 61 | 68 | 65 |

....

| Difference from 60 | +8 | ‑11 | +10 | +3 | +5 | ‑8 | +6 | ‑2 | ‑17 | +1 | +8 | +5 |

Total of positive differences: $8 + 10 + 3 + 5 + 6 + 1 + 8 + 5 = 46$ ⎫ Total difference
Total of negative differences: $^-11 + {}^-8 + {}^-2 + {}^-17 = {}^-38$ ⎬ $= 46 + {}^-38 = 8$
Mean $= 60 + \frac{8}{12} = 60.67$ (2 dp) ⎭

Exercise D3.3

1 The lengths of eight worms (in cm) were:

12, 14, 11, 16, 15, 13, 12, 14

   a Find the total length of all eight worms.
   b Find the mean length of the worms.

2 The table shows the lengths of the worms from question 1.

Length (cm)	12	14	11	16	15	13	12	14
Difference from 10 cm	2							

   a Copy and complete the table to show the difference from 10 cm for each length.
   b Find the total of the differences from your table.
   c Find the mean difference from 10 cm.
   d Use your answer to part c to find the mean length of the worms. Check your answer is the same as the mean you worked out in question 1.

3 Karen did an experiment to see how well people could estimate lengths.
She asked 10 people to estimate and cut 50 cm lengths of ribbon.
She measured the ribbons accurately, as shown in the table.

Length, cm	52	47	56	61	39	44	45	67	63	53
Difference from 50 cm	$+2$	-3								

   a Copy and complete the table to show the differences from 50 cm.
   b Find the total of the positive differences, and the total of the negative differences.
   c Use your answers to part b to find the total of all of the differences from 50 cm.
   d Use the formula on page 194 to find the mean length of the 10 ribbons.

4 In a television game show, five contestants had to guess the value of an antique vase.
Their guesses were: £650, £250, £500, £550 and £400.
Find the mean of the guesses, using an assumed mean of £500.

5 A matchbox is marked 'average contents 100'. Chloe decides to test this claim.
She counts the matches in 15 boxes – her results are shown in the table.

102	96	104	108	104	97	98	96	97	104	103	102	99	98	101

   a Find the mean number of matches in the boxes, using 100 as an assumed mean.
   b Explain whether or not you think the claim on the box is justified.

This spread will show you how to:
▶▶ Construct simple line graphs for time series.
▶▶ Construct simple scatter graphs.
▶▶ Identify which are most useful in the context of the problem.

KEYWORDS
Line graph   Scatter graph
Frequency diagram
Pie chart

You use a graph or chart to show patterns in data.

There are four main charts you can choose from:

You use the one that best shows the features of the data.

Frequency diagram

A frequency diagram compares the size of categories with each other.

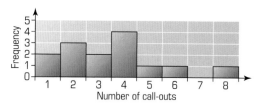

The graph shows the number of times per week the fire service is called out in a small town over a 14-week period.

Pie charts

A pie chart compares the size of a category with the whole.

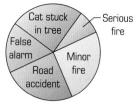

The pie chart shows the reasons for the fire service call-outs.

Scatter graph

A scatter graph shows if there is any relationship between two variables.

In a survey, students recorded the number of hours they spent watching television, and doing homework. The graph shows that the more television students watched, the less time they tended to spend on homework.

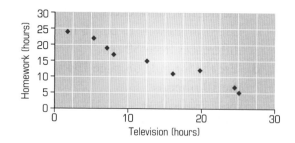

Line graph

A line graph shows a trend over time – a time series.
Plot time on the horizontal axis. Join the data points with straight lines.

A caretaker recorded the temperature in the school hall every hour from 8 am till 4 pm. We can use the graph to estimate the temperature between readings.

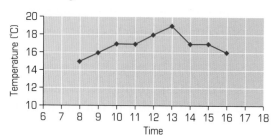

Exercise D3.4

1 The table shows the heights and weights for ten Year 9 students.

Height (cm)	160	152	176	164	148	149	177	172	158	141
Weight (kg)	45	37	72	43	37	41	70	55	45	35

a Copy the axes for the scatter graph.
b Plot a point on the graph for each pair of values.
c Describe the relationship between the height and weight data shown in the scatter graph.

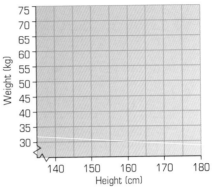

2 Robin boiled a kettle, and then let it cool down. He used a sensor to record the temperature of the water safely.
The table shows Robin's results.

Time	0	1	2	3	4	5	6	7	8	9	10	11	12	13	14	15
Temp	18	79	100	92	84	78	72	66	62	57	53	50	47	44	41	39

'Time' is the number of minutes after switching the kettle on.
'Temp' is the temperature in °C.

a Draw a set of axes, with 'Time' on the horizontal axis, and 'Temperature' on the vertical axis.
(The horizontal scale goes from 0 to 15 minutes, and the vertical scale goes from 0°C to 100°C.)
b Plot the data from the table on your. Each pair of numbers will give you one point on your graph.
c Join the points with straight lines to make a time-series graph.
d Describe the changes in temperature that are shown in the graph.

3 Select and draw the best type of graph for each of these sets of data.
You will need to choose your own scales for each graph.
a Sarah's height (in cm) was measured each birthday from the age of 2 to 18.

Age	2	3	4	5	6	7	8	9	10	11	12	13	14	15	16	17	18
Height (cm)	87	95	103	108	116	122	128	133	138	144	149	156	164	170	173	175	176

b The table shows the scores obtained by two opponents in 12 frames of snooker.

Player 1	45	71	60	101	67	43	0	68	98	67	65	0
Player 2	80	69	83	5	8	78	68	19	0	21	33	133

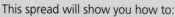

This spread will show you how to:
▶▶ Construct stem-and-leaf diagrams.

KEYWORDS
Stem-and-leaf diagram
Modal class   Order

A stem-and-leaf diagram is a combination of a table and a chart.

▶ Like a table, you can read off the individual data values.
▶ Like a chart, you can see the shape of the distribution

This makes it a good way to organise sets of data.

Always order the data before
you draw the diagram.

example

Yvonne asked 26 mobile phone owners to record the
number of text messages they sent in one month.
Here are their totals:

18, 24, 29, 36, 37, 37, 39, 43, 46, 48, 49, 49, 50, 54, 56,
57, 57, 58, 59, 62, 64, 68, 70, 76, 82, 90

Show the totals on a stem-and-leaf diagram.

The data is in order.
Choose a sensible stem: go up in 10s.
Put the data in order on the appropriate
stem.

90	0
80	2
70	0 6
60	2 4 8
50	0 4 6 7 7 8 9
40	3 6 8 9 9
30	6 7 7 9
20	4 9
10	8

Key: | 20 | 4 | means 24 text messages sent in the month.

It is easy to find the range of the data, the modal class, and the
median from a stem-and-leaf diagram.

▶ The range is 90 − 18 = 72 messages.
▶ The modal class is 50–59 messages.
▶ The median is between the 13th and 14th values:
  (50 + 54) ÷ 2 = 52 messages.

You need a key to be able to read a stem-and-leaf diagram.

This stem-and-leaf diagram shows the thicknesses of 18 books:

The thicknesses (in cm) are:
    0.7, 0.8, 1.3, 1.4, 1.4, 1.4, 1.5, 1.5, 1.6,
    1.7, 1.8, 2.0, 2.2, 2.2, 2.6, 2.7, 3.5, 4.1

4	1
3	5
2	0 2 2 6 7
1	3 4 4 4 5 5 6 7 8
0	7 8

Key: | 1 | 4 | means 1.4 cm.

Exercise D3.5

1 These are the numbers of items purchased by 20 customers at a supermarket.

> 2, 4, 9, 15, 17, 17, 18, 19, 22, 24, 24, 25, 25, 26, 29, 31, 33, 35, 40, 42

Copy and complete the stem-and-leaf diagram to show this set of data.

40	
30	
20	
10	
0	

Key: | 10 | 5 | means 15.

2 Use the stem-and-leaf diagram that you drew for question 1 to find:
   a the range of the number of items purchased
   b the modal class of the data.

3 A group of 20 students took a science test.
These are their marks (out of 50).

> 7, 9, 11, 16, 18, 19, 20, 21, 24, 25, 26, 27, 29, 30, 31, 32, 33, 37, 42, 48

   a Draw a stem-and-leaf diagram for this set of data.
   b Use your diagram to find the range and the modal class for this set of data.

4 These are the numbers of calls received by a computer help desk each day for 15 days.

> 7, 14, 12, 7, 9, 2, 18, 25, 5, 9, 6, 22, 16, 15, 3

Draw a stem-and-leaf diagram to show this data.
Remember to order the data first.

5 These are the weights (in kilograms, to 1 decimal place) of a series of packages.

> 0.3, 1.2, 1.3, 1.3, 1.5, 1.7, 1.8, 2.0, 2.4, 2.7, 2.8, 3.2, 3.2, 3.4, 3.9, 4.1, 4.7, 5.4, 5.8

5	
4	
3	
2	
1	
0	

Key: | 1 | 5 | means 1.5 kg.

Copy and complete the stem-and-leaf diagram to show this set of data.

6 The distance travelled by 15 different paper aeroplanes was measured in metres, accurate to 1 decimal place.

> 3.2, 3.9, 4.1, 4.5, 3.4, 2.8, 3.6, 3.8, 2.9, 1.8, 4.9, 5.7, 2.7, 4.3, 5.2

Draw a stem-and-leaf diagram to show this data.

This spread will show you how to:
- ▶▶ Discuss a problem that can be addressed by statistical methods.
- ▶▶ Interpret diagrams, drawing inferences.
- ▶▶ Communicate the results of a statistical enquiry.

KEYWORDS

Statistics	Hypothesis
Diagrams	Conclusions

In a statistical report, you need to present your findings.

- ▶ Choose statistics and diagrams that show up the most important features of your results.
- ▶ Draw some conclusions if possible. Put these in terms of the hypothesis you wrote at the start of the project.

Class 9C wanted to test the hypothesis that:

- ▶ Penguins that 'huddle together' will cool down more slowly than penguins that stand alone.

They used 2-litre cans of water at 40°C to represent the penguins. They placed the cans in a freezer, and used sensors to record the temperature of the cans every 5 minutes for 30 minutes.

For the 'huddled' penguins, the cans were touching.

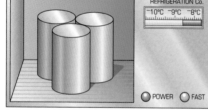

They ran the experiment again with the cans further apart.

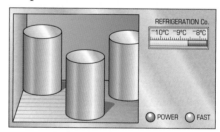

They decide to present the results in a line graph as it shows the change over time.

The graph shows that the cans cooled down more slowly when they were close together.

They state the conclusions of the project clearly.

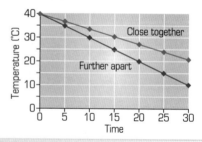

Our hypothesis was that putting the bottles closer together would make them cool down more slowly. The data from the experiment confirm the hypothesis.

They explain what the conclusions mean, and suggest other work that could be done.

The experiment suggests that penguins will use less energy keeping warm if they are huddled together, rather than standing separately.
We could go on to investigate the effects of different sizes of 'huddle'.

Exercise D3.6

1 A group of students were investigating the effect of insulation on the cooling rate of penguins. They recorded the temperature of a single can of warm water placed in a refrigerator. They ran the experiment with:

▶ The can without any insulation
▶ The can covered in a layer of bubble wrap
▶ The can covered in a layer of aluminium kitchen foil
▶ The can covered in bubble wrap *and* a layer of foil on top.

The group's hypotheses were:

▶ The can without insulation will cool fastest.
▶ The bubble wrap will give better insulation than the foil.
▶ The can will cool most slowly when the bubble wrap and the foil are used.

The table shows the results of the experiment.

Write a conclusion to the project. You should include a graph to show the results, and explain whether or not the results confirm the hypotheses.

Temperature (°C)		Time (in minutes) after start of the experiment						
		0	5	10	15	20	25	30
Covering	None	40	27	18	12	9	6	5
	Wrap	40	34	29	25	22	19	16
	Foil	40	31	23	18	14	11	9
	Both	40	38	36	35	33	31	30

2 Class 9D did a project about shopping. They asked people to fill in a questionnaire. One question was:

How did you travel to the shops today?	☐ Walk/ bicycle	☐ Own motor vehicle	☐ Public transport

They asked people at:

▶ a small shop in the high street
▶ a large supermarket
▶ an out-of-town shopping mall.

The table shows their results.

a Explain the hypotheses you would have used for this project.
b Write a conclusion for the project. You should present the data in a suitable way, and explain whether or not your hypotheses were confirmed.

		Types of transport		
		Walk/bike	Motor	Public
Shop type	High Street	12	11	7
	Supermarket	4	20	6
	Shopping mall	1	24	5

You should know how to …

1 Construct:

- ▶ simple line graphs for time series
- ▶ simple scatter graphs.

Identify which are most useful in the context of the problem.

2 Represent problems and interpret solutions in algebraic, geometric or graphical form.

Check out

1 Here are two sets of data.

Represent each of these sets of data with a suitable chart.

a In the final of a television talent show, two judges gave marks out of 10 to each of six singers.

The table shows the marks awarded.

Singer	A	B	C	D	E	F
Judge 1	10	8	4	6	7	3
Judge 2	7	6	2	8	9	1

b This table shows the depth of water in a stream, measured at hourly intervals.

Time	0	1	2	3	4	5	6	7	8	9	10	11
Depth	0.7	0.7	0.8	1.3	1.4	1.4	1.0	0.9	0.6	0.5	0.3	0.2

'Time' means the number of hours after the first measurement, and 'depth' is the depth of water in metres.

2 Give an example from your project work of a graph or chart that you used to represent a set of data.

Explain why you chose that particular type of chart, and what features of the data it showed.

Applying geometrical reasoning

This unit will show you how to:

- ▶▶ Solve geometrical problems using side and angle properties of triangles and quadrilaterals.
- ▶▶ Classify quadrilaterals by their geometric properties.
- ▶▶ Know and use geometric properties of cuboids and shapes made from cuboids.
- ▶▶ Begin to use plans and elevations.
- ▶▶ Make simple scale drawings.
- ▶▶ Use the formula for the volume of a cuboid.

- ▶▶ Construct nets of solid shapes.
- ▶▶ Calculate volumes and surface areas of cuboids and shapes made from cuboids.
- ▶▶ Solve more demanding problems and investigate in a range of contexts.
- ▶▶ Represent problems and interpret solutions in algebraic, geometric or graphical form.
- ▶▶ Use logical argument to establish the truth of a statement.

Packages come in all shapes and sizes.

Before you start

You should know how to ...

1 Name special triangles and quadrilaterals.

2 Find missing angles in triangles and quadrilaterals.

3 Find the area of a rectangle.

4 Use units of measure for area.

Check in

1 Give the full mathematical name for:
   a the yellow shape
   b the red shape
   c the green shape
   d the pink shape
   e the purple shape.

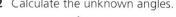

2 Calculate the unknown angles.

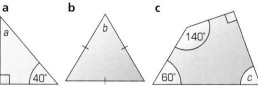

3 Write down the formula for the area of a rectangle.

4 Find the area of this rectangle. State the units of your answer.

This spread will show you how to:
▶▶ Solve geometrical problems using side and angle properties of triangles and quadrilaterals.
▶▶ Classify quadrilaterals by their geometric properties.

KEYWORDS
Triangle   Quadrilateral
Angles in a triangle
Angles at a point
Angles in a quadrilateral
Tessellate

Manufacturers often design packages so that they fit together.

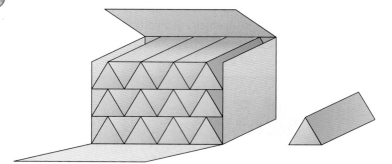

The packages tessellate – they leave no gaps so all the space in the box is used.

Triangles and quadrilaterals are good shapes for tessellating.

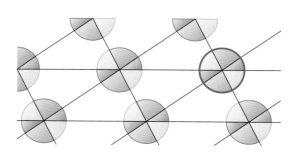

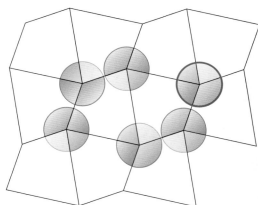

Any triangle tessellates:

The angles in a triangle add to 180°.
red + blue + yellow = 180°

At any point the angles add to 360°.

2 red + 2 blue + 2 yellow = 360°

Any quadrilateral tessellates:

The angles in a quadrilateral add to 360°.
red + blue + yellow + green = 360°

At any point the angles add to 360°.

red + blue + yellow + green = 360°

Exercise S4.1

1 Copy these shapes onto squared paper.
Show how each shape tessellates, using translations and rotations.

a 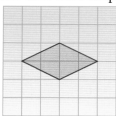 b 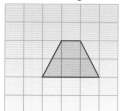 c 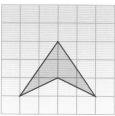 d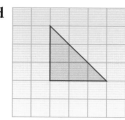

2 **a** Accurately draw two triangles with these measurements. Cut them out.
Mark the angles on both sides of the paper.
b Rearrange the two triangles to form a rhombus and then an arrowhead.
c In each case, draw the outline and mark the angles.
d What is the sum of the interior angles for each quadrilateral?
e Give reasons why it is possible to make each quadrilateral.
f Draw the diagonals in the rhombus.
g Give one geometrical property of these diagonals.

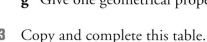

3 Copy and complete this table.

Shape	Opposite sides equal?	Opposite angles equal?	Diagonals perpendicular?	Order of rotational symmetry	Number of lines of symmetry	Tessellate?
Square	yes	yes	yes	4	4	yes
Rectangle						
Parallelogram						
Rhombus						
Isosceles trapezium						
Arrowhead (delta)						
Kite						

4 The interior angle of a regular hexagon is 120°.
a Explain why a regular hexagon tessellates.

b Calculate the values of *a* and *b*.
c Find and draw these shapes from the diagram:
▶ isosceles triangle
▶ equilateral triangle
▶ kite.
In each shape, find all the interior angles.

This spread will show you how to:
▶▶ Use 2-D representations to visualise 3-D shapes.
▶▶ Begin to use plans and elevations.

KEYWORDS
3-D
Plan
Isometric paper
View
Elevation

Boxes have three dimensions: length, width and height.

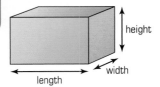

height
width
length

You can look at boxes from three different directions:

Top   **Side**   **Front**

These three directions are called:

Plan view   Side elevation   Front elevation

example

Draw the plan view, the side elevation and the front elevation of this shape:

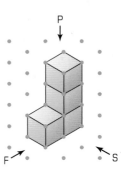

P

F   S

The shape is drawn on isometric paper.

To draw the ...
... plan view   ... side elevation   ... front elevation
look from above   look from the side   look from the front.

Exercise S4.2

1 Match each of these solids with its plan view.

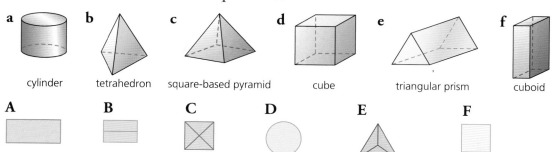

a cylinder   **b** tetrahedron   **c** square-based pyramid   **d** cube   **e** triangular prism   **f** cuboid

A   **B**   **C**   **D**   **E**   **F**

2 **a** On squared paper, draw the plan view, side elevation and front elevation of each shape.

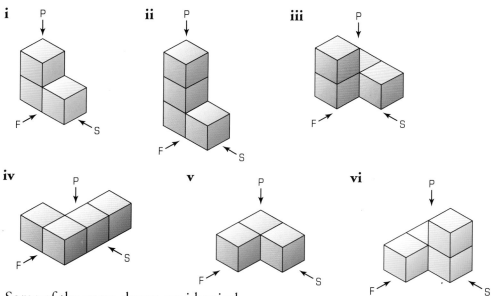

i   ii   iii   iv   v   vi

b Some of the seven shapes are identical.
Match the shapes and find the odd one out.

3 **a** Use multilink cubes to build each shape, given the three views.
   b Draw each 3-D shape on isometric dotty paper.
   c How many cubes are needed to make each shape?

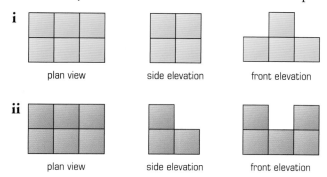

i   plan view   side elevation   front elevation

ii   plan view   side elevation   front elevation

207

Volume of a cuboid

This spread will show you how to:

▶▶ Know and use the formula for the volume of a cuboid.

▶▶ Calculate volumes of shapes made from cuboids.

KEYWORDS

Volume   Cuboid

Dimensions   Capacity

▶ **The volume of a box is the amount of space it takes up.**

You can measure volume in:

cm³

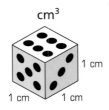

or m³

A cuboid is a box with rectangular faces.

It has three dimensions: length, width and height.

▶ **The volume of a cuboid = length × width × height**

You can find the volumes of shapes made from cuboids.

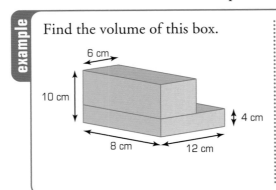

Find the volume of this box.

Split the box into two cuboids.
Find the volume of each:

Vol. A = 6 × 8 × 6   = 288 cm³

Vol. B = 8 × 12 × 4   = 384 cm³

Add the volumes   = 672 cm³

▶ **The capacity of a shape is the amount of liquid it will hold.**

You can measure capacity in:

litres (l)   or millilitres (ml)

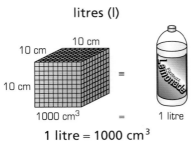

1000 cm³   =   1 litre

1 litre = 1000 cm³

1 cm³ = 1 millilitre = 1 ml

1 ml = 1 cm³

Exercise S4.3

1 Calculate the volumes of these cuboids.

a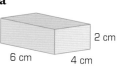
6 cm 4 cm 2 cm

b
10 cm 5 cm 5 cm

c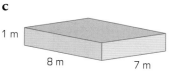
1 m 8 m 7 m

d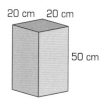
20 cm 20 cm 50 cm

2 **a** Draw a 10 by 10 square on squared paper.
Cut it out.
Cut off the four squares as shown and fold along the dotted lines to make an open-top cuboid.
Calculate the volume of this cuboid.

b Unfold the cuboid. Cut off three more squares in each corner as shown.
Fold along the dotted lines and calculate the new volume.

c Continue this process to copy and complete this table of results.

Length	Width	Height	Volume
8	8	1	
6	6	2	
4			
2			

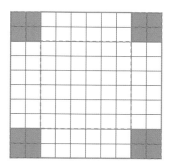

d What are the dimensions of the cuboid with the largest volume?

3 How many of these small cartons will fit into the large box?

10 cm 5 cm 5 cm

20 cm 30 cm 50 cm

4 Calculate the volumes of these shapes.

a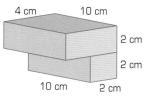
4 cm 10 cm 2 cm 2 cm 10 cm 2 cm

b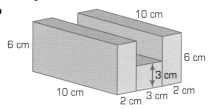
10 cm 6 cm 6 cm 3 cm 10 cm 2 cm 3 cm 2 cm

c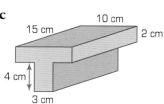
10 cm 15 cm 2 cm 4 cm 3 cm

S4.4 Surface area of a cuboid

This spread will show you how to:

▶▶ Know and use geometric properties of cuboids and shapes made from cuboids.

▶▶ Calculate the surface area of a cuboid.

KEYWORDS

Cuboid	Surface area
Edge	Vertices
Face	Plan
Net	Elevation

A cuboid has three dimensions: length, width and height.

It has:

▶ 12 edges

▶ 8 vertices

▶ 6 faces

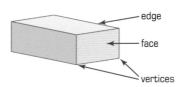

Most boxes are made up from a flat (2-D) shape called a net.

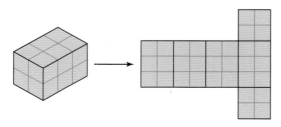

> Notice that opposite faces have the same area.

You find the area of the net by adding the areas of the faces.
$6 + 6 + 6 + 6 + 4 + 4 = 32$ cm^2

> ▶ The area of the net is the surface area of the cuboid.

You can use plans and elevations to find the surface area.

example

Find the surface area of this shape:

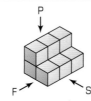

P

F   S

....

Opposite faces or views have the same area, so:

Plan view

Area = 6 cm^2

Side elevation

Area = 6 cm^2

Front elevation

Area = 3 cm^2

Surface area = $2 \times 6 + 2 \times 6 + 2 \times 3 = 30$ cm^2

Exercise S4.4

1 The opposite faces of a dice add up to 7.
Copy these nets and put the numbers 1 to 6 in the
appropriate places.

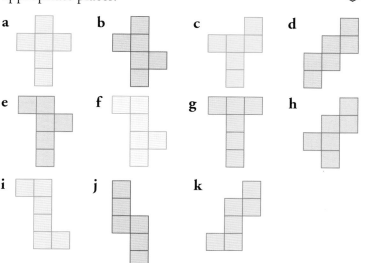

a   b   c   d

e   f   g   h

i   j   k

2 This cube has opposite faces that are the same colour.
   a How many edges are where the same-coloured faces meet?
   b How many edges are where different-coloured faces meet?
   c What are the colours of the faces at each vertex?

3 A cuboid is cut into two halves as shown.
What is the name of the shape of the new face that is created?

a   b   c   d

4   a Draw the net of this shape made from 12 cubes.
    b Find the surface area of the shape using the net.
    c On squared paper, draw the plan view, side
      elevation and front elevation.
    d Calculate the area of the plan view, side elevation
      and front elevation.
    e Calculate the surface area of the shape using your
      answers in part d.

5 Use 12 multilink cubes. Put the cubes together to make a cuboid.
   a Give the dimensions of all possible 1-layer cuboids.
   b Give the dimensions of all possible 2-layer cuboids.
   c Continue until you have found the dimensions of all the possible cuboids.
   d Calculate the surface area of each cuboid.
   e Which cuboid has the smallest surface area?

> Do not use the same
> combination twice.

S4.5 Nets and scale drawings

This spread will show you how to:
- ▶▶ Make simple scale drawings.
- ▶▶ Construct nets of solid shapes.

KEYWORDS
Cube   Net
Cuboid   Scale
Prism   Base
Pyramid   Apex
Cross-section
Triangular prism

Boxes and packages come in all shapes and sizes.

You should know these common 3-D shapes:

Cube	Cuboid	Prism	Pyramid

Square faces	Rectangular faces	Cross-section the same throughout the length.	Base tapers to a point called the apex.

The nets of these shapes look like this:

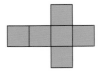 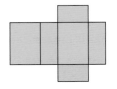 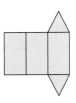

You name a:
prism by its cross-section   pyramid by its base.

This is a triangular prism.   This is a square-based pyramid.

You may need to use a scale to draw a real-life box.

This box measures 30 cm × 15 cm × 10 cm.

The scale drawing measures 6 cm × 3 cm × 2 cm.

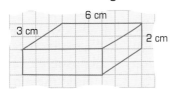

The scale is 1 : 5.
Use 1 cm to show 5 cm on the real box.

Exercise S4.5

1 Using squared paper, copy and cut out these nets.
Name the solid formed in each case.

a

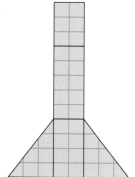

b

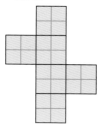

c

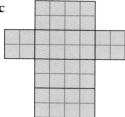

Now redraw the nets on squared paper and add flaps on alternate edges.
Cut out the nets to check your answers.

2 On squared paper, draw the nets of:
a a 2 cm by 3 cm by 5 cm cuboid
b a 3 cm by 3 cm by 3 cm cube.
Draw flaps on alternate edges.
Cut out the nets to check your answers.

3 These are nets for a scale model of the same box.

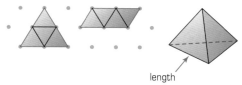

length

The scale is 1 : 5.
a What is the name of the shape of the box?
b Calculate the length of the real box.
c Draw the nets for the real box and add flaps to join up the net.
d Cut out and make the box.

4 This is the net for a scale model of another box.
The scale is 1 : 3.
a What is the mathematical name of the box?
b Calculate the length of the real box.
c Draw the net for the real box and add flaps as needed.
d Cut out and make the box.
e Measure the height of the box.
f Calculate the total surface area of the box.

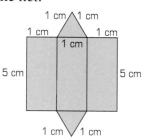

1 cm 1 cm
1 cm   1 cm
1 cm
5 cm   5 cm
1 cm 1 cm

height

length

S4.6 Designing a box

This spread will show you how to:
▶▶ Know and use geometric properties of cuboids and shapes made from cuboids.

KEYWORDS

Cuboid   Surface area
Dimensions   Volume
Plan view   Net
Elevation   Scale drawing

Chocolates come in all shapes and sizes.

To design the best box to keep the chocolates in, you consider:

1 The type of box you design
– no gaps means no waste!

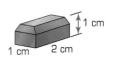

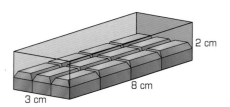

2 The dimensions of the box – the views, surface area and volume.

Plan view	Side elevation	Front elevation

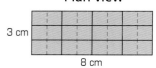 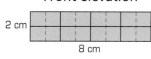

You can work out whether it will fit on a shelf or whether you can carry it!

▶ Surface area = 2 × plan area + 2 × side area + 2 × front area
= $2 \times 24 \text{ cm}^2 + 2 \times 6 \text{ cm}^2 + 2 \times 16 \text{ cm}^2 = 48 \text{ cm}^2 + 12 \text{ cm}^2 + 32 \text{ cm}^2 = 92 \text{ cm}^2$

▶ Volume of cuboid = length × width × height
= $8 \times 3 \times 2 \text{ cm}^3 = 48 \text{ cm}^3$

3 You would then construct the net.

First make a sketch ...

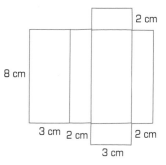

then an accurate scale drawing.

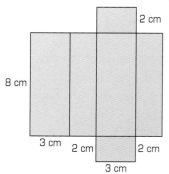

Choose an easy-to-use scale and make sure you can fit your drawing on one sheet of paper.

Exercise S4.6

1 A bar of chocolate has these dimensions:
  a Explain why this shape is good for packaging.
  b Calculate the volume of the chocolate bar.

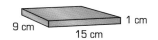

2 Three chocolate bars are sold in a bumper pack and a box is made to pack them.
The box has dimensions of 15 cm, 9 cm and 3 cm.
  a Calculate the volume of the box.
  b Draw the plan view, side elevation and front elevation of the box.
  c Calculate the surface area of the box, using the views in part **b**.

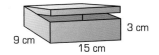

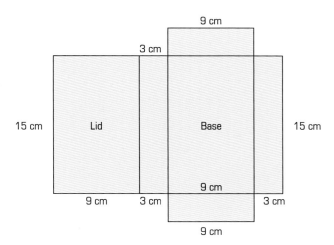

  d Copy this net onto squared paper and add the flaps and lid flaps.
  e Calculate the surface area of the box, using the net.
  f Draw a scale drawing of the net, using a scale of 1 cm to represent 3 cm or 1 : 3.

3 Design a box, with a lid, to package:
  a an orange or
  b 10 biscuits or
  c your choice of sweets.

The design should include:
  ▶ reasons for your choice of shape
  ▶ calculations of volume and surface area
  ▶ views
  ▶ the net
  ▶ a scale drawing.

Using your design, make a model box and then a full-size box.
Decorate the box with suitable labels.

You should know how to ...	Check out
1 Know and use the formula for the volume of a cuboid.	**1 a** Write down the formula for the volume of a cuboid. **b** The volume of this cuboid is 125 cm³. Calculate the height.

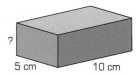

?　　5 cm　　10 cm

2 Calculate volumes and surface areas of cuboids.	**2 a** Calculate the volume of this cuboid.

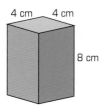

4 cm　　4 cm

8 cm

b Calculate the surface area.

3 Represent problems and interpret solutions in geometric form.	**3** Triangles are made by joining three of the vertices of a 3 cm by 3 cm by 3 cm cube.

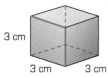

3 cm

3 cm　　3 cm

Accurately draw the different possible triangles. For each triangle name the type.

4 Use logical argument to establish the truth of a statement.	**4** Show that it is possible to make an equilateral triangle using three of the vertices of the cube.

Probability experiments

This unit will show you how to:

▶▶ Design and use two-way tables.
▶▶ Know that if the probability of an event occurring is p, then the probability of it not occurring is $1 - p$.
▶▶ Find and record all possible mutually exclusive outcomes for single events and two successive events in a systematic way, using diagrams and tables.
▶▶ Estimate probabilities from experimental data.
▶▶ Compare experimental and theoretical probabilities in different contexts.

▶▶ Understand that:
  ▶ If an experiment is repeated there may be, and usually will be, different outcomes.
  ▶ Increasing the number of times an experiment is repeated generally leads to better estimates of probability.
▶▶ Identify the necessary information to solve a problem.
▶▶ Give solutions to an appropriate degree of accuracy.
▶▶ Suggest extensions to problems, conjecture and generalise.

You can use chance to make decisions

Before you start

You should know how to ...

1 Find simple probabilities based on equally likely events.

2 Recognise equivalent fractions, decimals and percentages.

3 Find complements to 1.

Check in

1 There are 10 balls in a bag.
  5 are green, 3 are blue, 2 are red.
  What is the probability of choosing:
  a a green ball
  b a blue ball
  c a green or red ball?

2 Which of these values is not equivalent?
  60% $\frac{3}{5}$ 0.6 $\frac{15}{25}$ 55%

3 What is the complement to 1 of:
  a 0.3 **b** $\frac{1}{5}$ **c** 0.76?

Simple tree diagrams

This spread will show you how to:
▶▶ Know that if the probability of an event occurring is p, then the probability of it not occurring is $1 - p$.
▶▶ Find and record all possible mutually exclusive outcomes for single events in a systematic way, using diagrams and tables.

You toss a coin to decide who starts a game.

A tree diagram is a good way to show the possible outcomes.

▶ The two 'branches' of the 'tree' show the possible outcomes: heads and tails.
▶ The outcomes are written at the end of the branches, and the probability of each one is shown on the branch.
▶ This diagram has two branches, but tree diagrams can have any number of branches.

$\frac{1}{2}$ — Heads

$\frac{1}{2}$ — Tails

The probability of getting heads is $\frac{1}{2}$.
The probability of not getting heads is $\frac{1}{2}$.

▶ If the probability that an event occurs is p, then the probability that the event does not occur is $1 - p$.

You can use this idea to help you to complete tree diagrams.

example

A jar contains red counters and green counters.
The probability of getting a green counter is 0.3.
Draw a tree diagram to show the possible outcomes.

....

You know the probability of getting a green is 0.3.
You need to work out the probability of getting a red.

The probability, p, of getting a green is 0.3.
The probability of not getting a green is $1 - 0.3 = 0.7$.
▶ There are only two colours, so the probability of getting a red is the same as the probability of **not** getting a green.

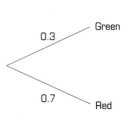

0.3 — Green

0.7 — Red

Exercise D4.1

1 Draw a tree diagram to represent each of these situations.

  a The probability of getting heads on a coin is $\frac{1}{2}$, and the probability of getting tails is $\frac{1}{2}$.

  b The probability of winning a prize in a raffle is 25%, and the probability of losing is 75%.

  c The probability that a car will start first time is 0.1, and the probability that it will not start first time is 0.9.

2 In each of these situations, there are just two possible outcomes. You are given the probability of one of them. Draw a complete tree diagram for each situation.

  a When a driver reaches a level crossing, the barriers will either be up or down. The probability that the barriers will be down is 0.1.

  b The probability of passing a cycling test is 65%.

  c When you roll a fair dice, you either get a multiple of 3 or you do not. The probability that you do get a multiple of 3 is $\frac{1}{3}$.

3 In each of these situations, work out the probability of each outcome and draw a tree diagram.

  a A student is chosen at random from a class. The person chosen will either be a boy or a girl, and there are 15 boys and 13 girls in the class.

  b A set of 10 digit cards numbered 0–9 are shuffled, and a card is picked at random. The number chosen may or may not be a multiple of 4.

  c In every 100 packs of crisps, there are 7 that contain prize tokens. Jonathan buys a packet, and checks to see if he has won a prize.

4 In each of these tree diagrams, there are three possible outcomes. Copy and complete the diagrams by filling in the missing probabilities.

  a A coloured counter is picked at random from a large jar.

  b A T-shirt is chosen at random from a rack in a shop.

  c A student picked at random takes a test with three possible results.

5 Draw a tree diagram for each of these outcomes.

  a A card is chosen at random from a pack of 12 cards marked A, B or C. There are 4 cards marked A, and 5 marked C.

  b A spinner has sections coloured red, gold and green. The probability of getting red is 0.3, and the probability of getting gold is 0.15.

219

More tree diagrams

This spread will show you how to:
▶▶ Find and record all possible mutually exclusive outcomes in a systematic way.
▶▶ Design and use two-way tables.

KEYWORDS
Tree diagram   Outcome
Event   Random
Two-way table

A tree diagram shows the different outcomes that can happen.

You can use it to show outcomes for two successive events.

example

Barry has two jars of counters.
The first jar contains red and green counters.
The second jar contains yellow and blue counters.
Barry picks a counter at random from each jar.
Show the possible outcomes on a tree diagram.

....

The two-stage tree diagram shows the possible outcomes.

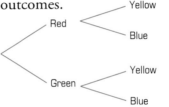

Red — Yellow, Blue
Green — Yellow, Blue

▶ To see all the possible outcomes for the two events, you read along the branches.

You can also show the outcomes in a two-way table:

A two-way table is useful when there are lots of possible outcomes.

	Red	Green
Yellow		
Blue		

You can sometimes restrict the outcomes to success or failure.

example

A player picks two cards from an ordinary pack of playing cards.
The player wins a prize if both cards are Kings.
Show the possible outcomes on a tree diagram.

....

Write 'Other' to show 'any card except a King'.
You do not need to show every possibility.

The tree diagram shows that the possible outcomes are:
(King, King), (King, Other), (Other, King) and (Other, Other).

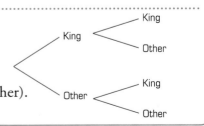

King — King, Other
Other — King, Other

Exercise D4.2

1 An ordinary coin is tossed twice.
Draw a tree diagram to show all the possible outcomes.

2 Karen sits a maths test and a science test.
Each test is graded either 'Pass' or 'Fail'.
Draw a tree diagram to show all the possible outcomes.

3 A shop sells a sweatshirt in:

▶ three sizes (small, medium and large), and
▶ two colours (red and black).

Copy and complete the tree diagram to show all the
possible combinations.

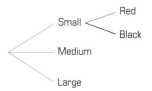

4 Each day, Simon uses an ordinary dice to decide what sort of
sandwich to make for lunch. He has:

▶ two choices of bread (white or brown), and
▶ three choices of filling (ham, cheese or tuna).

a Explain how Simon could use the dice to choose a type
of bread, and a filling.
b Draw a tree diagram to show all the possible outcomes.

5 When ordering a pizza at the Cherry Tree Café, you have
to pick one topping from each column of the table.

Draw a tree diagram to show all the possible combinations
of toppings.

Column A	Column B
Anchovies	Black olives
Pepperoni	
Pineapple	Green peppers
Chicken	

6 A shop sells light bulbs in three different powers
(40 W, 60 W and 100 W) and three different colours
(clear, frosted and peach).
a Draw a tree diagram to show all the possible choices of
light bulb.
b Draw a two-way table to show the possible choices.

Which diagram do you think is better?
Explain the reasons for your choice.

7 This two-way table shows all the possible outcomes
when a coin is tossed and a dice is rolled.

Show this information as a tree diagram.

	1	2	3	4	5	6
Head	(H, 1)	(H, 2)	(H, 3)	(H, 4)	(H, 5)	(H, 6)
Tail	(T, 1)	(T, 2)	(T, 3)	(T, 4)	(T, 5)	(T, 6)

Equally likely outcomes

This spread will show you how to:
▶▶ Find and record all possible mutually exclusive outcomes in a systematic way.

KEYWORDS
Random   Outcome
Equally likely Tree diagram
Probability

When you choose an item at random, each item is equally likely to be picked.

When the outcomes at any stage are equally likely, all the probabilities will be equal.

> **example**
>
> A card is chosen at random from this pack.
> Draw a tree diagram to show the possible outcomes.
>
>
>
> ·····
>
> The choice is at random, so each outcome is equally likely.
>
> The tree diagram shows five outcomes.
> Every probability is 0.2, or $\frac{1}{5}$, or 20%.
>
> 0.2 — A
> 0.2 — B
> 0.2 — C
> 0.2 — D
> 0.2 — E

You can use tree diagrams when you have two successive events with equally likely outcomes.

> **example**
>
> These two fair spinners are spun.
> Draw a tree diagram to show all the possible outcomes.
>
>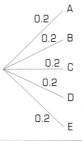
>
> ·····
>
> The tree diagram shows that there are 8 possible outcomes.
> All of these outcomes are equally likely.
>
> They each have a probability of $\frac{1}{8}$.
>
>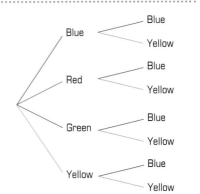
> Blue — Blue
> Blue — Yellow
> Red — Blue
> Red — Yellow
> Green — Blue
> Green — Yellow
> Yellow — Blue
> Yellow — Yellow

Exercise D4.3

1 This hexagonal spinner has sections coloured green, yellow and orange.

   a Draw a tree diagram to show the possible outcomes.
   b The spinner is fair, and the probabilities of all the outcomes are equal.
      Mark the probabilities on the tree diagram.

2 A fair, four-sided spinner has sides marked A, B, C and D. Draw a tree diagram to show all the possible outcomes when the spinner is spun, and mark the probability of each outcome on the diagram.

3 Draw tree diagrams for each of these pieces of apparatus. Mark the probability for each outcome.
Each piece of apparatus is fair, so the outcomes are equally likely.
   a A set of five cards marked A, B, C, D and E.
      (Write the probabilities as percentages.)
   b An ordinary dice. (Write the probabilities as fractions.)
   c A coin. (Write the probabilities as decimals.)

4 A fair dice has two faces marked '1', two faces marked '2', and two faces marked '3'.
   a Copy and complete the tree diagram to show all the possible outcomes when the dice is rolled twice.

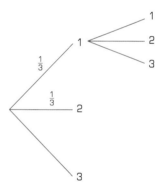

   b Mark the probability of each outcome on your diagram.
   c Use your tree diagram to work out the probability that the total score for the two rolls will be 6.

5 Julie pulls two Christmas crackers.
   ▶ The first cracker contains a comb, a whistle or a magnifying glass.
     All of these are equally likely.
   ▶ The second cracker contains a whistle or a pencil sharpener.
     These are also equally likely.
   a Draw a tree diagram to show all the possible outcomes.
      Mark the probability of each outcome on your diagram.
   b Find the probability that Julie gets two whistles when she pulls the crackers.

This spread will show you how to:
▶▶ Estimate probabilities from experimental data.
▶▶ Understand that if an experiment is repeated there may be, and usually will be, different outcomes.

KEYWORDS
Experiment   Estimate
Model   Equally likely
Predict

This is a game called 'Down the Nile'.

The map and the diagram both show part of the river Nile. A, B, C, D and E are towns where the river meets the sea.

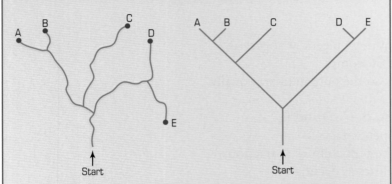

The map shows the river accurately, but the diagram shows all of the connections clearly.

A boat sails down the Nile, starting at the point shown.
Every time the river splits, the captain of the boat spins a coin to decide whether to go left or right.
Predict which town the boat will finish at!

Terri and Jan tried to work out where the boat was most likely to go.

The five towns are all equally likely. The probability of getting to any town is $\frac{1}{5}$, or 20%.

No! 50% of the time the boat will go to D or E, so that's 25% each. If others were the same, it would add up to more than 100%.

▶ Use a counter to represent the boat.
▶ Spin a coin to decide which way to move.
▶ Model a large number of trips down the river.
▶ Use this formula to estimate the probability:

$$\text{Probability of reaching a town} = \frac{\text{Number of trips that reach the town}}{\text{Total number of trips down the river}}$$

Exercise D4.4

You are going to carry out an experiment to estimate the probability of getting to each of the towns in a game of 'Down the Nile'.

1 First, make a prediction:
  ▶ Write down your predictions for the probability of getting to each town.
  ▶ Remember that the probabilities should add up to 1 (if you use decimals or fractions), or 100%.

2 Carry out an experiment to estimate the probability of reaching each of the towns A, B, C, D and E in a game of 'Down the Nile'.
  ▶ Follow the instructions given on page 224.
  ▶ You need a fairly large number of trials in your experiment.
  ▶ Work out the probability of getting to each town, using the formula on page 224.

3 Write a paragraph about the results of your experiment from question 2.
  ▶ Do you think that you are equally likely to get to any of the five towns?
  ▶ Did the experiment work out as you expected, or did the results surprise you?

4 The maps below show some other rivers.

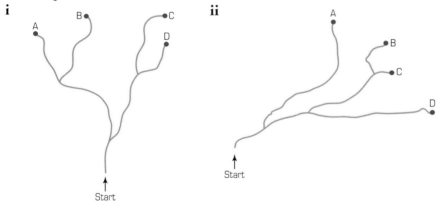

i

ii

Just like the game 'Down the Nile', a boat starts at the position shown and turns left or right at each fork in the river, until it reaches one of the towns.
Again, the captain of the boat spins a coin to decide whether to go left or right at each fork, so the probability of going in each direction is $\frac{1}{2}$.

  a For each river, predict whether the boat is equally likely to finish at any of the towns, or whether some towns are more likely than others. (You may find it useful to redraw the maps with straighter lines.)
  b Now carry out an experiment to test some of your predictions.
  c Write a paragraph explaining what you find out.

This spread will show you how to:
▶▶ Understand that:
  ▶ If an experiment is repeated there may be, and usually will be, different outcomes.
  ▶ Increasing the number of times an experiment is repeated generally leads to better estimates of probability.

KEYWORDS
Theoretical probability
Experiment
Predict

In the 'Down the Nile' game, the probabilities of turning left or right at each fork were equal.

The captain spun a coin to decide the way to go.

You can investigate what happens when the probabilities are different.

The map shows a section of river, marked with the probabilities that a boat will go in each direction.

Use theoretical probability to **predict** the town that the boat will finish at.

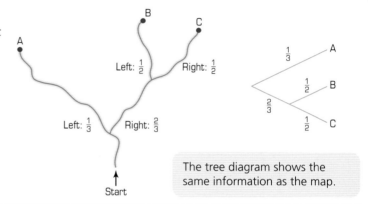

The tree diagram shows the same information as the map.

Imagine you made three trips down the river.
▶ You would expect to take the left fork, and get to town A, once – because the probability is $\frac{1}{3}$.
▶ With the other two trips, you would expect to get to B once and C once, because each probability is $\frac{1}{2}$.
So, in three trips, you would expect to get to each town once.
This shows that the probabilities are equal.

You can also carry out an experiment to test the predictions.

Use a dice.

▶ At the first fork, turn left to A if you roll a 1 or 2.
▶ If you roll a 3 or more, turn right.
  Roll again to decide whether you go to B or C.
  ▶ If you roll a 3 or less, go to B.
  ▶ If you roll a 4 or more, go to C.

You will not get the same results every time you roll the dice. You should carry out as many trials as possible so the results are fair.

Exercise D4.5

1 Maya and Kiran both carried out the experiment described on page 226.
Each experiment had 10 trials.

Maya's results:

B	B	B	B	C	C	B	B	A	B

Kiran's results:

C	C	A	C	A	B	A	C	C	A

a Copy and complete this table for Maya's results and again for Kiran's.

Student's name:			
Town	A	B	C
Frequency			

b Estimate of the probability of getting to each town, based on each person's results. Divide the frequency by the total number of trials – which is 10.

2 Maya and Kiran decided to combine their data, and work out a new set of estimates because their results were so different.

a Copy and complete this table.

Town	A	B	C
Total frequency			

b Work out an estimate of the probability of getting to each town, based on the combined results.

Hint: Add up the frequencies for each town from each person's data, and divide each total by 20.

3 Carry out your own version of the experiment.
Record your data in a copy of this table:

Town	Tally	Frequency
A		
B		
C		

▶ Use your answers to questions 1 and 2 to help you to decide how many trials you need to carry out.

▶ You can get a larger set of trials by combining your results with those obtained by other students.

▶ Work out the probability of getting to each town by dividing the frequency by the total number of trials.

▶ Write a paragraph to explain how closely your results agree with the prediction that the probabilities of getting to each town are equal.

Comparing experimental and theoretical probabilities

This spread will show you how to:
▶▶ Compare experimental and theoretical probabilities.

KEYWORDS
Trial   Experiment
Estimate   Simulation
Outcome

▶ The more trials you have in an experiment, the more reliable the estimates of probability will be.

Joe investigates how many trials he needs for an experiment to give reasonable results.

He experiments using this river journey.

The captain is equally likely to turn left or right at each fork.

There are four equally likely outcomes.
The theoretical probability of getting to each town is $\frac{1}{4}$.

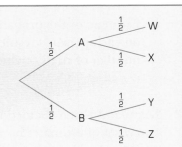

Joe carries out an experiment to estimate the probability of reaching town W.

▶ For each trial, he tosses a coin twice.
▶ A trial is 'successful' if it results in two heads.

He uses the formula for experimental probability:

$$\text{Probability of reaching town W} = \frac{\text{Number of successful trials}}{\text{Total number of trials}}$$

After 10 trials he has these results: P (W) = 0.4

This is not very close to the expected result of $\frac{1}{4}$ or 0.25.

Joe carries out a computer simulation of the experiment with 10 trials.
He runs the simulation four times.

The estimated probability of getting to town W changes each time:

Run number	1	2	3	4
P(W)	0.2	0.1	0.3	0.1

Joe finds the average probability over all five experiments:

0.4 + 0.2 + 0.1 + 0.3 + 0.1 = 1.1
1.1 ÷ 5 = 0.22

The average probability is now closer to the expected 0.25.

To get even closer he'd need to do lots more trials.
Alternatively, he can collect together data from other students.

Exercise D4.6

1 The map shows part of a river.

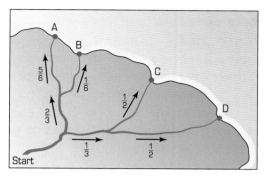

A boat sails down the river from the position shown, and eventually reaches the sea at one of the ports A, B, C or D.

Each time the boat reaches a fork in the river, the captain decides whether to go left or right by rolling an ordinary dice.

a Draw a tree diagram to show the possible outcomes.

b Explain how the captain could use a dice to decide on a route down the river, with the probabilities shown.

2 Carry out an experiment to estimate the probability of the journey finishing at each of the ports A, B, C and D in question 1.

a Start by modelling 10 trips down the river.
   Record your results in a frequency table, and use the formula to estimate each probability.

b Next, model another 10 trips, making 20 in all.
   Estimate the probability of getting to each of the towns, based on the new set of data.

c Finally, collect as much data as you can and make another estimate of the probabilities based on this larger set of data.

   (You can collect some more data yourself, or combine your data with some from another group.)

3 Carmel says:

> If 9 boats sailed down the river, I would expect 6 of them to take the left fork, and I would expect 5 out of these 6 to go to A. So 5 out of every 9 trips will finish at A, and the probability must be $\frac{5}{9}$ or about 0.55.

a Show how Carmel can work out the probability of finishing at each of the other ports B, C and D.

b Explain how these probabilities compare with the probabilities calculated in question 2.

D4 Summary

You should know how to ...

1 Find and record all possible mutually exclusive outcomes for single events and two successive events in a systematic way, using diagrams and tables.

2 Identify the necessary information to solve a problem.

Check out

1 A game uses two fair spinners.
Spinner 1 has red and blue segments.
Spinner 2 has green and yellow segments.
- ▶ The probability of Spinner 1 landing on a red segment is 0.5.
- ▶ The probability of Spinner 2 landing on a green segment is 0.6.

a Draw a tree diagram to show the possible outcomes when both spinners are spun. Mark on all the probabilities.

b Spinner 1 is spun twice. Draw a sample space diagram for all the possibilities.

2 When Spinner 1 is spun twice, as in question 1b, all the outcomes are equally likely. Explain how you could find the probability of getting one red and one blue when Spinner 1 is spun twice.

230

This unit will show you how to:

▶▶ Solve more demanding problems and investigate in a range of contexts.

▶▶ Compare and evaluate solutions.

▶▶ Identify the necessary information to solve a problem.

▶▶ Represent problems and interpret solutions in algebraic and graphical form.

▶▶ Suggest extensions to problems, conjecture and generalise.

▶▶ Design and use two-way tables.

You can use models to investigate problems.

Before you start

You should know how to ...

1 Continue number patterns.

2 Use letter symbols.

3 Plot graphs of simple linear functions.

Check in

1 Write the next two terms in each sequence:

    a 12, 5, ⁻2, __, __

    b 1, 4, 9, __, __

2 If $x = 5$ and $y = 3$, work out:

    a $x + y$

    b $3x$

    c $4x + 2y$.

3 Plot the graph of $y = 2x - 3$ using values for x from 0 to 7.

    Copy and complete this table of values to help you:

x	0	1	2	3	4	5	6	7
y								

Starting an investigation

This unit will show you how to:
▶▶ Solve more demanding problems and investigate in a range of contexts.
▶▶ Identify the necessary information to solve a problem.

KEYWORDS
Investigate
Units
Rectangle

Rods and connectors

A model construction kit is made with rods that slide into connectors.

There are three different types of connector.

This is an L-connector.

This is a T-connector.

This is an X-connector.

L-connectors cost 2p.

T-connectors cost 3p.

X-connectors cost 4p.

The rods cost 1p each, and they are all the same length.

The diagram shows a rectangle made with the kit.

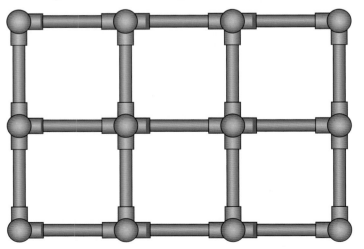

This rectangle has an area of 6 square units.

It uses these connectors:
  4 Ls
  6 Ts
  2 Xs
It also uses 17 rods.

This rectangle would cost 51p.

Investigate:
  ▶ the largest rectangle that can be built for a total cost of £1 or less
  ▶ the cost of other rectangles made from the kit.

Exercise B1.1

This exercise will help you structure your investigation.

> Start by trying a few examples, to make sure that you understand how the investigation works.

1 Work out the cost of making the following rectangles with the construction kit.
Show your working carefully.

> Simple diagrams like these are all you need to draw in your work.

> Try to get some very general ideas about how the results change.

2 Jackie says:

> I am going to make a rectangle with an area of 12 square units. Does the cost change if I make the rectangle a different way?

All of these rectangles have an area of 12 square units.
Work out the cost of each one.

Use your results to answer Jackie's question.

> Once you understand the problem, go back to the instructions. The first part of the investigation asks you to find the biggest rectangle you can make with £1 or less.

3 You should see that you can make a rectangle with an area of 12 square units for less than £1.
You should now check whether it is possible to make a bigger rectangle.

This spread will show you how to:
- ▶▶ Identify the necessary information to solve a problem.
- ▶▶ Solve more complex problems by breaking them down into smaller steps or tasks.
- ▶▶ Design and use two-way tables.

KEYWORDS
Systematic
Two-way table
Diagram

You start an investigation by trying lots of examples.
You then need to work systematically and organise your results.

Break the problem into steps

There are two things you can change about a rectangle – its width and its height.
Fix one of these and change the other so it is easier to see what is going on.

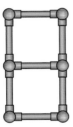 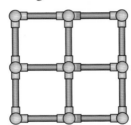 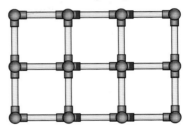

These rectangles all have a height of 2. The width increases by 1 each time.
You can work out how much the cost increases each time the width increases by 1.

▶ To work systematically, change just one thing at a time.

Record your results

You can record the cost of each rectangle in a table like this:

Cost of rectangles with a height of 2

Width	1	2	3	4	5	6
Cost (p)						

You can then go on to find the cost of rectangles with different heights.

You can put all of the results into a two-way table like this:

Cost of rectangles	Width					
	1	2	3	4	5	6
Height 1						
Height 2						
Height 3						
Height 4						

▶ Putting the results into a table makes it easier to spot patterns.

Exercise B1.2

1 **a** You may already have found the cost of these rectangles.
If not, work out the cost of each of them now.

 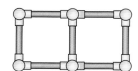 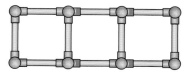

b Copy the table, and fill in the cost of each of the rectangles.

		Width of rectangle		
		1	2	3
Height	1			

2 Extend your results table to include rectangles up to 12 squares wide.

		Width of rectangle											
		1	2	3	4	5	6	7	8	9	10	11	12
Height	1												

Fill in the blank spaces in the table.
You may need to draw some of the rectangles to find the results.

3 Extend your table of results downward by adding some extra rows.

		Width of rectangle											
		1	2	3	4	5	6	7	8	9	10	11	12
Height	1												
	2												
	3												

Fill in as many results as you can.
▶ You should find that there are number patterns in the results,
and you can use these patterns to help you fill in the table.
▶ You should still draw some of the diagrams, and work out their cost,
to check that the number patterns give the correct result.

4 Use this idea to help you to check some of the results in
your table:

> A rectangle that is 3 squares across and 1 square down
> will cost exactly the same as one that is 1 square across
> and 3 squares down.

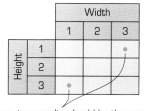

		Width		
		1	2	3
Height	1			●
	2			
	3	●		

These two results should be the same.

Finding patterns and rules

This spread will show you how to:
▶▶ Represent problems and interpret solutions in algebraic form.

KEYWORDS
Algebra
Flow chart
Systematic

You should now have a set of results, organised into a table.

You should explain why the number patterns work, and describe them in words.

These rectangles are two rods high:

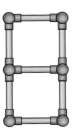 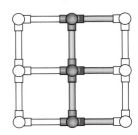 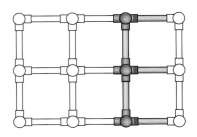

The results for this set of rectangles are in the second row of the table.

The numbers in the table go up by 15 each time.		Width of rectangle				
To make a rectangle one square wider, you need to add 5 rods, 2 T-connectors, and 1 X-connector. The extra cost is 5p + 6p + 4p = 15p.	Height:	1	2	3	4	5

Table (right side):

		Width of rectangle				
		1	2	3	4	5
Height:	1					
	2	•	•	•		
	3	+15p +15p				

You should describe any rules and patterns using algebra.

This table shows the results for some rectangles with a height of 1 square.

The cost of the rectangles goes up by 9p as the width increases by 1 square.
You can use w to stand for the width of the rectangle, and c for the cost (in pence).

		Width of rectangle				
		1	2	3	4	5
Height:	1	12	21	30	39	
	2					
	3					

The rule will be similar to: $c = 9w$.

When $c = 9w$, the numbers are: 9, 18, 27, 36

The actual numbers are: 12, 21, 30, 39

You add 3 each time, so the correct rule is $c = 9w + 3$.

Exercise B1.3

The flow chart shows the steps you need to take to describe and explain the number patterns in your table of results.

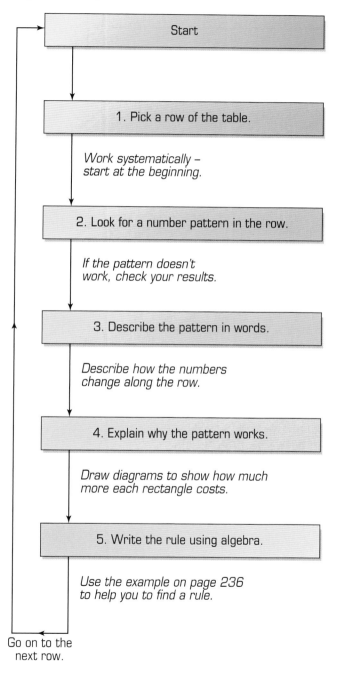

Start

1. Pick a row of the table.

*Work systematically –
start at the beginning.*

2. Look for a number pattern in the row.

*If the pattern doesn't
work, check your results.*

3. Describe the pattern in words.

*Describe how the numbers
change along the row.*

4. Explain why the pattern works.

*Draw diagrams to show how much
more each rectangle costs.*

5. Write the rule using algebra.

*Use the example on page 236
to help you to find a rule.*

Go on to the
next row.

Explain the number patterns in your table of results by working through the steps in this chart.

This spread will show you how to:
▶▶ Represent problems and interpret solutions in graphical form.

KEYWORDS
Graph
Axis
Data

A graph is a good way to describe your results as it shows up trends.

This graph shows the cost of rectangles with a height of 1.

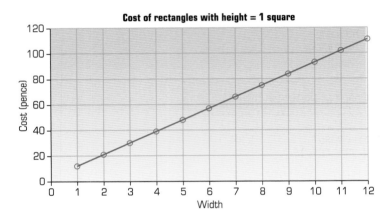

Cost of rectangles with height = 1 square

Part of the data for this graph was shown in the table on page 236.

The graph makes some features of the results clearer:

▶ If the height is 1 unit, the biggest rectangle you can make for £1 or less is 10 squares wide.
▶ The line shows the trend in the results. The line is straight, which shows that the cost increases by the same amount each time the width increases by one unit.

You need to read the graph carefully:

▶ Notice that the points marked on the graph represent the only rectangles that can actually be made.
The line between the points is only there to make the trend clearer.
▶ It is not easy to read off actual values from the graph. You need to include a table of results **and** a graph in your investigation.

You could also have other lines on the graph, to show the cost of rectangles with other heights.

Exercise B1.4

The sketch shows how you could include all of the information from your table of results in a single graph.

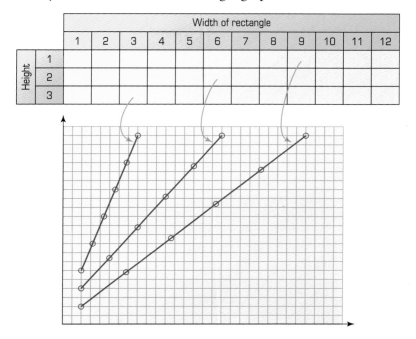

Use the sketch to draw your own graph to show some of the results from your table.

Remember:

▶ Plot the width of the rectangles on the horizontal axis.
▶ Plot the cost of each rectangle on the vertical axis.
▶ Choose the scales for each axis so that the graph will include the widest rectangle you want to include, and the most expensive one.
▶ Your graph will need a title, and will need to be carefully labelled.

Your graph gives you another chance to check your results, because the points you plot for each row of the table should make a straight line.

Your lines should look like this.

If they look like this, check your results!

This spread will show you how to:

▶▶ Suggest extensions to problems, conjecture and generalise.

KEYWORDS
Investigate
Extend
Condition

You have now investigated the original problem quite thoroughly. You have:

▶ found the cost of a range of rectangles
▶ organised your results in a table
▶ looked for patterns in your results, and described these in words, and using algebra
▶ explained why the number patterns work
▶ drawn graphs to illustrate your results.

You should be able to work out the biggest rectangle that you can make for £1.

You can now change some of the original conditions, and investigate the effect of the changes. For example:

You could work out the effect of changing the cost of some of the pieces.

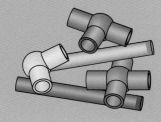

Special offer!
For a limited time, you can buy any piece for just 1p! That's right – any connector is now yours for a penny!

You could also change the kit so that you can build 3-D models. As well as the connecting rods, you would need pieces like these:

3p

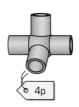
4p

5p

6p

You could now investigate the volume of the cuboids that you can make for a particular amount of money.

Exercise B1.5

Extend the problem and ask some questions of your own.
There are three different types of extensions:

> **1 Asking different questions**
> Keep the basic situation the same, but extend the problem by changing the questions that you are investigating.

In the original problem you found the biggest rectangle you could make for £1.
What if the money available was increased to £2? or £3?

You could investigate these questions, and put the results in a table.

Money available	£1	£2	£3	£4	£5
Area of biggest rectangle					

> **2 Changing the starting information**
> Change some of the details of the investigation, and see what effect the changes have.

You can change the prices of the pieces.
To find anything significantly different you need to make the changes very clear – like making all the pieces the same price.

> **3 Major extensions to the problem**
> Use the original problem as a starting point, and then design a new investigation of your own.

You could extend to investigate 3-D problems.

You must decide on the cost of the new connectors – the example on page 240 has new connectors that cost one penny for every rod that can be connected to them which is the same as in the original problem.

This kind of extension gives a completely new and more complicated investigation to carry out – make sure you have time to do it!

Reports and conclusions

This spread will show you how to:
▶▶ Compare and evaluate solutions.

KEYWORDS
Systematic
Conclusion
Predict

Coursework can be worth a lot of marks at GCSE, and by following these three steps, you can make sure that you get the best mark your work deserves.

You have already worked through the first two steps.

1 Work systematically to generate results
- ▶ Do not try to change everything at once.
  Make small controlled changes so that you can see their effect.
- ▶ Record and present your results in an organised way such as a table.
- ▶ Check your results carefully.
  Do not just continue a number pattern without checking that it is correct.

2 Describe and justify patterns and rules
- ▶ Describe patterns in your results, using words, algebra and graphs.
- ▶ Explain why your rules work, by showing the connection between the number patterns and the situation you are investigating.
- ▶ Use your rules to predict and check some further results.

When you do a piece of Maths coursework, you will produce a report giving your solutions to the questions asked.

The third step should help:

3 Communicate your results effectively
- ▶ Use appropriate tables, diagrams and algebra to present your findings.
- ▶ Use headings to make your report easy to follow.
- ▶ Make conclusions based on the question asked.
- ▶ Justify any conclusions by referring to your findings.
- ▶ You do not have to include all of your working out in the main part of your report, although you should give some examples showing how you worked things out.
  (Your working can be included as an appendix.)

Exercise B1.6

Your finished investigation will probably include these sections:

1 Title page

2 Contents page

3 Introduction
Explain briefly what the investigation is about.

4 Results
Explain how you found and checked your results.
Present the results that you need, using tables and graphs.
You only need to include a few examples to show what you did.

5 Analysis
Describe and explain the patterns in your results.
Use words and algebra to describe the patterns in your results.
It is very important to try to explain why the rules work.

6 Conclusions
Look back at the original questions, and give your answer to them clearly.
In this investigation there was one question with a single answer (finding the largest rectangle you can make for £1), and a more open extension that you could answer in lots of ways.

7 Appendix
Include any detailed working and rough work that you want to show, but which would make the main part of the report too cluttered.

It is a good idea to have page numbers on your report, and to label every chart and diagram (for example, 'Table 2', 'Diagram 6').
This makes it much easier to refer to other parts of your report (for example, 'See Diagram 3 on page 6').

If you extended the investigation, you may be able to include your extension work in the sections shown.
If the extension was a major one, you may need to write a separate report!

You should know how to ...

1 Identify the necessary information to solve a problem.

2 Represent problems and interpret solutions in algebraic and graphical form.

Check out

1 Write a set of **Hints and Tips** that you would give to somebody starting on a mathematical investigation.

You could include advice about how to:

▶ Organise the work
▶ Set out the results
▶ Check the results
▶ Find rules
▶ Report the findings of the investigation.

2 In your investigation, you had the opportunity to represent your results in various forms:

▶ Tables of results
▶ Graphs to represent your results
▶ Rules in words or using algebra.

Explain the advantages and disadvantages of each of these ways of presenting your results. You should describe how easy each method is to carry out, and how clearly it describes what is going on.

accuracy
D3.1

The accuracy of data is how exact it is, for example, the number of decimal places.

add, addition
N1.1, N1.9, N2.4

Addition is the sum of two numbers or quantities.

algebra
A3.6, B1.3

Algebra is the branch of mathematics where symbols or letters are used to represent numbers.

algebraic expression
A3.1, A3.2, A5.1, A5.2, A5.3

An algebraic expression is a collection of numbers and letters linked by operations but not including an equals sign.

alternate angles
S1.3, D1.5

A pair of alternate angles are formed when a line crosses a pair of parallel lines. Alternate angles are equal.

angle: acute, obtuse, right, reflex
S1.1, S1.2, S1.3, D1.3, P1.5

An angle is formed when two straight lines cross or meet each other at a point. The size of an angle is measured by the amount one line has been turned in relation to the other.

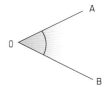

An acute angle is less than 90°.

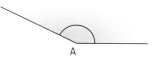

An obtuse angle is more than 90° but less than 180°.

A right angle is a quarter of a turn, or 90°.

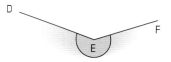

A reflex angle is more than 180° but less than 360°.

angle bisector
S1.9

An angle bisector divides an angle in half. For example, QX is the angle bisector of ∠PQR.

angles at a point
S1.2, S4.1

Angles at a point add up to 360°.

$a + b + c = 360°$

angles in a quadrilateral
S4.1

Angles in a quadrilateral add up to 360°.

$a + b + c + d = 360°$

angles in a triangle
S4.1

Angles in a triangle add up to 180°.

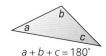

$a + b + c = 180°$

Glossary

angles on a straight line
S1.2, S1.3, S1.5

Angles on a straight line add up to 180°.

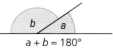

apex
S4.5

The highest point of a solid is the apex.

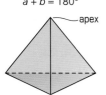

approximate, approximately
N2.3

An approximate value is a value that is close to the actual value of a number.

arc
S1.6, S1.7, S1.8, S1.9

An arc is a part of a curve.

area: square millimetre, square centimetre, square metre, square kilometre
S2.2, P1.5

The area of a surface is a measure of its size.

arithmetic sequence
A1.3

In an arithmetic sequence each term is a constant amount more or less than the previous term.

ascending, descending
N1.1

Ascending means going up or getting bigger. Descending means going down or getting smaller.

associative
A3.1

Addition and multiplication are associative because when adding or multiplying three or more numbers it doesn't matter which pair you add or multiply first.
$(1 + 2) + 3 = 1 + (2 + 3)$
$(1 \times 2) \times 3 = 1 \times (2 \times 3)$

assumed mean
D3.3

An assumed mean is used to simplify the arithmetic when calculating the mean. The assumed mean is subtracted from all the data and added back on once the mean of the smaller numbers has been calculated.

average
D1.1, D1.6

An average is a representative value of a set of data.

axis, axes
A4.8, B1.4

An axis is one of the lines used to locate a point in a coordinate system.

bar chart
D1.4, D1.5

A bar chart is a diagram that uses rectangles of equal width to display data. The frequency is given by the height of the rectangle.

base (of plane shape or solid)
S2.2, S2.3, S4.5

The lower horizontal edge of a plane shape is usually called the base. Similarly, the base of a solid is its lowest face.

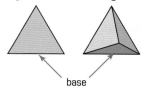

bearing, three-figure bearing
S3.1

A bearing is measured from the North in a clockwise direction.
The bearing of B from A is 045°.

best estimate
A4.4

The best estimate of a value is the closest you can achieve.

billion
N2.2

One thousand million or 1 000 000 000 or 10^9.

bisect, bisector
S1.8, S1.9

A bisector is a line that divides an angle or another line in half.

brackets
N1.9, N2.8, A5.2

Operations within brackets should be carried out first.

calculator: clear, display, enter, key, memory
N2.8

You can use a calculator to perform calculations.

capacity: litre, millilitre centilitre
S2.5, S2.6, S4.3

Capacity is a measure of the amount of liquid a 3-D shape will hold.

category
D1.3, D1.4

A category is a class of data.

centre of enlargement
S3.5

The centre of enlargement is the point from which an enlargement is measured.

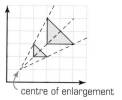
centre of enlargement

centre of rotation
S3.2

The centre of rotation is the fixed point about which a rotation takes place.

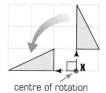
centre of rotation

change
N1.6

Change is the amount of increase or decrease.

collect like terms
A3.1

Collecting like terms means collecting all similar terms together. For example, $2x + 3x + 4 + 2 = 5x + 6$.

common denominator
N1.1, P1.4

Fractions have a common denominator if their denominators are the same.

compare
N1.1, N1.5

Compare means to assess the similarity of.

compasses (pair of)
S1.7, S1.8, S1.9

Compasses are used for constructions and drawing circles.

compensation, compensate
N2.4, N2.5

The method of compensation makes some calculations easier, for example, some multiplications are easier if you double one of the numbers and then compensate by halving the answer.

Glossary

complementary angles S1.5	Complementary angles sum to 90°. For example, $a + b = 90°$, so a and b are complementary.
conclude, conclusion D3.6, B1.6	To come to a decision after a series of logical steps.
condition B1.5	A condition is something that must be satisfied.
congruent, congruence S1.1, S2.3, S3.2	Congruent shapes are exactly the same shape and size.
consecutive A4.4	Consecutive means following on in order. For example 2, 3 and 4 are consecutive integers.
constant N1.8	A constant is something that does not change.
construct S1.7	To draw a line, angle or shape accurately.
construction lines S1.6, S1.7	Lines drawn to help in constructing bisectors of angles and lines, for example, when you use a straight edge and compasses.
continuous (data) D1.4, D3.2	Continuous data can take any value between given limits, for example, less than 1 m.
conversion graph A2.3	A graph that converts between units is a conversion graph.
convert A2.3	To change.
coordinate pair A2.2	A coordinate pair is a pair of numbers that gives the position of a point on a coordinate grid. For example, (3, 2) means 3 units across and 2 units up.
coordinates S2.1	Coordinates are the numbers that make up a coordinate pair.
corresponding angles S1.3, S1.5	A pair of corresponding angles are formed when a straight line crosses a pair of parallel lines. Corresponding angles are equal.
corresponding sides S1.1	Corresponding sides in congruent shapes are equal in length.
counter-example P1.2, P1.4	A counter-example disproves a statement.
cross-section S4.5	A cross-section is what you get when you cut across a solid.
cube root N2.1, A4.3	The cube root of a number is the value that gives the number when multiplied by itself twice. For example, $2 \times 2 \times 2 = 8$, so 2 is the cube root of 8, or $2 = \sqrt[3]{8}$.
cube, cube number N2.1, A4.3	A cube number is the product of three equal integers. For example, $27 = 3 \times 3 \times 3$, so 27 is a cube number.

cubed
N2.1

A number is cubed if it is multiplied by itself twice. 2 cubed, written 2^3, is $2 \times 2 \times 2 = 8$.

data
D1.1, B1.4

Data are pieces of information.

data log
D3.1

Data logging collects information automatically by instruments. This data can then be sent to a computer.

decimal number
N1.4, N1.5, N2.2

A decimal number is a number written using base 10 notation.

decimal place (dp)
N2.3, N2.8

Each column after the decimal point is called a decimal place. For example, 0.65 has two decimal places (2 dp).

deduce
S2.2

To deduce is to draw a logical conclusion.

degree of accuracy
D3.1

A degree of accuracy is a measure of accuracy. This can be a number of decimal places or significant figures.

denominator
N1.2, N2.8, A5.4

The denominator is the bottom number in a fraction. It shows how many parts the whole has been divided into.

diagonal
S1.4, S1.5, A4.6

A diagonal of a polygon is a line joining any two vertices but not forming a side.

This is a diagonal.

diagram
D3.6, B1.2, P1.2

A diagram is a line drawing that illustrates a situation.

difference
D3.3

You find the difference between two amounts by subtracting one from the other.

difference pattern
B1.3

The differences between consecutive terms in a sequence form a difference pattern.

dimensions
S2.5, S4.3, S4.6

The dimensions of an object are its measurements.

direct proportion
N1.8, A3.5

Two quantities are in direct proportion if they are always in the same ratio.

direction
S3.1

The direction is the orientation of a line in space.

discrete (data)
D1.4, D3.2

Discrete data can only take certain definite values, for example, integers between 10 and 20.

displacement
A2.3

Displacement is a measure of how something has been moved.

distance–time graph
A2.3, A4.9

A graph showing distance on the vertical axis and time on the horizontal axis.

distribution
D1.6

Distribution describes the way data is spread out.

distributive
A5.2

Multiplication is distributive over addition and subtraction. For example, $a(b+c) = ab + ac$.

divide, division
N1.2, N1.3, N1.4, N1.9,
N2.5, N2.6, N2.7

Divide (÷) means share equally.

edge (of solid)
S4.4

An edge is a line along which two faces of a solid meet.

edge

elevation
S4.2, S4.4, S4.6

An elevation is an accurate drawing of the side or front of a solid.

enlarge, enlargement
S3.5, S3.6

An enlargement is a transformation that multiplies all the sides of a shape by the same scale factor.

equal (sides, angles)
S1.2

Equal sides are the same length. Equal angles are the same size.

equally likely
D4.3, D4.4

Events are equally likely if they have the same probability.

equation
A3.1, A3.2, A3.4, A5.1, A5.3

An equation is a statement linking two expressions that have the same value.

equation (of a graph)
A4.6

The equation of a graph links the two variables together and can be used to give coordinates.

equidistant
S1.6, S1.9

Equidistant means the same distance apart.

equivalent, equivalence
N1.1

Equivalent fractions are fractions with the same value.

estimate
N2.5, D2.1, D2.4, D4.4,
D4.6, P1.6

An estimate is an approximate answer.

even
A4.4

The even numbers are 2, 4, 6, 8, 10, 12, ...

event
D2.2, D4.1, D4.2

An event is an activity or the result of an activity.

exceptional case
P1.2, P1.4

An exceptional case is one which is used to disprove a rule or hypothesis.

expand
A5.2, A5.3

To expand brackets, you multiply them out.

expect
D2.4

What you expect is what you think will happen.

experiment
D2.1, D2.4, D4.4, D4.5, D4.6

An experiment is a test or investigation to gather evidence for or against a theory.

experimental probability
D2.4

Experimental probability is calculated on the basis of the results of an experiment.

extend
B1.5

To extend a problem, you ask further questions about it.

exterior angle
S1.2

An exterior angle is made by extending one side of a shape.

face
S2.5, S4.4

A face is a flat surface of a solid.

face

factor
N2.5, A4.1

A factor is a number that divides exactly into another number. For example, 3 and 7 are factors of 21.

fair, biased
D2.4

In a fair experiment there is no bias towards any particular outcome.

flow chart
A1.1, B1.3

A flow chart is a diagram that describes a sequence of operations.

formula, formulae
A1.3, A3.1, A5.1, A5.5, A5.6
S2.2, S2.3, P1.6

A formula is a statement that links variables.

fraction
N1.1, N1.3, N1.4, N1.5, N1.7,
A5.4, P1.3

A fraction is a way of describing a part of a whole. For example, $\frac{2}{5}$ of the shape shown is shaded.

frequency diagram
D1.4, D3.4

A frequency diagram uses bars to display grouped data. The height of each bar gives the frequency of the group, and there is no space between the bars.

frequency table
D1.4, D3.1

A frequency table shows how often each event or quantity occurs.

function
A2.1, A3.1, A4.6, A5.1

A function is a rule. For example, $+2$, -3, $\times 4$ and $\div 5$ are all functions.

function machine
A2.1, A2.2, A3.3

A function machine links an input value to an output value by performing a function.

general term
A1.2

The general term of a sequence is an expression which relates its value to its position in the sequence.

generate
A1.1

Generate means produce.

gradient, steepness
A4.6, A4.7, A4.9

Gradient is the measure of the steepness of a line.

grid method
N2.6

To multiply two numbers by the grid method, you work out the values in the grid, then add them. For example, 34×17.

	30	4	300
10	300	40	210
7	210	28	40
			28
			578

grouped data
D3.2

Grouped data are groups of data values.

hectare

A hectare is a unit of area equal to 10 000 m^2.

height, high
S2.2, S2.3

Height is the vertical distance from the base to the top of a shape.

heptagon
S3.4

A seven-sided shape.

highest common factor (HCF)
A4.1, A4.2

The highest common factor is the largest factor that is common to two or more numbers.
For example, the HCF of 12 and 8 is 4.

horizontal
A3.3, A4.6

A horizontal line is parallel to the bottom of the page.

hypothesis, hypotheses
D3.6

A hypothesis is a statement that has not been shown to be true or untrue.

identity
A5.1

An identity is an equation that is always true.

imperial unit: foot, yard, mile, pint, gallon ounce, pound, ton
S2.6

Imperial units are the units of measurement historically used in the UK and other English-speaking countries.

increase, decrease
N1.6

Increase means make greater. Decrease means make less.

index, indices, power
N1.9, N2.8, A4.3, A4.4

The index of a number tells you how many of the number must be multiplied together. When a number is written in index notation, the index or power is the raised number.
For example, the index of 4^2 is 2. The plural of index is indices.

input, output
A2.1, A2.2

Input is data fed into a machine or process. Output is the data produced by a machine or process.

integer
N2.4, N2.6

An integer is a positive or negative whole number (including zero). The integers are: ..., $^-3$, $^-2$, $^-1$, 0, 1, 2, 3, ...

intercept
A2.2, A4.6, A4.7

The y-intercept is the point where a graph crosses the y-axis.

interest
N1.6

Interest is the amount paid by someone who borrows money. Interest is calculated as a percentage of the sum borrowed.

interior angle
S1.2

An interior angle is inside a shape, between two adjacent sides.

interpret
D1.1, A4.8, A4.9, P1.1, P1.2

You interpret data or a question when you make sense of it.

intersect, intersection
S1.1, S1.8, A5.6

Two lines intersect at the point where they cross.

intersection

inverse
N1.3, A3.3, N2.7, A5.4

An inverse operation has the opposite effect to the original operation. For example, multiplication is the inverse of division.

investigate
B1.1, B1.5, P1.6

To investigate something, you find out more about it.

isometric
S4.2

Isometric grids are designed to make it easier to draw shapes.

justify
N1.4

To justify is to explain or to prove right.

length: millimetre, centimetre, metre, kilometre; mile, foot, inch
S2.6, P1.5

Length is a measure of distance. It is often used to describe one dimension of a shape.

line graph
D1.4, D3.4, B1.4

Points are joined by straight lines on a line graph.

linear equation, linear expression, linear function, linear relationship
A2.2, A4.5, A5.6

An equation, expression, function or relationship is linear if the highest power of any variable it contains is 1.
For example, $y = 3x - 4$ is a linear equation.

linear sequence
A1.1, A1.2

The terms of a linear sequence increase by the same amount each time.

locus, loci
S1.8, S1.9

A locus is the position of a set of points, usually a line, that satisfies some given condition. Loci is the plural of locus.

lowest common multiple (LCM)
A4.1, A4.2

The lowest common multiple is the smallest multiple that is common to two or more numbers.
For example, the LCM of 4 and 6 is 12.

map
A2.1

A mapping maps one set of numbers to another.

mapping
A2.1

A mapping is a rule that can be applied to a set of numbers to give another set of numbers.

mass: gram, kilogram, tonne; ounce, pound
S2.6

Mass is a measure of the amount of matter in an object. An object's mass is closely linked to its weight.

mean
D1.2, D1.6, S2.1, D3.2

The mean is an average value found by adding all the data values and dividing by the number of pieces of data.

median
D1.2, D3.2

The median is an average which is the middle value when the data is arranged in size order.

metric unit: gram, metre, litre
S2.6, B1.1, P1.1

Metric units are the measurements used in the metric system.

midpoint
S1.8, S2.1

The midpoint of a line is halfway between the two endpoints.

mirror line
S3.2

A mirror line is a line or axis of symmetry.

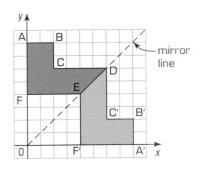

modal class
D3.2, D3.5

The modal class is the most commonly occurring class when the data is grouped. It is the class with the highest frequency.

mode
D1.2

The mode is an average which is the data value that occurs most often.

model
D4.4

A model is an experiment that attempts to copy a real-life pattern.

multiple
A4.1

A multiple of an integer is the product of that integer and any other. For example, these are multiples of 6: $6 \times 4 = 24$ and $6 \times 12 = 72$.

multiply, multiplication
N1.2, N1.3, N1.9, N2.5, N2.6, N2.7

Multiplication is the operation of combining two numbers or quantities to form a product.

multiply out (expressions)
A5.2

A bracket is multiplied out when each term inside it is multiplied by the term outside it.
For example, $3(x + 1)$ multiplied out is $3x + 3$.

negative number
N2.4, N2.5

A negative number is a number less than zero.

net
S2.5, S4.4, S4.5, S4.6

A net is a 2-D arrangement that can be folded to form a solid shape.

nth term
A1.2, A1.3

The nth term is the general term of a sequence.

numerator
N1.2

The numerator is the top number in a fraction. It shows how many parts you are dealing with.

object, image
S3.2

The object is the original shape before a transformation. The image is the position of the object after a transformation.

occur
D2.2

To occur means to happen.

odd
A4.4

The odd numbers are 1, 3, 5, 7, 9, 11, ...

order
D3.5

To order means to arrange according to size or importance.

order of operations
A3.2, N1.9, N2.8

The conventional order of operations is:
brackets first,
then division and multiplication,
then addition and subtraction.

order of rotational symmetry
S3.4

The order of rotational symmetry is the number of times that a shape will fit on to itself during a full turn.

origin
A3.5

The origin is the point where the *x*- and *y*-axes cross, that is (0, 0).

outcome
D2.1, D2.3, D4.1, D4.2, D4.3, D4.6

An outcome is the result of a trial or experiment.

parallel
S1.1, S1.3, S1.4, S2.3

Two lines that always stay the same distance apart are parallel. Parallel lines never cross or meet.

partition, part
N2.4, N2.5

To partition means to split a number into smaller amounts, or parts. For example, 57 could be split into 50 + 7, or 40 + 17.

percentage (%)
N1.4, N1.5, N1.6, P1.3

A percentage is a fraction expressed as the number of parts per hundred.

perimeter
S2.2

The perimeter of a shape is the distance around it. It is the total length of the edges.

perpendicular
S1.1, S1.6, S2.2, S2.3

Two lines are perpendicular to each other if they meet at a right angle.

perpendicular bisector
S1.6, S1.8

The perpendicular bisector of a line is at right angles to the line at its midpoint.

pie chart
D1.3, D1.5, D3.4, P1.2

A pie chart uses a circle to display data. The angle at the centre of a sector is proportional to the frequency.

place value: thousands hundreds, tens, units, tenths hundredths, thousandths
N2.2, N2.3, N2.6

The place value is the value of a digit in a number. For example, in 3.65 the digit 6 has a value of 6 tenths.

plan, plan view
S4.2, S4.4, S4.6

A plan view of a solid is the view from directly overhead.

polygon: pentagon, hexagon, heptagon, octagon
S3.4

A polygon is a closed shape with three or more straight edges.

A pentagon has five sides. | A hexagon has six sides. | A heptagon has seven sides. | An octagon has eight sides.

population pyramid
D1.5 (Homework)

A population pyramid is a back-to-back bar chart showing the differences between two populations.

predict
D4.4, D4.5, B1.6

Predict means forecast in advance.

primary source
D1.1, D3.1

Data you collect yourself is data from a primary source.

prime
A4.1

A prime number is a number that has exactly two different factors.

Glossary

prime factor decomposition
A4.2

Expressing a number as the product of its prime factors is prime factor decomposition.
For example, $12 = 2 \times 2 \times 3 = 2^2 \times 3$.

probability
D2.1, D2.2, D2.3, D4.1, D4.3, P1.3

Probability is a measure of how likely an event is.

profit, loss
N1.4

Profit is the amount of money gained.
Loss is the amount of money lost.

proof, prove
S1.3, S1.5

A proof is a chain of reasoning that establishes the truth of a proposition.

proportion
N1.5, N1.7, N1.8, D1.5, P1.4

Proportion compares the size of a part with the size of a whole. You can express a proportion as a fraction, decimal or percentage.

quadrant
S2.1

A coordinate grid is divided into four quadrants by the x- and y-axes.

quadrilateral: kite, parallelogram, rectangle, rhombus, square, trapezium
S1.4, S4.1, B1.1

A quadrilateral is a polygon with four sides.

rectangle

All angles are right angles. Opposite sides equal.

parallelogram

Two pairs of parallel sides.

kite

Two pairs of adjacent sides equal.

rhombus

All sides the same length. Opposite angles equal.

square

All sides and angles equal.

trapezium

One pair of parallel sides.

questionnaire
D1.1

A questionnaire is a list of questions used to gather information in a survey.

random
D4.2, D4.3

A selection is random if each object or number is equally likely to be chosen.

range
D1.2, D1.6

The range is the difference between the largest and smallest values in a set of data.

ratio
N1.7, N1.8, S3.5, S3.6, P1.3

Ratio compares the size of one part with the size of another part.

rearrange
A5.5

To rearrange a formula, you reposition the terms.

recurring decimal
N1.5

A recurring decimal has an unlimited number of digits, which form a pattern, after the decimal point.

reflect, reflection
S3.2, S3.3

A reflection is a transformation in which corresponding points in the object and the image are the same distance from the mirror line.

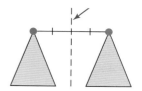

reflection symmetry
S3.4

A shape has reflection symmetry if it has a line of symmetry.

regular
S3.4

A regular polygon has equal sides and equal angles.

relationship
A3.5

A relationship is a link between objects or numbers.

rotate, rotation
S3.2, S3.3

A rotation is a transformation in which every point in the object turns through the same angle relative to a fixed point.

round
N2.3, P1.6

You round a number by expressing it to a given degree of accuracy. For example, 639 is 600 to the nearest 100 and 640 to the nearest 10.
To round to one decimal place means to round to the nearest tenth. For example, 12.47 is 12.5 to 1 dp.

sample
D3.1

A sample is part of a population.

sample space (diagram)
D2.3

A sample space diagram records the outcomes of two events.

scale, scale factor
S3.5, S3.6, S4.5

A scale gives the ratio between the size of the object and its diagram. A scale factor is the multiplier in an enlargement.

scale drawing
S3.6, S4.6

A scale drawing of something has every part reduced or enlarged by the same amount, the scale factor.

scatter graph
D1.4, D3.4

A scatter graph is a graph on which pairs of observations are plotted.

secondary source
D1.1, D3.1

Data already collected is data from a secondary source.

sector
D1.3

A sector is a division of a pie chart.

service charge
N1.6

The cost for providing the service.

sign change key
N2.8

The sign change key [+/−] on a calculator changes a positive value to negative or vice versa.

simplest form
N1.7

A fraction (or ratio) is in its simplest form when the numerator and denominator (or parts of the ratio) have no common factors.
For example, $\frac{3}{5}$ is expressed in its simplest form.

simplify
S3.6, A5.2

To simplify an expression you multiply out any brackets and collect like terms together.

simulation
D4.6

A simulation is a mathematical model.

slope
A4.8

A slope or gradient is the measure of steepness of a line.

solid (3-D) shape: cube, cuboid, prism, pyramid, square-based pyramid, tetrahedron
S2.4, S2.5, S4.3, S4.4, S4.5, S4.6

A solid is a shape formed in three-dimensional space.

cube

six square faces

cuboid

six rectangular faces

prism

end faces are the same shape and size

pyramid

the faces meet at a common vertex

tetrahedron

all the faces are triangles

square-based pyramid

the base is a square

solve (an equation)
A3.4, A5.3

To solve an equation you need to find the value of the variable that will make the equation true.

square number, squared
N2.1, A4.1, A4.3

If you multiply a number by itself the result is a square number. For example, 25 is a square number because $5^2 = 5 \times 5 = 25$.

square root
N2.1, A4.3

A square root is a number that when multiplied by itself is equal to a given number. For example, $\sqrt{25} = 5$, because $5 \times 5 = 25$.

statistic, statistics
D3.6

A statistic is a value that represents a set of data.
A mean, median, mode and range are statistics.

stem-and-leaf diagram
D3.5

A stem-and-leaf diagram is a way of displaying data.
For example, the numbers 29, 16, 18, 8, 4, 16, 27, 19, 13 and 15 could be displayed as:

0	4 8
1	3 5 6 6 8 9
2	7 9

Key: | 0 | 4 | means 4

straight edge
S1.7

A ruler.

straight-line graph A2.2, A4.5	When coordinate points lie in a straight line they form a straight-line graph. It is the graph of a linear equation.

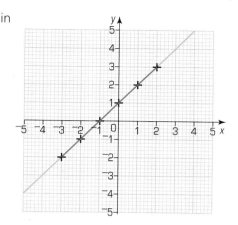

strategy N1.8, P1.3, P1.5	A strategy is a way of tackling a problem.
substitute A3.2, A3.4, A3.6, A5.1, A5.5	When you substitute you replace part of an expression with a numerical value.
subtract, subtraction N1.1, N1.6, N1.9, N2.4	Subtraction is the operation that finds the difference in size between two numbers.
supplementary angles S1.5	Supplementary angles add up to 180°. For example, 60° and 120° are supplementary angles.
surface, surface area S2.5, S4.4, S4.6	The surface area of a solid is the total area of its faces.
systematic D2.3, B1.2, B1.3	To work systematically means to break a problem down into simple steps, which you can solve individually. To list data systematically, you could divide the data into groups and list items for one group at a time
T(*n*) A1.2	T(*n*) is the notation for the general, *n*th, term of a sequence. For example, T(3) is the third term.
tax N1.4	Taxes are paid to the government. They are often expressed as a percentage.
term A1.1, A1.2, A1.3	A term is a number or object in a sequence. It is also part of an expression.
terminating decimal N1.5	A terminating decimal has a limited number of digits after the decimal point.
tessellate, tessellation S1.3, S3.3, S4.1	A tessellation is a tiling pattern with no gaps. Shapes will tessellate if they can be put together to make such a pattern.
theoretical probability D4.5	A theoretical probability is worked out without an experiment.
theory	A theory is a collection of ideas explaining something.
three-dimensional (3-D) S2.4, S4.2	Any solid shape is three-dimensional.

Glossary

to the power of n
A3.6, N2.1

This is the index in a number expressed in index notation in general form, for example x^n.

total
D3.3, P1.1, P1.3

The total is the result of an addition.

transform
D3.4

You transform an equation by doing the same to both sides.

transformation
S3.2, S3.3

A transformation moves a shape from one place to another.

translate, translation
S3.2, S3.3

A translation is a transformation in which every point in an object moves the same distance and direction. It is a sliding movement.

tree diagram
D4.1, D4.2, D4.3

A tree diagram shows the probabilities of the outcomes of an event. For example, if you roll a dice:

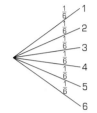

trial
D2.1, D4.6

In probability, a trial is one attempt in an experiment.

triangle: equilateral, isosceles, scalene, right-angled
S1.2, S1.4, S1.5, S4.1

A triangle is a polygon with three sides.

equilateral

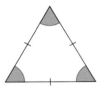

three equal sides

isosceles

two equal sides

scalene

no equal sides

right-angled

one angle is 90°

triangular prism
S4.5

A triangular prism has a triangular cross-section all the way through.

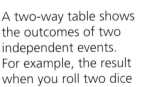

two-way table
D4.2, B1.2, P1.2

A two-way table shows the outcomes of two independent events. For example, the result when you roll two dice and add the scores.

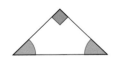

		Dice 1				
		1	2	3	4	5	6
Dice 2	1	2	3	4	5	6	7
	2	3	4	5	6	7	8
	3	4	5	6	7	8	9
	4	5	6	7	8	9	10
	5	6	7	8	9	10	11
	6	7	8	9	10	11	12

unit fraction
N1.2

A unit fraction has 1 as the numerator.
For example, $\frac{1}{2}$, $\frac{1}{7}$, $\frac{1}{23}$.

unitary method
N1.8, P1.4

In the unitary method, you first work out the size of a single unit and then scale it up or down.

value added tax (VAT)
N1.4

A tax imposed on goods and services by the government.

variable
A3.1, A5.1

A variable is a symbol that can take a range of values.

vary
D2.4

Results vary if they are different each time.

verify
P1.2, P1.4

To verify something is to show it is true.

vertex, vertices
S2.1, S4.4

A vertex of a 3-D shape is a point at which three or more edges meet. A vertex of a 2-D shape is where two sides meet.

vertex

vertical
A4.6

A vertical line is parallel to the side of the page.

volume: cubic millimetre, cubic centimetre, cubic metre
S2.4, S2.5, S4.3, S4.6

The volume of an object is a measure of how much space it occupies.

x-axis, y-axis
A4.5

On a coordinate grid, the x-axis is the horizontal axis and the y-axis is the vertical axis.

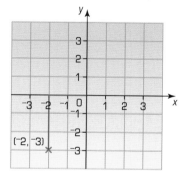

(⁻2, ⁻3)

Answers

A1 Check in

1 a 14, 17
   b 0, ⁻4
2 a 9
   b 1
   c ⁻11
   d 46
3 a 2
   b ⁻7
   c ⁻1
   d ⁻16

A1 Check out

1 a 3, 7, 11, 15, 19
   b 1, 2, 5, 14, 41
   c 5, 16, 38, 82, 170
   d 5, 8, 11, 14, 17
   e 1, 7, 13, 19, 25
   f 1, ⁻1, ⁻3, ⁻5, ⁻7
2 a 2, 5, 8, 11
   b Start with 2 squares,
      add 3 each time
   c 5th pattern : 14 squares
      7th pattern : 20 squares
      10th pattern : 29 squares
      Add on 3 each time.
   d $3n - 1$

A2 Check in

1 a $3n$ b $n + 10$ c $6 - n$
   d $\frac{n}{3}$ e $3n + 4$
2 a ⁻7   b ⁻2   c 2
   d ⁻4   e ⁻12   f 0
3

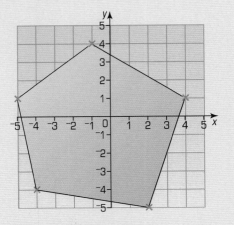

The shape is a pentagon.

A2 Check out

1 a ⁻7, ⁻3, ⁻1, 1, 3   b
2

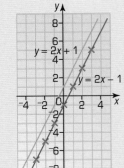

The graphs have the same gradient.
B also has the same gradient.
3

1. a 35
   b 6
   c 5
2. a $\frac{5}{7}$
   b $\frac{7}{12}$
   c $\frac{9}{10}$
3. a $\frac{4}{5}$
   b $\frac{4}{5}$
   c $\frac{7}{8}$
   d $\frac{7}{11}$
4. a 5p
   b £12
   c 6.5 m

1.

	Fraction	Decimal	%
School	$\frac{1}{4}$	0.25	25%
Sleep	$\frac{7}{20}$	0.35	35%
Homework	$\frac{3}{20}$	0.15	15%
Other	$\frac{1}{4}$	0.25	25%

2. a 30p b 6p   c 6.4 cm d 2 mm
   e 18p f 18 cm   g 91p   h 51 mm
   i i 8.8 ii 27.6 j i 28.8 ii 7.5
3. a £40 : £20   b £10 : £50
   c £50 : £10   d £25 : £35
   e £10 : £20 : £30 f £12 : £30 : £18
4. a i 42p ii £2.10
   b i 16p ii 64p iii £1.20
5. Jim is not correct.
   He would end up with 79.2 (99% of 80).

1. a 5n   b 4n
   c 3n   d n^2
   e 2n + 2p   f 3n + 4p
2. a ⁻7   b ⁻2
   c 1   d 0
3. a 8   b 11
   c ⁻1   d 5
4. a £1.80
   b £3.60
   c £3

1. a 10x + 4
   b 3x − 6
2. a x = 2   x = 10
   b i   x = 2
     ii   x = 3
     iii x = 12
     iv   x = 10
     v   x = 60
     vi   x = 3
     vii x = ⁻1
3. a 4   b $\frac{1}{4}$ c 3
   d $1\frac{1}{2}$ e 8   f 5
   g 2   h $1\frac{1}{2}$
4. 2(n + 3) = 14, n = 4

S1 Check in

1. a Obtuse
   b Right angle
   c Acute
2. a $a = 75$
   b $b = 45$

S1 Check out

1. a e
   b h
   c a
2. a 180°; angles in a triangle sum to 180°
   b 360°; angles in a quadrilateral sum to 360°
3.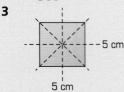
4. 60°, 120°, 60°, 120°

D1 Check in

1. ⁻12.9, ⁻1.6, 3.2, 5.6, 9.7, 15.3
2.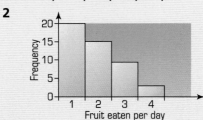
3. $\frac{1}{4}$ of the students ate an apple.
   $\frac{1}{4} \times 36 = 9$ students

D1 Check out

1. a Pie chart – shows proportions
      Bar chart – shows actual values
      Line graph – shows changes in data
      Scatter graph – shows two variables
   b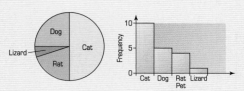
   c It is easier to compare proportions on the pie chart. The number of each type of pet can be read off the bar chart.
2. Design an experiment with each person estimating 30 seconds a number of times, say 10. Then collate results.
3. Scatter graph with data shown: 2 variables
   Roughly, the more time spent reading the fewer hours spent watching TV. On average, people spent much more time watching TV than reading.

S2 Check in

1 5
2 For example

3 Check your answers with your teacher.

S2 Check out

1 **a** 10 cm²
   b 10 cm²
   c 50 cm²
   d 50 cm²
2 **a** Volume = length × width × height
   b 2 cm
3 **a** 36 cm³
   b 72 cm²

N2 Check in

1 **a** 42
   b 7
   c 8
   d 27
   e 32
   f 8
2 **a** 42, 30, 12, 60, 20
   b 12, 60, 20
   c 42, 30, 12, 60
   d 30, 60, 20

N2 Check out

1 **a** 618   **b** 664
   c £402   **d** £556
   e 777   **f** 35
   g 7242   **h** 63 pupils
2 **a** 182.7   **b** 7.824
   c 5.7   **d** 12.7
   e £146.25   **f** 2.4 m
3 **a** 206.72   **b** 20 672
   c 20.672   **d** 0.323
   e 64

1 a 6
  b ⁻40
  c 8
  d 4
2 35, 90, 125, 150
3 $\frac{12}{16} = \frac{3}{4} = \frac{75}{100}$
4 a ⁻9
  b 3

1 a i 24   ii 36   iii 20   iv 182
  b i 24   ii 9   iii 6   iv 2
  c i $\frac{6}{13}$ ii $\frac{1}{2}$
2

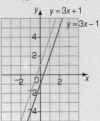

Same gradient, different intercept
(⁺1 and ⁻1)

3

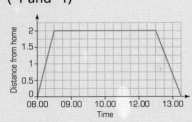

  b 1 hr 15 mins

1 a $\frac{1}{6}$
  b $\frac{1}{2}$
  c $\frac{1}{2}$
2 a i 0.6
    ii 0.75
    iii 0.62
  b i 35%
    ii 55%
    iii 60%

1

	Spinner 2			
		2	4	6	8
Spinner 1	1	3	5	7	9
	2	4	6	8	10
	3	5	7	9	11
	4	6	8	10	12

2 Construct a sample space diagram like this:

	Set 2			
		1	2	3	4
Set 1	A				
	B				
	C				
	D				

and write in the probabilities – they are all the same.

Total number of outcomes = 16

Probability of each outcome = $\frac{1}{16}$

To combine probabilities, add them together. So probability of picking a vowel and an even number is

p(A2) + p(A4) = $\frac{1}{16} + \frac{1}{16} = \frac{1}{8}$

1 a 20°
  b 140°
  c 220°
2 a, b, d
3 a 2 : 5
  b 5 : 6
  c 3 : 2

1

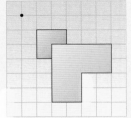

2 a i   Reflection in the x-axis
     ii Rotation through 180° about (0, 0)
     iii Reflection in the y-axis
     iv Translation $\begin{pmatrix} 2 \\ 2 \end{pmatrix}$
  b i   Reflection in the y-axis,
         translation $\begin{pmatrix} 2 \\ 2 \end{pmatrix}$
     ii Reflection in the x-axis,
         translation $\begin{pmatrix} 2 \\ 2 \end{pmatrix}$
     iii Rotation through 180° about
         (0, 0), translation $\begin{pmatrix} 2 \\ 2 \end{pmatrix}$

1 a 75% of 64,
     $\frac{1}{4}$ of 192,
     $\frac{2}{3}$ of 72,
     200% of 24
  b £504
  c 12 cm², 14 cm;
     8 cm, 22 cm;
     5 cm, 125 cm²
2 a i $a = 70°$, $b = 40°$
     ii $c = 80°$, $d = e = 100°$
  b i $3n$
     ii $4n - 2$
3 a i   71p
     ii 73p
  b 500 g

1 a $2(x - 3)$

b $\dfrac{(y + 9)}{2}$

2 a 115

b 2592

c 4080

d 12 650

3 a $x = 1$

b $x = {}^-2$

c $x = 12$

d $x = 15$

1 All lines, rows and diagonals add up to $3x$

2 a $3x - 6 = 5x - 20$

$14 = 2x$

$x = 7$

b $4a + 8 = 6a - 12$

$20 = 2a$

$a = 10$

3 a 9

b 8

c 3

4 5, 8, 11

Graph with coordinates:
(0, 2), (1, 5), (2, 8), (3, 11)

5 Cost, C, in pounds: $C = 5 + 0.03m$
where m = minutes used per month

1 Mean = 3.9 (to 1 dp)

Range = $7 - 0 = 7$

2

Items of post	0–2	3–5	6–8	9+
Frequency	6	13	5	0

3 a 3

b 10

1 a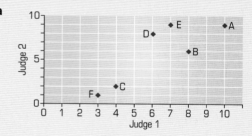

b

2 Your own example. Ask your teacher to check your answer.

1. a Isosceles triangle
   b Isosceles trapezium
   c Right-angled triangle
   d Rhombus
   e Kite
2. $a = 50°$, $b = 60°$, $c = 70°$
3. Area = length × width
4. 15 cm^2

1. a Volume = length × width × height
   b 2.5 cm
2. a 128 cm^3
   b 160 cm^2
3. Right-angled triangles (isosceles and scalene) and equilateral triangles are possible.

Isosceles   Scalene   Equilateral

4. Join the inside vertices at opposite corners.
   This means that each side of the triangle is the diagonal of a 3 cm square, so all the sides are of equal length.

1. a $\frac{1}{2}$
   b $\frac{3}{10}$
   c $\frac{7}{10}$
2. 55%
3. a 0.7
   b $\frac{4}{5}$
   c 0.24

1. a
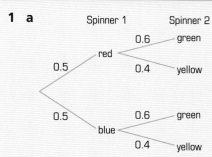

b
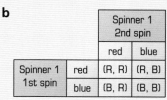

2. One red and one blue: (R, B) or (B, R)
   Probabilities are equally likely.
   So p(R, B) = $\frac{1}{4}$ and p(B, R) = $\frac{1}{4}$
   p(R, B) + p(B, R) = $\frac{1}{4}$ + $\frac{1}{4}$ = $\frac{1}{2}$

B1 Check in

1 a ⁻9, ⁻16
   b 16, 25
2 a 8
   b 15
   c 26
3

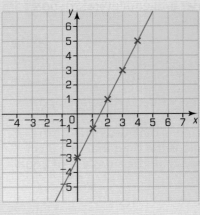

B1 Check out

1, 2 Ask your teacher to check your answers.

Index

Index

Index

×	1	2	3	4	5	6	7	8	9	10
1	1	2	3	4	5	6	7	8	9	10
2	2	4	6	8	10	12	14	16	18	20
3	3	6	9	12	15	18	21	24	27	30
4	4	8	12	16	20	24	28	32	36	40
5	5	10	15	20	25	30	35	40	45	50
6	6	12	18	24	30	36	42	48	54	60
7	7	14	21	28	35	42	49	56	63	70
8	8	16	24	32	40	48	56	64	72	80
9	9	18	27	36	45	54	63	72	81	90
10	10	20	30	40	50	60	70	80	90	100